GW01003743

# A Question of Balance

# A Question of Balance

Game animals and their role in the British countryside

Edited by Stephen Tapper

THE GAME
CONSERVANCY
TRUST

First published in 1999

The Game Conservancy Trust,
Fordingbridge
Hampshire, SP6 1EF

ISBN 1 901369 05 6

The costs of this publication have been met by the
Bernard Sunley Charitable Foundation

Designed and produced by: GoodallJames,
Bournemouth, UK
Reproduction by: The Faculty, Poole, UK
Printed and Bound by: Focus on Print, Poole, UK

Maps produced from the Countryside Information
System (CIS). Copyright Natural Environment Research
Council and Department of Environment, Transport and
the Regions, with acknowledgements to The Met. Office,
the Ordnance Survey and the Institute of Terrestrial Ecology, Monks Wood. Bird and mammal distributions based
on BTO and BRC atlas data[1,2].

1. Gibbons, D. W., Reid, J. B. & Chapman, R. A. (1993)
The New Atlas of Breeding Birds of Britain and Ireland:
1988–1991. British Trust for Ornithology. T. & A. D.
Poyser, London.

2. Arnold, H. R. (1993) The Atlas of Mammals in Britain.
ITE Research Publication, NERC, HMSO London.

# Contents

# A Question of Balance

Britain's game animals and their predators are the most dramatic of our wildlife species and have been pursued by man since prehistoric times. Game animals tend to be substantial in size and may need large areas to accommodate them, so, apart from specific exceptions, such as wintering concentrations of waterfowl, their populations cannot be accommodated on nature reserves or protected through Sites of Special Scientific Interest or Special Areas of Conservation. They run in, swim through or fly over lands used for growing crops, grazing livestock or forestry. Therefore it is the owners and managers of such countryside enterprises who are in the best position to conserve these animals. Unlike nations with a vast area of state-owned lands, where the state can organise game seasons and bag limits, most of Britain is privately owned. Thus the responsibility for the well-being of game rests with the land-occupier.

Land-occupiers are usually keen to conserve game animals but the economics of their enterprises often force them to make decisions which are detrimental to the well-being of the game they want to help. In many cases, at the root of these decisions lies a Government agricultural policy, such as the Common Agricultural Policy, which deliberately skews the economics of crop growing and livestock rearing to such an extent that wildlife conservation interests are seriously jeopardised.

It is our view that these subsidies need to be rebalanced and partly replaced by grants for wildlife habitat conservation and creation. This would better serve the interest of the public, who are increasingly concerned about wildlife on farmland, while at the same time allowing farmers and landowners to conserve game without severe detriment to their agricultural businesses. Even farmers who have no personal interest in field sports will find that improving their land for game may bring them additional income from letting the shooting, fishing or stalking rights. At the same time, the value of their property increases if it has an improved sporting potential as a result of improved habitat. This in turn benefits a range of other wildlife species.

Not all aspects of game management appear to coincide with conservation interests, eg. the control of predators to improve game survival. However, predation control is linked to habitat conservation because, without it, game stocks can become so reduced that habitat improvements on their own have no game value. Also, in most cases, the predators in question are common and successful generalists, so reductions in their numbers locally or regionally will not jeopardise their status. Indeed, we think that, without predator control, we may also lose some of the less numerous and more vulnerable members of the fauna, such as some of the ground-nesting birds.

Other predators are far less common and we believe that, in the national interest, it is right that the Government should safeguard those predators, such as birds of prey, which have been threatened and could be threatened in the future by an over-zealous desire to increase the game bag. There is no doubt that legal protection has benefited some of these species. However, success can bring problems and we think that, in the future, we will need management as well as species protection if we are to retain a rich and diverse predator fauna as well as prolific game stocks.

# Acknowledgements

*Capercaillie*

Picture credits:

*Photographs by* **Laurie Campbell**

*Additional photographs by* Nigel Boatman *56, 57;* Simon Everett *208;* Game Conservancy *60, 68, 72;* Nick Giles *61, 195, 203, 204;* Sophia Miles *108;* Peter Moore *70, 75, 90;* NHPA *25, 64, 110, 144, 157, 220, 266;* Stephen Tapper *39, 54, 55, 78, 87, 94, 98, 120, 124, 130, 142, 146, 150, 170, 178, 188, 194, 197, 198, 202, 218, 228, 229, 238, 244, 254;* Alexis de la Serre *149;* Chris Stoate *83;* Mike Swan *76;* Andy Walker *200;*

*A Question of Balance* is the work of both the staff and trustees of The Game Conservancy Trust. It was written principally by our research staff because we believe that good conservation policy is based on good science. However, our advisory and technical staff have contributed substantially to deriving policies that will be effective and workable. Our trustees have concentrated on evaluating and assessing the text, discussing and resolving contentious issues, and recommending changes where necessary.

The authors are Nicholas Aebischer, David Baines, Nigel Boatman, John Carroll, Nick Giles, Andrew Hoodless, David Newborn, Charles Nodder, Dick Potts, Richard Prior, Jonathan Reynolds, Peter Robertson, Rufus Sage, Nick Sotherton, Chris Stoate, David Summers, Stephen Tapper and Simon Thirgood.

Other staff who have helped by reading and commenting on various sections are David Jackson, Ian Lindsay, Ian McCall, Hugo Straker, Peter Thompson and Martin Tickler. We would also like to thank Johnny Birks, Robert Kenward and Graham Cox for comments on some of the accounts.

The trustees of The Game Conservancy Trust, under the chairmanship of The Earl Peel, appointed a working party to oversee the *A Question of Balance* project. This consisted of Hugh Oliver-Bellasis (Chairman), David Caldow, David Clark, Tom Cook, Oliver Doubleday, John Drysdale, The Hon. Sir Charles Morrison, The Hon. Matt Ridley and Baron Georges van Tuyll van Serooskerken.

*A Question of Balance* was co-ordinated and edited by Stephen Tapper, with sub-editing by Nicholas Aebischer, Charles Nodder, Dick Potts, Sophia Miles and Mike Swan. Special thanks to Maggie O'Hanlon for her editorial contribution.

Angela Knight, James Long, Judy Pittock and Michele Trebilco assisted by entering text changes, printing out documents, verifying references and organising meetings.

Finally, we are extremely grateful to the Bernard Sunley Charitable Foundation for funding the publication of *A Question of Balance*.

# The Game Conservancy Trust

**The principal activity of The Game Conservancy Trust is scientific research into game and game habitats, the results of which can be turned into practical conservation advice for farmers, landowners, game-managers and Government agencies. Its objectives are encapsulated in the Trust Deed as follows:**

- **To promote for the public benefit the conservation and study of game species, their habitats and the other species associated with those habitats.**

- **To conduct research into the ecology and biology of game species and their environmental requirements and to publish the useful results of such research.**

- **To advance the education of the public in game biology and in the conservation of game (especially, but not exclusively, in the conservation of game as a sustainable resource).**

This work is urgent because the numbers of many of Britain's game species are declining. Moreover, the Trust is in a unique position to assess what is required in this very wide area of conservation concern because few other conservation organisations have an equivalent research base. Dozens of research reports and papers by the Trust's staff are published in scientific (peer-reviewed) journals every year – over 770 since the foundation of the Trust in 1969 – all of which contribute to the knowledge of game and wildlife ecology.

The research of the Trust is complemented by the Advisory Service of Game Conservancy Limited, a wholly owned subsidiary. This service helps land-managers to implement the research findings and runs courses to train new and existing managers in the latest approaches to conservation. Taken together, the research and advisory work improve the management and the conservation of a substantial amount of the British countryside, including that of Northern Ireland and the Isle of Man.

Because the Trust is principally supported by 'hunters' (ie. all those who shoot, hunt and fish for game animals), many people have confused its role with other organisations whose aim is to support and defend field sports. Hunters, of course, support the Trust because without game there would be no field sports. Nevertheless, it should be emphasised that the Trust, should a conflict of interests arise, would always put the long-term interests of the game before the short-term interests of the hunters.

Today's countryside is a busy place. Farmers, foresters, developers and landowners shape the landscape, and people from all walks of life participate in a diversity of business, recreational and leisure activities. No single interest should be allowed to dominate and balancing these interests is ultimately the job of Government. This job will be easier if the disparate groups can agree on a way forward and what is to be done.

The Game Conservancy Trust recognises that its own interests and those of others may diverge and looks forward to continuing discussion with other bodies on how various aspirations for the 21st century can be achieved for the public benefit.

# Introduction

**A *Question of Balance* is the first comprehensive policy document produced by The Game Conservancy Trust. It is not a scientific review but a conservation plan based on scientific observation. To a large extent it draws on the Trust's own research but, as it is impossible to prove everything in this plan scientifically, much has had to be based on empirical knowledge or even plain common sense. Often we have to make decisions now rather than wait for long-term experiments to provide definitive answers.**

In 1989, the Trust published a broad policy statement in a short paper entitled Game 2000[1]. *A Question of Balance* is more detailed and more specific. It tackles all the main game conservation issues and puts forward research needs and a conservation plan for each of the principal game species in Britain and for the management of habitats in which they are found.

Readers unfamiliar with the history of game preservation in Britain may be surprised and confused by the inclusion of conservation and management proposals for a range of predatory birds and mammals; after all these animals are not quarry species and many are fully protected in law. Earlier generations of landowners and keepers, however, regarded all predators as enemies of game and, in many cases, the predators suffered as a consequence. The Victorians and Edwardians demonstrated clearly that, by putting game interests first, they could sustain very high game numbers and high shooting bags – but at the expense of some other species[2]. Today, such a self-centred approach is generally unacceptable but so too are the views of those who fail to recognise the role that game conservation has played, and still plays, in maintaining habitats and improving biodiversity in the wider countryside.

The Trust cannot dismiss the impact of predators on game as being of little consequence. Indeed, research shows that the combined effect of a range of predatory species on numbers of prey can have serious consequences for game abundance[3]. It is not thus good sense to aim to have all predatory species abundant in every locality. The impact of some, such as the carrion crow and the fox, not only compromises the management of game and species that depend on game habitats but may also jeopardise the status of less common, non-game prey species[4]. On the other hand, if the actions recommended in *A Question of Balance* are carried through, national wild game numbers and productivity, as well as biodiversity (including predators), will substantially improve while the long-term interests of the hunter will be sustained.

Game management engenders an incentive to manage and create habitats specifically for wildlife – something which is only incidental to other forms of land use, such as forestry or farming. This is critical to an appreciation of its conservation value. The habitat management needed to encourage a wild game species, whether it be brown trout, red grouse or brown hare, depends on an appreciation of the ecological needs of these animals at all stages of their life-cycle and throughout different seasons. Young animals often have quite different needs from adults so, for example, to maintain a self-sustaining population of trout, a stream-manager must ensure that there are gravel beds to hold trout eggs as well as deep pools for the adult fish. Likewise, grey partridge numbers can only be sustained if farmland is managed in such a way that ample insects are available for growing chicks; this is achieved by increasing the biodiversity of the cereal ecosystem.

Habitat diversity is needed for most game and intensive monocultures are usually unsuitable. Maintaining this critical and appropriate diversity is a feature of our habitat proposals and we seek measures from Government and its agencies to encourage farmers and landowners to improve biodiversity. We do not favour subsidies to support intensive land use, nor do we support 'conservation' measures that are inappropriate to a particular habitat.

Many of our game animals depend on a landscape of a specific character, such as open arable farmland or upland heather moor. Injecting biodiversity by, for example, planting trees, whether as blocks of forestry or small farm woodlands, can totally destroy this character and imperil the wild game dependent on it. In this context we see the *Character of England*[5] map, recently launched by the Countryside Commission (now the Countryside Agency) and English Nature, as a blueprint defining these landscapes. By acting as a bench-mark, it will help to ensure that these landscapes are not lost and that habitat conservation into the next century will maintain the regional flavour of the countryside.

Internationally many bodies now accept that conservation aims are dependent on the support of local inhabitants and that conservation through wise use is an important practical means of maintaining species and habitats[6]. We believe this also applies in the British Isles. *A Question of Balance* is not the last word on these matters. As the debate moves on, as new research is carried out, and as the understanding of the complex relationships between the fauna, flora and man improves still further, this plan will continue to evolve.

## Sources and references

1. Morrison, C. (1989) *Game 2000: A Manifesto for the Future of Game in Britain.* The Game Conservancy Trust, Fordingbridge, Hampshire.

2. Tapper, S. C. (1992) *Game Heritage: An Ecological Review from Shooting and Gamekeeping Records.* Game Conservancy Limited, Fordingbridge, Hampshire.

3. Tapper, S. C., Potts, G. R. & Brockless, M. (1996) The effect of an experimental reduction in predation pressure on the breeding success and population density of grey partridges *(Perdix perdix).* Journal of Applied Ecology, 33: 965–78.

4. Lovegrove, R., Shrubb, M. & Williams, I. (1995) *Silent Fields* Gwlad Tawel: The Status of Farmland Birds in Wales. Royal Society for the Protection of Birds, Sandy, Bedfordshire.

5. Anon. (1996) *The Character of England: Landscape, Wildlife and Natural Features.* Countryside Commission and English Nature, Cheltenham and Peterborough.

6. McNeely, J. A. (In press) The problems with concentrating on mammals when the world is thinking about biodiversity. In: Entwhistle, A. & Dunstone, N. (Eds) *Has the Panda Had its Day? Future Priorities for the Conservation of Mammalian Biodiversity.* Fauna & Flora International/Mammal Society Symposium, Zoological Society, London.

# Part 1
# Game management
# and the countryside

# 1. Game management logic – conservation through wise use

The Game Conservancy Trust, in setting this strategy for game management

into the 21st century, is concerned principally with two matters:

- Biodiversity;

- Sustainability with respect to Britain's game management heritage.

*Heather burning*

## Historical aspects

One respect in which we may differ from other conservation agencies, and where the clearest exposition of our view is necessary, is the role of our own species. For a long time man has influenced almost all matters to do with the flora, fauna and countryside in Britain and this has fundamental implications for the justification of active management or intervention to conserve species or habitats. At the same time we believe that man has always been part of nature, giving us a right and a responsibility to 'conserve for wise use'.

### Early agricultural practices

In reference to agricultural practices, the terms 'natural' or 'balance of nature' are often used inappropriately. By 'natural' some conservationists mean an 18th-century approach in which man manages the land in a sympathetic and 'traditional' way. In the 18th and 19th centuries agricultural practices in Britain did indeed have much to commend them: they relied on ecological cycles to maintain and build soil fertility and, although yields were low compared with those of today, they were achieved largely without using fossil fuels and pesticides.

However, this kind of farming was not traditional. It followed a much longer period – from the Neolithic era to the Middle Ages – during which soils were gradually impoverished, woodland was destroyed, and the treeless uplands that we now cherish were produced[1]. The main problem with the word 'natural' is the implication that anything 'unnatural' is undesirable. Man has affected the environment for so long that such a distinction can be as unhelpful as it is illogical.

### Impact of hunting

Many people find it hard to understand how game harvesting can be beneficial to wildlife conservation. This is not surprising because many species have become extinct as a result of hunting by man. Indeed, evidence from the oceanic islands, the Americas and Australia led one recent reviewer to conclude that:

> *Whenever anatomically and behaviourally modern man has reached land previously*

*unoccupied by humans – whether a continent or an island, an extinction spasm of the species hunted has resulted[2].*

Only in regions such as Africa, where man and game have evolved together, has the bulk of the large game species survived. In North America, many large mammals were lost soon after the first humans arrived[3, 4], and populations of game and fur-bearers were hugely depleted following the first European contact[5].

### Early conservation measures

The origins of 'conservation through wise use' are obscure but certainly pre-date St Cuthbert, who, in the 7th century, protected the eider colonies off the north-east coast of England to improve the supply of eider down. Later, the first European colonists reported clear examples of habitat management being practised by the North American Indians, who regularly burnt forest undergrowth to increase game and aid hunting[6].

## Current conservation problems

### Human pressures

In Europe today one of the biggest conservation problems is that a variety of species – including most game – live over wide areas that can never be regulated by the site protection policies of parks or reserves. These species cannot be conserved through a system of nature reserves because the cost is too high but, at the same time, they cannot be left to fend for themselves because the pressures of pesticides, pollution and human development are too great. The growing human population, together with technological advances and the demand for higher living standards, is making

disproportionately increasing demands on the environment. Therefore, in addition to what is being achieved by the network of nature reserves and Sites of Special Scientific Interest, we need to reduce these pressures in the wider environment. We believe that 'conservation through wise use' can make a significant contribution to alleviating wider environmental pressures.

### Intensive agriculture

The biggest obstacle to the wise use of game in the developed world is intensive agriculture. The wise use of farmland in Britain, be it lowland arable or upland rough pasture, could be encouraged by a more discriminate use of subsidies. Currently both sustainable and non-sustainable agriculture are equally rewarded and the costs of the detrimental effects of modern agricultural practices are not borne by the farmers themselves. The situation is worst where subsidies actually encourage over-production[7].

Some progress is now being made in rebalancing the objectives of the European Union's Common Agricultural Policy and there is a growing acceptance that compromise between farm production and conservation is essential. We are not opposed to modern agricultural systems; indeed it is arguable that, without modernisation and its consequent increase in yields, much more land in Britain and continental Europe would have to be farmed in order to achieve even the minimum necessary production[8]. Thus, in a sense, modern farming practices actually help to protect habitats[9].

## Conservation through wise use

There are two significant components to this approach.

### An optimal sustainable yield of managed game

A vital ingredient is the concept of sustainability, ie. a yield (or game harvest) that is sufficiently high to produce economic benefits, yet not so high as to reduce future yields. The yield of a species is directly related to its reproduction rate and its survival rate. Both can be improved by game management, which affects an animal's living conditions in one or more of the following ways:

- Better habitat;

- Better nutrition;

- Less predation;

- Less disease;

- Less poaching.

Thus, although annual harvesting removes a sizeable portion of the population (typically 10–30% of gamebirds), this is offset by gains due to a lower natural mortality and/or better reproduction rate. The populations of game and other species on managed land are therefore generally much greater throughout the year than those on unmanaged land[10].

This association of management with improved reproduction and survival, together with harvesting, contrasts markedly with *cropping*, ie. harvesting a wildlife resource in a situation where no management is undertaken. Even if cropping is carried out sustainably it inevitably leads to lower numbers of both game and other species. In some instances, there may be an economic incentive to over-exploit if the economic value of an animal is currently higher than it is likely to be in future[11]. Cropping by itself is therefore *not* 'conservation through wise use'.

## A realisable income from the ownership of the resource

The *market value* of the game harvest consists principally of the *sporting value* of the shooting, hunting or fishing rights but also includes the *value of the meat*. It is this overall value that provides the main incentive for the long-term conservation of the quarry and its habitat.

However, the overall value does not by itself prevent *over-exploitation* and, unless a wildlife resource is subject to clearly defined *property rights*, there may well be an incentive for individuals to take as large a share as possible while they can[12]. History is full of examples of such over-exploitation, ranging from whales to elephants and from fur-bearers to fish. Often in such scrambles for a common resource values tend to increase as stocks diminish, thus driving the hunted species further towards extinction. This is clearly the case, for example, with rhinoceros horn, where market values are set to soar should the rhinoceros become extinct[13].

## Conservation actions

- The wise use of farmland, with better-targeted chemical inputs, environmentally sensible stocking levels and an undistorted price structure for agricultural inputs and outputs is the most urgent of all conservation priorities within the EU. This would lead to an increase in many game populations and would provide additional opportunities for wildlife conservation in the countryside at large.

- Over-exploitation in Britain can best be prevented where there is clear ownership of a wildlife resource, either by an individual or by an association of individuals, eg. a fishing club, wildfowling club or local community[14]. In this way the owner has an incentive to reap a sustained annual income, rather than depleting the capital in a few short seasons, and to protect the resource against unwise use.

This is the basis for conservation through wise use. It is not solely wise use, nor is it just sustainable use. The key word, often omitted by others, is conservation, ie. the active intervention by man to improve the habitats, food chain and environmental conditions of the species in question. Such action often carries with it benefits for many other, non-game species, from wild flowers and butterflies to songbirds and crayfish.

## Sources and references

1. Rackham, O. (1986) *The History of the Countryside*. J. M. Dent & Sons Ltd, London.

2. Diamond, J. M. (1991) Twilight of Hawaiian birds. *Nature*, **535**: 505–6.

3. Martin, P. S. (1967) Prehistoric overkill. In: Martin, P. S. & Wright, H. E. (Eds) *Pleistocene Extinctions: The Search for a Cause*. Yale University Press, New Haven. 75–120.

4. Ward, P. D. (1997) *The Call of Distant Mammoths: Why the Ice Age Mammals Disappeared*. Copernicus, Springer-Verlag, New York.

5. Tapper, S. & Reynolds, J. (1996) The wild fur-trade: Historical and ecological perspectives. In: Taylor, V. J. & Dunstone, N. (Eds) *The Exploitation of Mammal Populations*. Chapman & Hall, London. 28–44.

6. Budiansky, S. (1995) *Nature's Keepers. The New Science of Nature Management*. Weidenfeld & Nicholson, London.

7. Harvey, G. (1997) *The Killing of the Countryside*. Jonathan Cape, London.

8. Ridley, M. (1996) Why famine forecasts are wrong. In: Ridley, M. (Ed.) *Down to Earth. II Combating Environmental Myths*. Institute of Economic Affairs, London. 38–9.

9. Avery, D. (1995) Preserving wildlife habitat – with agrochemicals. *Agronomist* (Spring): 10–12.

10. Aebischer, N. J. (1991) Sustainable yields: Gamebirds as a harvestable resource. *Gibier Faune Sauvage*, **8**: 335–51.

11. Caughley, G. & Sinclair, A. R. E. (1995) *Wildlife Ecology and Management*. Blackwell Science, Cambridge, Massachusetts.

12. Ridley, M. (1996) *The Origins of Virtue*. Viking, London.

13. Bowles, D. (1996) Wildlife trade – a conserver or exploiter? In: Dunstone, N. & Taylor, V. J. (Eds) *The Exploitation of Mammal Populations*. Chapman & Hall, London. 266–91.

14. Kock, M. D. (1996) Zimbabwe: a model for the sustainable use of wildlife and the development of innovative wildlife management practices. In: Dunstone, N. & Taylor, V. J. (Eds) *The Exploitation of Mammal Populations*. Chapman & Hall, London. 229–49.

# 2. Key game habitats

Britain's countryside owes much of its character to field sports. Throughout historic times the requirements of preserving game have always mitigated against the pressures of intensive land use, particularly agriculture. In the years following the Second World War, successive governments, and particularly the European Union, have sought to promote agricultural production through subsidy which, in conjunction with other factors, has been to the detriment of habitats for game.

The Game Conservancy Trust recognises that Britain's countryside reflects change and that future conservation depends on managing this change and not simply trying to preserve the status quo. We will strive to develop new ways to conserve habitats and encourage governments to move away from production-based subsidies towards environmental payments to farmers and landowners which benefit a range of wildlife in the open countryside.

**Areas of moorland ground in Britain:** kilometre squares containing more than 25 hectares of heath and heath shrub. From ITE Land Cover Map.

# 2.1 Heather moorland

## Current status

Moorland dominated by heather *(Calluna vulgaris)* is largely restricted to the uplands of Britain and Ireland and a few other areas on the European mainland and the western coast of Norway. Heather moorland in Britain is considered to be internationally important and its retention is a high conservation priority[1].

The assemblages and particular variation of habitats and wildlife in the uplands are unique. A quarter of the 81 upland plant communities described in the national vegetation census are globally rare or particularly well represented in Britain. Upland bird species assemblages are not rich by European standards but they contain many species which are uncommon or unusual nationally: twite, golden plover, merlin, golden eagle, dotterel, ptarmigan and red grouse.

## History and character

*Golden plover*

Open heather moorland is a semi-natural habitat created, most usually from woodland, by the influence of man. The original upland forest cover was probably at its greatest 5,000 years ago, when most ground below 700 metres in the south and east, and below 450 metres in the north and west, was wooded. As the climate became wetter and cooler, and as forest clearance by humans increased, so the extent of open heath, rough grass and bogs began to form the pattern now so characteristic of the British uplands. Early settlers also used fire and grazing as management tools to clear woodland and suppress regeneration, creating the open landscapes with which we are familiar today.

From the 1500s to 1800s, grouse and grouse hunting were only infrequently mentioned in the literature, with the uplands being dominated by cattle-, sheep- and deer-grazing interests. However, from the early 1880s, grouse shooting increased in popularity and the advent of the breech-loading shotgun gave rise to the style of grouse shooting seen today, with large areas of the uplands being managed to produce a shootable surplus of grouse. In the 1940s we estimate that 54% of heather ground in Scotland was actively managed for driven grouse shooting. By the 1980s this had fallen to 26% but grouse conservation still remained the primary land use in many areas[2].

## Changes after the Second World War

The post-war period saw a great rise in numbers of sheep in the uplands, the advent of subsidies for forestry and increases in red deer numbers in the Scottish Highlands. The war years had demonstrated the need for greater self-sufficiency, and subsequent improvements in research and development for upland farming, coupled with subsidies for sheep production, led to a rapid expansion of the national hill flock. For example, the number of ewes in the Less Favoured Areas of England and Wales increased from 2.5 million in 1949 to 7.9 million in 1987. The area of forestry also increased, thanks to government incentives, from 5% of total land area in 1919 to its current 2.3 million hectares, or 10% of total land area. Since 1919, 90% of the new woodlands in Britain have been in Scotland, leading to losses of large areas of open moorland.

It is estimated that 47,989 square kilometres (62%) of Scotland consisted of semi-natural vegetation in the late 1940s[3]. Of this, 15,377 square kilometres comprised heather moorland and 20,004 square kilometres were blanket mire, often with a high heather component. By the 1970s the areas of heather moor and blanket mire had been reduced by 18% and 8% respectively. These reductions were largely attributed to increases in afforestation and, to a lesser extent, conversion to grassland. Over a similar period it has been estimated that the area of heather moorland in England and Wales declined by 20%[1,4].

The remaining heather is still under threat. With the current area of moorland (ground dominated by dwarf shrubs) in both England and Wales estimated at 7,790 and 6,360 square kilometres respectively[4], it was found that 24% of moorland in England and 43% in Wales contained suppressed heather (<25% cover) that was vulnerable to loss[4].

### Grouse shooting and heather loss

In Scotland it has been possible to compare the rates at which heather has been lost on areas with and without grouse-shooting interests. Based on the aerial photographic surveys of Scotland[3], and only considering areas that contained at least 10% heather cover in the 1940s, rates of heather loss can be contrasted for four levels of grouse-shooting interest[2].

It is clear from the graph *(left)* that, although heather has been lost from all of the categories, losses have been least on those areas with a continuing interest in grouse management. It seems reasonable to conclude that this interest has slowed the otherwise catastrophic rates of heather loss seen throughout the uplands. From the above, we calculate that an additional 953 square kilometres of heather would have been lost from the Scottish uplands since 1945 were it not for grouse interests[2].

## Conservation plan

We see the future for the upland moors as a multiple land-use system with grouse management and grazing working together to protect the vegetation. The commercial afforestation of the uplands is, we feel, detrimental to sporting and conservation interests and we would like the

*Amount of heather on Scottish upland estates: moors where grouse shooting was retained between 1940 and 1980 (left); moors where grouse shooting was lost after 1940 (centre); areas of moor where there has been no grouse interest since at least 1925 (right). Active grouse moors clearly retain more heather than other areas. Data from 171 moors.*

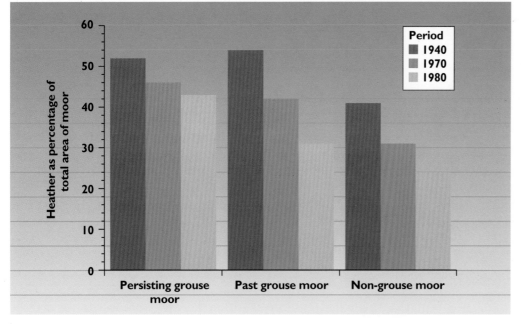

removal of Government support for new commercial planting on heather ground. While the promotion of native woodland plantings is to be encouraged, we feel that the loss of significant areas of open heather moorland in this way is undesirable.

We wish to see grazing pressure reduced across much of the heather uplands. In many areas sheep are the most important grazing species and their numbers are bolstered by Government subsidy. We wish to see Government support for upland farming maintained but through payments other than the existing Hill Livestock Compensatory Allowance. Area payments, as opposed to the current headage-based systems, or subsidies for stock removal, such as the Countryside Premium Scheme and some Environmentally Sensitive Area options, should be encouraged.

Much heather loss is caused by winter 'fothering' on the hill margin. Schemes to reduce such damage, either by encouraging off-hill wintering or by increased hill shepherding, should be promoted. The hill margin is an important habitat for species such as the black grouse and has suffered particularly from increases in grazing pressure. Reducing grazing pressure and planting suitable native woodlands on the moorland fringe would be of particular benefit.

## Conservation actions

Our main aim is to maintain and improve the condition of the existing heather acreage while promoting heather restoration in many parts of its previous range. Our approach to this is three-fold.

- To guarantee a continued interest in heather retention and management throughout the uplands, we must ensure that heather is a valued resource for landowners, primarily through its use for grouse shooting.

- There should be a reduction in the pressures leading to heather loss, principally Government subsidy systems that encourage commercial afforestation and overgrazing.

- The management of the existing heather ground should be improved through education to ensure its long-term viability.

## Sources and references

1. Thompson, D. B. A., MacDonald, A. J., Marsden, J. H. & Galbraith, C.A. (1995) Upland heather moorland in Great Britain: a review of international importance, vegetation change and some objectives for nature conservation. *Biological Conservation*, **71**: 163–78.

2. Barton, A. F. & Robertson, P. A. (1997) *Land Use Change in the Scottish Uplands, 1945–1990, in Relation to Grouse Shooting Interests*. The Game Conservancy Trust, Fordingbridge, Hampshire.

3. Tudor, G. & Mackay, E. G. (1995) Upland land cover change in post-war Scotland. In: Thompson, D. B. A., Hester, A. J. & Usher, M. B. (Eds) *Heaths and Moorland: Cultural Landscapes*. HMSO, London. 28–42.

4. Bardgett, R. D., Marsden, J. H., Howard, D. C. & Hossel, J. E. (1995) The extent and condition of heather in moorland, and the potential impact of climate change. In: Thompson, D. B. A., Hester, A. J. & Usher, M. B. (Eds) *Heaths and Moorland: Cultural Landscapes*. HMSO, London. 43–51.

**Areas of forest and
woodland in Britain:**
kilometre squares containing
more than 10 hectares
of woodland.
**Light green =** deciduous.
**Dark green =** mixed.
**Blue** = coniferous. From ITE
Land Cover Map.

# 2.2 Forest and woodland

## Current status

Britain has over 2.5 million hectares of tree cover, about 10% of the land area. Of this, deciduous woodland (60%) has a predominantly southerly distribution and coniferous woodland (40%) is mainly in the north. Ancient semi-natural woodland contributes 318,000 hectares to the total while secondary native woodland contributes a further 250,000 hectares[1]. The remainder consists of non-native woodlands and forests, including many large coniferous plantations in Scotland and elsewhere. Around 25% of the total tree cover is estimated to be in small pockets scattered among mainly arable and grassland areas.

## History and character

The history of British woodland and its relationship to the rest of the landscape is well understood[2]. Tree cover in Britain reached its greatest extent about 5,000 years ago, with most but not all ground below 700 metres elevation in the south and 450 metres elevation in the north consisting of forest. Much of this area would have been covered by oak, hazel and elm, with birch and pine in the Scottish uplands and lime in the Midlands and the south-east of England.

## Decline

Deforestation began in Neolithic times in the east and in chalkland areas, before spreading west and north. Outside Scotland, the Romans and Saxons continued to convert more of the countryside from forest, using the wood for building and industry, but also clearing for agricultural purposes.

Pasture-woodlands came into use at the time of the Normans. The last extensive wildwoods in England probably disappeared around 1100 AD, given that the records in the *Domesday Book* (1086) suggest only 15% of the land area in England contained continuous tree cover. During the medieval period coppicing became important as a management tool, creating large areas of woodlands with oak in the overstorey and coppice species of ash, maple, hazel and others underneath. Royal hunting forests, such as the New Forest, Cranborne Chase and Sherwood Forest, helped to retain extensive woodland in some areas.

In the Scottish Highlands large-scale clearances of woodlands did not begin until the 17th century, although many of the forests that existed 4,000 years ago had by then been converted to blanket bog and moorland by a combination of man's fires and climatic changes. The systematic clearance of the pinewoods began as timber supplies from English woodlands fell short of demand. Throughout Britain, while the sustainable management of some woodlands by coppicing and regeneration continued, the rate of woodland clearance accelerated in response to demands for ship building up until the early 20th century.

## Forest expansion in the 20th century

At the turn of the last century, tree cover in the UK was at an all-time low of around 5% of the land area. Most woodland outside Scotland contained broad-leaved species and was concentrated in the south-east of England. In Scotland the native pinewoods had been severely depleted. The consequent reliance on imported timber concerned the Government, which responded by introducing a policy of forest creation in 1919. The Forestry Commission was established to implement it and began a programme of extensive planting of commercial timber trees. The private sector was also encouraged to plant by a combination of tax incentives and grant aid aimed specifically at timber-producing trees.

For 50 years, up until the early 1980s, new coniferous woodlands were created on previously unwooded ground and existing broad-leaved woodlands were felled and restocked with conifers or mixtures. Fast-growing non-native coniferous species, such as sitka spruce, were widely planted as monocultures in upland areas of Britain, particularly in Scotland. Most plantings were by the Forestry Commission but private sector involvement increased during the 1960s as a result of financial incentives so that, by the 1980s, the proportion of woodland planted by the Forestry Commission was diminishing rapidly.

By the late 1970s, some of the new coniferous plantations in the uplands and elsewhere were being criticised for being environmentally insensitive. Priorities began to change and, in 1985, the Forestry Commission's official remit was itself altered to include wildlife conservation. Preferential grants became available for broad-leaved species for the first time. In 1988 the Forestry Commission introduced a new Woodland Grant Scheme which increased this differential and was more flexible, with options for mixed planting. In the same year, the Farm Woodland Scheme was introduced, which, for the first time, gave compensation for loss of income from farming. Tax incentives to private forestry investors were removed, thus dramatically reducing the planting of extensive non-native woodlands on marginal land. Since the founding of the Forestry Commission, however, tree cover in Britain had doubled to about 10% and the original aim, to reduce Britain's reliance on imported timber, had to some extent been met.

Alongside this overall increase, the clearance (and replanting) of semi-natural and other native woodland by the Forestry Commission and others has continued in some areas until very recently. Around 40% of the Scottish semi-natural pinewoods remaining in the 1950s were cleared during the following 30 years. Throughout Britain 8% of all ancient woodlands were removed over the same period. Areas of farmland that reverted to native woodland during the 1920s and 1930s have since been reclaimed. Despite the reversion of some neglected land to woodland, it is unlikely that there has been an overall gain in the extent of native woodland in Britain this century[3]. In addition there have been many changes in management as a result of agricultural intensification, notably the virtual disappearance of coppicing and the loss of hedgerows, which has isolated many small areas of native trees.

## Forestry policy in the 1990s

In 1991 the Government set itself two principal policy aims:

- To expand tree cover steadily to increase the many diverse benefits that forests provide;

- To manage existing forests and woodlands sustainably[4, 5].

These aims led to further developments in grant support for certain types of tree planting and woodland management in the 1990s.

*Grant support*
The Forestry Authority's Woodland Grant Scheme is now more flexible than its predecessor and includes a range of incentives targeted at specific environmental objectives in conjunction with the Ministry of Agriculture, Fisheries and Food. The incentive to plant on agricultural land was given a further boost by the Farm Woodland Premium Scheme and the Better Land Supplement. In 1995, the Government defined its objective of woodland expansion in its Rural White Paper[6], which called for the doubling of woodland cover in England within 50 years. In the same year, changes to the set-aside rules allowed woodland planting on set-aside for the first time. The Farm Woodland Premium Scheme (which replaced the Farm Woodland Scheme) changed again in 1997, with higher payment rates for broad-leaves and a simplified application procedure.

The Woodland Grant Scheme also includes a Community Supplement for plantings near towns and cities and where access is allowed. Woodland Improvement Grants provide an incentive to manage existing woodlands with specific objectives. Already many of these have been orientated towards the conservation of certain wildlife species or have biodiversity targets in mind. Grants are available for replanting woodlands with native species and for excluding stock where natural regeneration is required. Areas of locally native, woody-shrub species can be included up to a limit of 10% of the total area. In Scotland new native pinewood plantings attract the same payment rate as broad-leaved species. The minimum planting density of 2,250 trees per hectare in the Woodland Grant Scheme is also relaxed for small plantings or where the creation of a semi-natural native woodland is the long-term aim.

### The UK Forestry Standard

Guidelines for the design and location of new woodlands and the management of existing ones within the Woodland Grant Scheme are given in the Government's UK Forestry Standard[1]. The Standard was published in January 1998 after a lengthy consultation period and reflects the Government's White Paper objective of sustainable forest management by encouraging woodland management for multiple benefits. It will be interpreted through the grant system and will need to be taken into account by all those involved in woodland management and planting.

The Standard defines criteria for sustainable forestry management, including nature conservation, and defines indicators at different levels for monitoring. For example, the UK Biodiversity Action Plan and European Union Habitats and Birds Directives are referenced at the national level, while guidance is provided on identifying conservation interest at the local level. In some cases a formal environmental assessment is required. Importantly, it also recognises the significance of game on beneficial woodland planting and management practices.

The Standard recommends that 10–20% open space is included in new woodland planting, increasing to over 20% in new native woodlands where nature conservation objectives are high. New conifer woodlands should include broad-leaved tree and shrub plantings and all new woodlands should be to some extent mixed. It recommends maximum stand and coupe sizes to fit the landscape. Existing woodlands and forests, including large coniferous monocultures, are to be managed through felling and restocking to achieve these limits and this process is now under way. Recommended options for the man-agement of existing semi-natural woodland are as a high forest – with an emphasis on small-scale felling systems, as coppice or as wood-pasture, or by using minimal intervention.

## Policy into practice

The design of new woodlands in Britain and the management of existing ones between 1986 and 1998 have seen a fundamental change in policy away from timber production as a sole purpose and towards sustainable forestry and multiple benefits. This change has had an almost immediate effect on the nature of new woodland planting, in particular because almost all tree planting is now undertaken within the Woodland Grant Scheme.

Some foresters and the timber industry are concerned about the scale of the changes and question the future profitability of the new woodlands. In 1996, timber production was the sole objective in less than 10% of new woodland planting; in the 1970s this figure was nearer 90%. Unlike commercial coniferous plantings, many of the new woodlands – it is argued – will not provide a significant financial return within a lifetime and, even at maturity, their economic value is uncertain. The changes have, however, been broadly welcomed by most conservation organisations, including ourselves. The movement away from large monoculture plantings of non-native conifers, often on ecologically inappropriate sites, towards mixed or deciduous plantings, the greater use of native species and the inclusion of open spaces and shrub planting will, in most instances, be of benefit to game and other wildlife.

### Farm woodlands and wildlife

Woodland conservation and game have been linked for hundreds of years in Britain and many existing semi-natural woodlands have remained because they provided a habitat for game species. More recently, woodland planting and management outside commercial forestry has been driven in many instances by sporting interests and game conservation. In a recent study, landowners in England were found to be three times more likely to undertake new woodland planting where pheasant releasing was practised. In existing woodlands, ride management, coppicing and shrub planting were also much more commonly practised where owners were interested in pheasants[7]. Such people were also three times more likely to plant new woodlands in the future. Some traditional woodland management practices, such as coppicing, regarded as beneficial for wildlife conservation, continue because the woodlands are managed primarily for game. Potential conflicts between nature conservation interests and the most intensive of woodland game management practices, such as pheasant releasing, are easily mitigated and often measures can be introduced that benefit both[8].

The Farm Woodland Premium Scheme, combined with the incentive of game habitat provision, has already led to the planting of large numbers of small woodlands on arable or improved grassland, with an average size in England of 3 hectares (in Scotland, the average Farm Woodland Premium Scheme planting is larger and includes a significant proportion of unimproved land). The recent changes to the Farm Woodland Premium Scheme and the significant step of allowing woodland planting on set-aside land are likely to encourage further planting of this sort. While it is clear that many forest wildlife species require much larger areas of continuous tree cover, appropriately sited small plantings of broad-leaves on improved land undoubtedly have a significant contribution to make as habitats for wildlife in intensively farmed areas of the country.

For pheasants these small farm woodlands provide roosting and other cover in winter and access to nearby farm crops where they spend most of the summer and rear broods. The edges are a vital component of their spring breeding cover. Even in winter, pheasants spend most of their time near the woodland edge and it has been shown that small woodlands with a high edge:area ratio hold greater densities of pheasants than other woods[9]. The woodland-edge zone is also important to most of the other wildlife that uses woodlands and, in many instances, greater attention could be paid to its design and management. In particular, graded woodland edges that contain a mix of shrubs, coppiced trees and standing herbage can provide attractive cover and improve the microclimate within the woodland itself for game and other wildlife[10].

## Skylighting

Within the woodland interior, opening the canopy to let in light and planting shrubs also creates structural diversity. Indeed, in many cases the shrub layer is more critical than the overstorey but it is often overlooked. The provision for including native shrub species in new and existing woodlands within the Woodland Grant Scheme (displacing up to 10% of the usual tree requirement) is therefore an important step for woodland wildlife and game. The Woodland Grant Scheme also allows for new native woodland plantings that have lower planting densities.

Where wildlife conservation is a primary aim, this relaxation is also of benefit; the reduced reliance on later thinning encourages shrub and herb species and hence greater woodland diversity. Similarly, the inclusion of open spaces within the Woodland Grant Scheme is a major improvement and was something we encouraged for many years. Even so, more guidance within the Woodland Grant Scheme literature and Forestry Standard is required. The area limits are restrictive and, for small woodlands in particular, rides and glades incorporated into new plantings are often too small to be of any long-term benefit to wildlife or game. Open spaces need to be of considerable size to be of value in a mature woodland, typically at least as wide as the projected woodland height. Rides wider than 30 metres begin to simulate the woodland edge but narrower ones are of limited extra benefit to pheasants[9].

## Felling and replanting

Within the forestry industry a change in felling and replanting methods has been observed in recent years, encouraged partly by developments in the Woodland Grant Scheme but also by the changing priorities of the foresters themselves. Large-scale clear felling and replanting with monocultures has to some extent given way to coupe and selective felling to maintain continuous cover. In many instances continuous-cover forestry methods require natural regeneration in areas which have been heavily thinned but which retain a number of mature seed trees. In time this approach will lead to timber-producing woodlands with mixed age-classes and hence increased diversity. Continuous-cover forestry is a good example of sustainable woodland management for the multiple benefits described in the Forestry Standard and it is now being practised in a number of woodlands where natural regeneration is possible. It does, however, require rigorous deer control.

The Government's Rural England White Paper target[6], to double England's woodland cover in 50 years, is an ambitious one. Currently the area of planting each year is about one quarter of the 20,000 hectares per year required. It is possible, however, that major Common Agricultural Policy reform will make forestry a more attractive alternative to farmers and that the rate of woodland planting will increase. A drive towards a steady increase in the area of woodland planting may, however, create further conflicts as the potential for inappropriate planting of woodland on characteristically open habitats increases. Some open habitats are valuable to wildlife and game for their spatial continuity and size and there is a danger of fragmenting these with even relatively small areas of woodland[11]. The planting of non-native conifers in the uplands, particularly on areas of blanket bog, is an example of this.

In the lowlands, tree planting on traditionally open landscapes has occurred recently in some areas. These open habitats are home to many declining bird species, such as the grey partridge, lapwing, skylark and corn bunting. These and other species all avoid woodland cover, partly because of the increased risk of predation. For them at least, a new small woodland can affect a relatively large open area. While the Forestry

Standard recommends that new woodland plantings on previously unwooded sites with an existing high conservation value should be avoided, we believe that the scope for inappropriate plantings on other sites is large and that greater general guidance and site-by-site advice is required.

In Scotland, the new incentives to plant native pinewoods within the Woodland Grant Scheme may improve habitat opportunities for woodland grouse in the long term. Further woodland management support schemes to benefit both the black grouse and capercaillie are required.

*Deer control*
While the impact of red deer on the regeneration of native pinewoods in Scotland has been recognised, a similar effect on the conservation value of lowland woodlands by rapidly increasing numbers of roe, fallow and muntjac has largely been overlooked. Although of historical value in some places, lowland woodlands grazed by deer (and other large herbivores) usually have an underdeveloped ground flora and shrub layer with little, if any, natural regeneration of trees – an effect similar to that observed in the upland pinewoods. They tend to become increasingly

open at all levels, eventually resembling pasture-type woodland with few trees, and are of low value to wildlife and game. Deer control, through shooting or through fencing newly planted or regenerating areas, is an expensive but crucial component of woodland planning, regardless of the management aims.

### Short-rotation coppice

The cultivation of willows and poplars on agricultural land as a source of wood chips for conversion to heat and electricity has recently been encouraged by the Government in order to meet its commitment to the use of renewable energy sources. If appropriate markets develop, these short-rotation coppice crops will need to be widely planted and have considerable potential as an alternative to the mainstream food crops on farmland. Short-rotation coppice therefore provides a rare opportunity for many landowners to include an unintensively managed woody-type crop in a cropped area. While it does not compete with mature native woodlands as a wildlife habitat, it does provide new habitat opportunities for wildlife and game in intensively farmed areas[12]. Short-rotation coppice crops can be planted on set-aside land and qualify for a planting grant within the Woodland Grant Scheme (but at a lower rate than other trees). Despite these incentives, short-rotation coppice does not attract an area payment and is currently an unattractive alternative to most other crops.

## Conservation actions

- Further incentives to encourage short-rotation coppice on agricultural land.

- The expansion of native woodlands to increase existing wildlife populations.

- The linking of existing native woodlands to facilitate colonisation by wildlife species and to diversify gene pools.

- Continued support for small farm woodlands on agricultural land except where new planting is inappropriate.

- Advice on and further encouragement of woodland-edge design and open-space management in new and existing woodlands.

- Recognition of the value of scrub and shrub habitats to wildlife and further encouragement of shrub planting within woodlands.

## Sources and references

1. Anon. (1998) *The UK Forestry Standard.* The Forestry Commission, Edinburgh.

2. Rackham, O. (1986) *The History of the Countryside.* J. M. Dent & Sons Ltd, London.

3. Peterken, G. F. (1995) An overview of native woodland creation. In: Ferris-Khan, R. (Ed.) *The Ecology of Woodland Creation.* Wiley, Chichester. ix–xviii.

4. Anon. (1991) *Forestry Policy for Great Britain.* The Forestry Commission, Edinburgh.

5. Anon. (1994) *Sustainable Forestry, The UK Programme.* HMSO, London.

6. Anon. (1995) *Rural England, a Nation Committed to a Living Countryside.* HMSO, London.

7. Short, C. (1994) *Implications of Game Management for Woodland Management, Landscape Conservation and Public Recreation.* Centre for Rural Studies, Royal Agricultural College, Cirencester.

8. Carroll, J. P. & Robertson, P. A. (1997) *Integrating Pheasant Management and Woodland Conservation.* Game Conservancy Limited, Fordingbridge, Hampshire.

9. Robertson, P. A. (1990) *Woodland Management for Pheasants.* Forestry Commission Research Information Note. HMSO, London.

10. McCall, I. (1988) *Woodlands for Pheasants.* The Game Conservancy, Fordingbridge, Hampshire.

11. Anon. (1986) *Nature Conservation and Afforestation in Britain.* Nature Conservancy Council, Peterborough.

12. Sage, R. B. & Robertson, P. A. (1996) Factors affecting songbird communities using new short rotation coppice habitats in spring. *Bird Study,* **43**: 201–13.

**Areas of tilled ground in Britain:** kilometre squares containing more than 25 hectares of tilled ground. From ITE Land Cover Map.

# 2.3 Arable land

## Current status

Approximately 32% of kilometre squares in Britain contain more than 25 hectares of tilled ground. A survey in 1996 revealed that arable crops (excluding rotational grassland, outdoor vegetable production, bulbs, flowers and fruit) were grown on over 4.5 million hectares in Great Britain[1]. Cereal crops made up the majority of tilled land (3.36 million hectares in 1996) followed, in descending order of area, by oilseed crops, sugar beet, pulses and potatoes. In fact, 14% of Britain's land surface is planted with cereal crops alone. In comparison, 1% of land is currently managed as nature reserves[2]. This is a huge area of habitat with a great potential for game and wildlife.

## History and character

Arable farmland is not a primeval habitat, but it does boast an ancient history. Arable farming has been practised in Britain since the land was first cleared by Neolithic farmers over 6,000 years ago. Starting on the lighter soils on higher ground in southern England, arable farming later spread to the lower, heavy soils of valley bottoms. Introduction of Iron Age implements allowed dense forests to be cleared and clay soils to be drained and ploughed. Within 1,000 years arable cultivation had spread to Shetland. This long history of cultivation means that arable farmland has developed its own rich flora and fauna which are uniquely adapted to the seasonal cycle of cultivation, sowing, management and harvest.

The recent history of farming in Britain is one of boom and bust, usually dependent on levels of Government support (particularly as a result of the threat of war), competition from abundant, cheap supplies from overseas producers, and climate. In times of agricultural depression, arable land would revert to grass or not be farmed at all. Certainly, since the Napoleonic Wars, the size of the area cultivated has gone through large fluctuations. For example, in 1984, there were 5 million hectares of arable land with 4 million hectares of cereals. Even during the last decade, as a result of the European Union's Common Agricultural Policy (CAP) and set-aside, the cereal area fell for a time by almost 25% while the total arable area fell by 12%.

Arable farming has also been greatly influenced by technical innovation. It started with the rudiments of plant breeding when Neolithic man planted early tetraploid varieties of cereals, such as emmer (*Triticum dicoccum*, a type of wheat). In the late 18th and 19th centuries the farming revolution brought the adoption of the four-course rotation, the use of inorganic compounds, eg. copper sulphate as an early herbicide, and the use of industrial by-products, eg. ammonium sulphate as early fertiliser[3].

Technical developments, especially in the last 50 years, have led to the destruction of many wildlife-rich sites by conversion to arable land. Technological advances have also allowed farmers to achieve previously unattainable productivity, thereby making it economically viable to plough up species-rich grassland and wetlands for arable crops. One consequence of this has been that many conservationists viewed the modernisation of farming as a destructive influence.

We, however, have never accepted that arable crops are a wildlife desert and we undertook some of the first research into the communities of insects found in cereal crops[4]. Our subsequent work on cereal crops has catalogued their value as wildlife habitats. For Britain, Potts[2] lists up to 300 species of flowering plants (up to 700 species in western and central Europe), up to 700 species of arthropods and 70 species of birds in some way dependent on arable land. A distinct and diverse cereal flora and fauna has been present for thousands of years, in many cases pre-dating heather moorland, woodland coppice and chalk downland, habitats that are the traditional focus of conservationists' attention.

### Intensification after the Second World War

The post-war period of agricultural intensification has seen unprecedented changes in the manage-

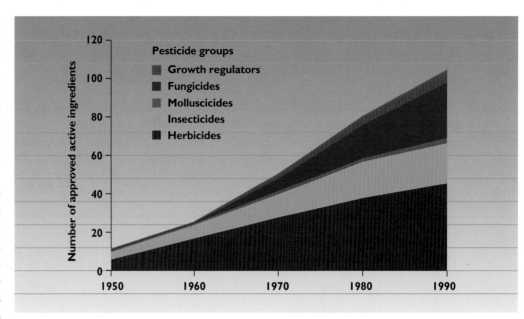

The number of active pesticide ingredients approved for use in UK cereal fields by decade

ment of arable land and, in consequence, its wildlife. More recently the high levels of price support following Britain's EU membership have meant that high levels of production have been sustained. Crop breeding has resulted in the development of cereal varieties responsive to the application of nitrogen fertilisers. As a result, mean levels of nitrogen applied to winter wheat crops have increased by almost 900% since the early 1950s and those to spring barley by almost 500%.

Pesticide use has similarly increased. The number of active ingredients available has increased from 11 in 1957 to over 100 in the 1990s. This, in itself, would not be detrimental if the products were becoming increasingly specific but, in fact, the number of times an area is treated has increased along with the spectrum of action of the active ingredients used. In 1994 a cereal field was sprayed an average of 2.3 times with

herbicides, 2.7 times with fungicides (including seed treatments) and 0.7 times with insecticides or molluscicides[5].

### Effects on biodiversity

To increase production and improve efficiency of farming operations, hedges, other boundary features and non-cropped cover have been destroyed to make fields larger. The Institute of Terrestrial Ecology calculates that the annual rate of hedgerow loss was 121,000 kilometres between 1984 and 1990 and 18,000 kilometres between 1990 and 1993. Fields have become larger and the diversity of the landscape mosaic has become less complex, while rotations have become simpler and, during the 1980s, all but disappeared. Traditional mixed farms have been largely replaced by specialised areas of production: grass in the wetter west, arable in the drier east. All these

changes have brought about a massive decline in biodiversity in the countryside[2].

So great is the impact of intensification on wildlife, that cereal-field-margin ecosystems were recently included as one of only 14 Habitat Action Plans in the Government's Biodiversity Action Plan. The list of wildlife considered under threat in Britain contained many arable species, including the grey partridge and brown hare.

### Effects of pesticides

Consequences of the change brought about by these post-war improvements have been well doc-umented, especially the direct poisoning of wildlife by the early cyclodiene insecticides, such as aldrin and dieldrin. Latterly, indirect effects of pesticides have also become accepted as a major cause of species decline. The best-known example of this is the grey partridge, in which population declines (83% in the last 25 years) were triggered by wors-ening levels of chick survival[6]. Chick survival was shown to be linked to the availability of preferred insects, essential in the diet of young chicks[7]. The use of insecticides and herbicides disrupts the food chain of partridge chicks, which feed on invertebrates, which, in turn, feed on weeds.

Other farming practices or their abandonment have also reduced densities of those so-called 'chick-food' insects. Sawflies in particular are asso-ciated with mixed arable and grass-ley rotations where the grass is established by undersowing spring cereals. Mixed farming has been much reduced, undersowing has all but disappeared and sawfly numbers have been more than halved in the 20 years to 1991[8].

### Effects on habitat

As well as these pesticide-related problems, the value of farmland as wildlife habitat has also decreased as a result of other processes associated with intensification. Winter food availability for farmland birds is thought to have been reduced because of better weed control techniques, fewer weed seeds and fewer over-winter stubbles brought about by a reduction in the area devoted to undersowing. The reduction in the quality and quantity of non-cropped habitats has reduced the number of nesting habitats. Where grass features in the rotation, silage making has replaced hay production and, again, has reduced nesting opportunities. Improving grassland through fertilisation has led to a reduction in the number of invertebrates, especially grasshoppers.

Research, mainly on the grey partridge and its preferred insect chick-foods over the past 25 years, has given us a much clearer understanding of the ecology of arable land, the nature of the problems reducing its suitability as wildlife habitat and, most importantly, what measures need to be taken to improve the wildlife potential of these vast tracts of ground[5,9].

## Conservation plan

The main object of conservation within arable systems should be to halt further degradation of existing habitats and to restore some of the huge biodiversity lost as a consequence of modern farming techniques. The aim should be to reduce the pressure of damaging farming practices within existing cultivated fields. This approach is known as extensification. However, it is vital to recognise that British farms have to remain profitable and at the forefront of new technological advances to compete internationally, perhaps in the near future, in a subsidy-free world market.

Within cultivated fields, however, the priority must be to conserve and resurrect a diverse weed flora and its associated complex of invertebrates. In this respect the most important area is the field margin. Field margins are crucial because they often retain elements of a relict seed bank from a pre-herbicide era[10], as well as providing buffers between crops and other wildlife habitats, such as hedgerows, woodlands and streams, where many animals including gamebirds spend part of their life-cycle[11].

By concentrating on the field margins (boundaries, grass margins and crop headlands) the much-sought-after compromise between efficient farming and wildlife conservation is most likely to be achieved. However, we cannot disregard the management of the whole field or farm. The effects of broad-spectrum pesticides, especially insecticides, may still need to be mitigated. Large blocks of monoculture crops may severely reduce cover and food resources for species over wide areas, and practices such as undersowing should be encouraged where appropriate.

### Policy into practice

The so-called 'Agri-environment Measures' which accompanied the reform of the CAP in 1992 contain, at present, the mechanisms by which these objectives can be best delivered. Although a mechanism designed to reduce production, the Arable Area Payments Scheme, and the set-aside regulations which it contains, allows farmers to use set-aside around the farm to recreate wildlife habitats. Since 1992 the scheme has evolved into one that is now wildlife-friendly and has flexible management options and great potential, eg. the Wild Bird Cover Option.

However, habitat creation schemes like this should not be based on a delivery mechanism which has such an uncertain future or which can change so radically from year to year. Margin set-aside is available only at a minimum width of 20 metres, a size considered too wide by many farmers. The best elements of set-aside should be incorporated into more-focused, better-funded schemes.

Such schemes are potentially in place. Each country currently runs management and habitat restoration schemes focusing on field margin management. Hedgerow restoration, planting and field margin management schemes, among others, are available in England (as Countryside Stewardship), in Scotland (as Countryside Premium) and in Wales (as Tir Cymen - now Tir Gofal). Although they could be better funded, these schemes provide the kinds of initiatives needed to implement any policy for wildlife conservation on arable land. A pilot Arable Stewardship Scheme, incorporating management methods for whole fields, such as undersowing and leaving winter stubbles, was started in 1998 and we anticipate this will greatly strengthen this approach.

Farmland conservation within specific areas of unique landscape, archaeological and wildlife value is also supported within Environmentally Sensitive Areas. In a few of these areas field margin prescriptions are grant-aided.

Therefore, in summary, many of our objectives can be fulfilled under the Agri-environment Measures currently managed by the Ministry of Agriculture, Fisheries, and Food, which were brought in as part of the Accompanying Measures at the last round of reform of the CAP. However, at present only 3% of the EU's agricultural subsidies are spent on such environmentally important measures, the rest being spent on support to the farmer. Just a slight re-balancing in the monies spent on these measures could lead to a disproportionately large benefit to arable wildlife.

## Research needs

Arable land has been the focus of much research attention, primarily as a result of declining partridge populations and currently as a result of declining populations of farmland birds. However, some questions remain:

- What are the environmental benefits of organic and integrated farming systems?

- What is the exact nature of the benefits to wildlife, other than grey partridges, brought about by undersowing and mixed arable and grass-ley rotations?

- What further environmental management practices could be introduced as grant-aided schemes in the next round of Common Agricultural Policy reform?

- How can set-aside be further improved to benefit arable wildlife?

- What are the impacts of farming practices, particularly insecticide use on arable wildlife over increasingly greater areas? So far, studies have only considered plots up to 10 hectares.

In addition, we believe it is imperative to continue monitoring wildlife within agricultural systems so that we can continually assess the consequences of a shifting agricultural policy.

## Conservation actions

- Increase the grants available under EU Regulation 2078/92 to support arable conservation schemes, such as Arable Stewardship, on a national scale.

- Provide long-term research funding to undertake multi-disciplinary studies of the impacts of farming systems on a large scale.

- Improve the national network of professional agricultural advisors, trained in the British Agro-chemicals Standards Inspection Scheme, with specialist knowledge of farmland wildlife.

- End the use of broad-spectrum insecticides on field margins (outer 12 metres) during the period between 15 March and 1 September. The use of such compounds should in some way be discouraged from the rest of the field during the summer.

## Sources and references

1. Nix, J. (1997) *Farm Management Pocket Book*. Wye College, Kent.

2. Potts, G. R. (1991) The environmental and ecological importance of cereal fields. In: Firbank, L. G., Carter, N., Darbyshire, J. F. & Potts, G. R. (Eds) *The Ecology of Temperate Cereal Fields*. British Ecological Society Symposium, Blackwell Scientific Publications, Oxford. 3–21.

3. Stoate, C. (1995) The changing face of lowland farming and wildlife. Part 1: 1845–1945. *British Wildlife*, 6: 341–50.

4. Potts, G. R. & Vickerman, G. P. (1974) Studies on the cereal ecosystem. *Advances in Ecological Research*, 8: 107–97.

5. Sotherton, N. W. (1998) Land use changes and the decline of farmland wildlife: An appraisal of the set-aside approach. *Biological Conservation*, 83: 259–68.

6. Potts, G. R. (1986) *The Partridge. Pesticides, Predation and Conservation*. Collins, London.

7. Southwood, T. R. E. & Cross, D. J. (1969) The ecology of the partridge. III. Breeding success and the abundance of insects in natural habitats. *Journal of Animal Ecology*, 38: 497–509.

8. Aebischer, N. J. (1991) Twenty years of monitoring invertebrates and weeds in cereal fields in Sussex. In: Firbank, L. G., Carter, N., Darbyshire, J. F. & Potts, G. R. (Eds) *The Ecology of Temperate Cereal Fields*. British Ecological Society Symposium, Blackwell Scientific Publications, Oxford. 305–22.

9. Sotherton, N. W. (1991) Conservation headlands: A practical combination of intensive cereal farming and conservation. In: Firbank, L. G., Carter, N., Darbyshire, J. F. & Potts, G. R. (Eds) *Ecology of Temperate Cereal Fields*. British Ecological Society Symposium, Blackwell Scientific Publications, Oxford. 373–97.

10. Wilson, P. J. & Aebischer, N. J. (1995) The distribution of dicotyledonous arable weeds in relation to distance from the field edge. *Journal of Applied Ecology*, 32: 295–310.

11. Longley, M. & Sotherton, N. W. (1997) Factors determining the effects of pesticides upon butterflies inhabiting arable farmland – a review. *Agriculture, Ecosystems & Environment*, 61: 1–12.

# The Sussex study:

## Thirty years of monitoring changes in agriculture and wildlife

The diagnosis of ecological problems associated with agricultural change is complicated by natural year-to-year fluctuations in the abundances of the flora and fauna that live on farmland. Long-term monitoring measures the scale of ordinary year-to-year variation, thus providing a background against which abnormally large changes or long-term trends may be assessed. Generally speaking, the longer a run of monitoring data, the more valuable it becomes, as the sensitivity of statistical techniques used to detect such changes improves with length. Monitoring helps to formulate hypotheses concerning the reasons for change through correlation with extrinsic factors. It thus acts as an early warning system, whose alerts then need independent confirmation by experimentation before remedial management recommendations can be made.

Our Sussex monitoring study is one of the longest-running sets of data on the cereal ecosystem in the world. It started in 1968 as the Partridge Survival Project, whose aim was to investigate the causes of a decline in numbers of the grey partridge – a decline that, by the late 1960s, was already cause for concern. Dick Potts, the project officer, began a detailed ecological study of the partridge on 62 square kilometres of the South Downs, in Sussex. He soon established that one of the causes of the decline was a shortage of chick-food insects in cereals, which led to poor survival of the partridge chicks[1]. The changes in insect densities reflected the reduction in arable weeds (which provide invertebrates with both food and shelter) following the introduction of herbicides in the late 1950s. Consequently, from 1970 onwards, we have monitored cereal invertebrates and weeds annually on the South Downs study area in the third week of June (the peak hatching time for grey partridge chicks) and recorded crop details on a field-by-field basis each year. The partridge monitoring has been maintained as well, with the whole area being counted every autumn after harvest. The databank also contains information on other species, eg. corn buntings and predators.

The Sussex data have demonstrated that, overall, invertebrate density in cereals has fallen by half over the last 25 years. Many invertebrate groups have been affected, at all levels in the food chain[2]. In terms of the main chick-food insects, the densities of caterpillars (sawfly and Lepidoptera larvae) in particular have followed the general trend – except on one farm where traditional mixed farming with ley rotations is still practised[3]. Interestingly, this farm is the only part of the study area where partridge numbers have not declined since 1970 and it is notable for its abundance of corn buntings and skylarks, both declining farmland birds which feed their chicks on invertebrates, including caterpillars.

Although the Sussex study began a decade after the introduction of herbicides in cereals, its start pre-dates the use of foliar fungicides and of insecticides. One feature of the Sussex data is the dramatic decline of mycetophagous (fungus-eating) species, such as mould beetles and rove beetles, which appears to coincide with the rise in use of foliar fungicides[4]. Of greater relevance to partridges, however, is the increased application, in summer, of broad-spectrum insecticides. This has happened since the late 1980s.

Computerised projections based on the Sussex data have shown that slow-reproducing insects such as sawflies can take up to four years to recover from a single summer application of dimethoate[5]. Partridge chick survival rates on areas that are currently intensively treated with summer insecticides average a third lower than on areas with no or slight treatment, whereas there had been no difference in pre-insecticide years[3]. It is now accepted that this study of the grey partridge and its environment provides the best evidence of the indirect effects of pesticides on farmland birds[6].

## Sources and references

1. Potts, G. R. (1970) Recent changes in the farmland fauna with special reference to the decline of the grey partridge (Perdix perdix). Bird Study, 17: 145–166.

2. Aebischer, N. J. (1991) Twenty years of monitoring invertebrates and weeds in cereal fields in Sussex. In: Firbank, L. G., Carter, N. , Darbyshire, J. F. & Potts, G. R. (Eds) The Ecology of Temperate Cereal Fields. British Ecological Society Symposium, Blackwell Scientific Publications, Oxford. 305–31.

3. Aebischer, N. J. & Potts, G. R. (In press) Spatial changes in grey partridge (Perdix perdix) distribution in relation to 25 years of changing agriculture in Sussex, U.K. Gibier Faune Sauvage.

4. Aebischer, N. J. & Potts, G. R. (1990) Long-term changes in numbers of cereal invertebrates assessed by monitoring. 1990 Brighton Crop Protection Conference – Pests & Diseases. 163–72.

5. Aebischer, N. J. (1990) Assessing pesticide effects on non-target invertebrates using long-term monitoring and time-series modelling. Journal of Functional Ecology, 4: 369–73.

6. Campbell, L. H., Avery, M. I., Donald, P. F., Evans, A. D., Green, R. E. & Wilson, J. D. (1997) A review of the indirect effects of pesticides on birds. Joint Nature Conservation Committee Report, No. 227. Peterborough.

Distribution of grey partridge coveys censused on the Sussex Downs study area in autumn 1970. The study area is 22 kilometres from east to west.

Distribution of grey partridge coveys censused on the Sussex Downs study area in autumn 1994.

**Distribution of
river habitat:** kilometre
squares containing more than
0.75 hectares of river or
tidal coast. From OS
Geographic Reference map.

# 2.4 Rivers

## Current status

Britain has an oceanic climate dominated by a westerly air-stream off the Atlantic. This gives a rainfall pattern in which the west and north are wetter than the south and east. Moreover, many western districts are composed of igneous and metamorphic rocks, which are impervious to water, whereas the central and eastern areas consist of mainly sedimentary rocks, such as chalk and limestone, which are porous and can accumulate water.

Thus the landscape of the western districts contains a myriad rain-fed streams that feed river systems which spate quickly after heavy rain. In the east, lower rainfall and an absorbent land surface mean fewer streams, often spring-fed, running into rivers of a more consistent flow. This difference is reflected in the character of the counties, with 71% of kilometre squares in Scotland containing a river compared with 57% in Wales and only 47% in England.

## History and character

British rivers vary greatly in their form and, consequently, their habitat value to different species.

This variation stems from the great differences in gradients, geology, soil type and rainfall across the British Isles.

## River types

Broadly speaking, it is possible to distinguish several general river types[1,2].

### Steep-gradient rivers

In the uplands of Scotland, northern England, Wales and Devon, hard rocks and steep slopes give rise to rocky, turbulent rivers which carve into the land surface. Where these rivers feed onto shallower slopes, coarse material is deposited and their character changes to one of a gravel-bed river, still with a swift current. Such rivers mostly have good water quality but the chemistry can vary greatly according to geology. For example, rivers in Scotland and Devon, which flow off granite, tend to be acidic and lack nutrients, while, at the other extreme, those flowing off the limestones of the Pennines and Peak District have hard, nutrient-rich water.

Upland rivers are characterised by species of plants, insects and fish which are adapted either

to remain securely attached to rocks or to obtain protection from them. Plants include algae and mosses while the insect community includes species which are agile swimmers but also have low, flattened bodies to help them remain on the surface of the stones (eg. stoneflies and some ephemerid species). Typical fish species include trout, which seek out slack current areas, and juvenile salmon, which shelter in crevices among stones in fast currents.

### Moderate-gradient rivers

In moderate-gradient areas in eastern Scotland, northern and south-western England and Wales, rivers typically flow over deposited material (gravel, sands, silt and clay) instead of eroding the bedrock as happens in the uplands. These rivers meander and are characterised by successions of deep pools on the bends, with undercut banks and shallow gravel 'riffles' between the pools. Although much less powerful than upland rivers, spates still result in active bank erosion and movements of the gravel.

The ecology of such rivers can be more diverse than upland rivers. Invertebrates may be present, living on rooted plants, burrowing into silts on the beds of pools – or occupying the faster stony riffles, as they do in upland streams. The fish community may still contain salmon but trout do better because pools are more frequent. Coarse fish species, such as barbel, chub, dace and grayling, can also thrive.

In southern England there is another type of moderate-gradient stream which differs from the above stereotype. Because these streams flow off chalk, which is porous, they do not suffer from spates but have a more constant flow of very clear nutrient-rich water. Typically, they have a gravel bed and abundant plant growths.

### Low-gradient rivers

In areas of low-gradient, typically sedimentary basins in southern England (eg. Cambridgeshire, Somerset), slow rivers tend to flow over deposits of fine sediment. These rivers are relatively narrow and deep, with silty beds. There may be rich and diverse plant communities but species adapted to slow-flowing water dominate. The fish species present are largely coarse, eg. roach, chub, bream, pike and perch.

## Problems affecting British rivers

British rivers, apart from being naturally diverse, have also been greatly affected by man's actions. These actions vary according to the river and different river types may be affected differently by the same action.

### Upland rivers

Apart from forestry and hydro-electric schemes, upland rivers have been less affected by human activities than lowland agricultural areas. However, in some areas the problems that do occur can be very damaging.

- **Acid rain** affects parts of Wales, Cumbria and south-western Scotland and has completely eliminated fish from some streams in these areas. The susceptibility of a river to acidification by acid rain depends on geology (a granite catchment is more vulnerable than a limestone one, for example) and also on the proximity of coniferous forests which filter pollutants from the air[3].

- **Over-grazing** has resulted in major physical changes to rivers in some areas because of bank damage caused by increased livestock densities. Densities of sheep and, in some localities, cattle have increased markedly in recent decades. As a result, upland streams tend to be wide, shallow and lack the bank-side cover they once had. This has reduced the amount of habitat, not only for fish but also for otters and nesting wildfowl[4,5]. The problem is, however, less serious in the north.

- **Coniferous afforestation** has had a major impact in some upland areas, where it has led to increased erosion following ploughing for planting, reduced flows as the trees become established, a concentration of airborne acidic pollutants[6] and overshading. Overshading reduces bank-side vegetation, resulting in increased erosion.

- **Drainage**, through both the dredging of streams and rivers and the no longer approved ditching, or 'gripping', of moorland areas, has had a significant impact through the loss of channel features, changing flow regimes and increased erosion in some upland areas, especially in the north of England[7].

- **Hydro-electricity and reservoir construction** have had a major impact on a number of rivers in the Scottish Highlands. The development of hydro-electric power stations in the 1950s has greatly altered the flow regimes of some rivers[8] and, in parts of England and Wales, water reservoirs have had a similar effect.

- **Sheep dip** is a potentially alarming problem that has recently arisen from the use of synthetic pyrethroid sheep-dipping chemicals that are extremely toxic to aquatic life. Invertebrate populations have recently been wiped out along many kilometres of stream by these chemicals[9].

*Lowland rivers*

Rivers in lowland areas have been widely affected by urbanisation, industrialisation and an increased demand for water.

- **Land drainage** in lowland areas of Britain, as a consequence of agriculture and urbanisation, has led to much river modification. In fact, it is estimated that up to 97% of all natural river and stream channels in some areas have been modified by man[10]. Such impacts can have a long history and include the draining of fens, the creation of water-meadow systems in the 18th and 19th centuries and the intensification of field drainage in the 19th century. In England and Wales, large co-ordinated drainage schemes took place, even in major rivers, after the Second World War to improve land drainage for agriculture[11]. However, in Scotland, where there is no statutory body in charge of land drainage, co-ordinated schemes did not occur; farmers acted independently.

  Land drainage by dredging affects the ecology of rivers by destroying the natural stream structure of pools and riffles, vegetation cover, channel shapes and flow regimes. In fact, most land drainage schemes have created completely artificial watercourses, a process known as 'channelisation'[12]. Channelisation and dredging can drastically reduce fish populations and species diversity generally, both within rivers and in adjacent wetland areas. Fortunately, the large schemes of the 1950s are regarded with some distaste nowadays but stream- and river-clearing operations are still widespread.

- **Water-quality effects** in lowland rivers are especially marked because of the greater use of these areas by man. During the 19th century most rivers in urbanised or industrial areas

became polluted but these problems are gradually being overcome. Now, a less serious but more insidious and widespread type of pollution results from modern agricultural practices. Leached fertilisers have resulted in a general enrichment of rivers in lowland Britain, altering their ecology as a consequence. However, inputs of other, more obvious pollutants, such as pesticides, slurry and silage run-off, are fortunately now more rigorously controlled.

  Inputs of fine sediment into rivers have increased; these result from erosion of arable land, especially where autumn sowing is practised. Sediment inputs also occur where high densities of stock have access to stream banks. Sediment can fundamentally change a stream's ecology by favouring different plant, invertebrate and fish communities. This subject was comprehensively reviewed by the National Rivers Authority[13] (now the Environment Agency, or EA).

  Clearly the occurrence of agricultural effects depends on the nature of the agriculture in an area. For example, in western England, problems arising from intensive dairy production are common while, in the east, problems stemming from arable production prevail. Furthermore, the nature of the river catchment is also important. For example, the soft clay soils of much of lowland England give rise to turbid rivers, whereas southern chalk streams, and Scottish lowland streams flowing off crystalline rocks, have clearer water.

- **Impoundment of water** by weirs, which were probably intended to provide a water supply to industries and mills, to aid navigation or for irrigation, has frequently altered the physical form of rivers in many parts of lowland Britain.

Impoundment produces slow, silty rivers with a radically different ecology to what would otherwise exist[5].

- **Over-grazing** of riverbanks by livestock has a major impact on the ecology of lowland rivers in many areas. This is particularly true in western England and Wales. Cattle especially denude bank-side vegetation and consequently increase erosion rates. Rivers become wider, shallower and more silty than in the absence of grazing[5,14].

- **Water abstraction** in urbanised areas puts great pressure on water resources. In England there are few lowland rivers which are not affected to some extent by the increasing demand for abstraction. Some, such as the River Darent in Kent, are now prone to drying up altogether[15].

- **Woodland planting** with poplars and other trees was carried out in many areas of old water-meadow after the Second World War. This has resulted in soil erosion problems similar to those caused by conifers in the uplands.

## Conservation plan

Almost all British rivers have been, and are being, affected to a considerable degree by human activities. Some of these impacts are lessening but, where they are not, measures are needed to remove the on-going causes of the problems and to rectify past damage. Many solutions are known and are technically simple. The major stumbling block is their implementation. Rivers are a resource often shared between conflicting interests and therefore riverine habitats are inherently difficult to manage. To do so requires co-operation,

understanding and compromise between all river-users.

## Co-ordination of statutory conservation bodies

A fundamental requirement in achieving successful river management is a co-ordinating body (or bodies) to reconcile the different interests. Currently numerous bodies exist and each one fulfils some aspect of river management.

Some bodies have a statutory mandate to regulate against particular river uses that are not in the public interest. For example, in England and Wales the EA has statutory powers to maintain water quality and to prosecute polluters. It also has statutory duties to maintain fisheries and is responsible for land drainage. Some of these actions (especially land drainage) may be damaging to riverine habitats, so a conservation division also exists within the EA to advise on methods of minimising harmful effects. In Scotland a similar role is performed by the Scottish Environmental Protection Agency (SEPA) but there is no fisheries or land drainage division. The only statutory fisheries management in Scotland is performed by District Salmon Fishery Boards.

## Regulation of river use

English Nature, the Countryside Council for Wales and Scottish Natural Heritage advise Government ministers on aspects of river conservation and can impose constraints on river use by designating rivers with a particular conservation interest as Sites of Special Scientific Interest or Special Areas of Conservation. Until recently few rivers have been designated but this is changing, with some 27 rivers currently being designated in England alone[16]. It is intended that these designations will prevent further problems affecting these rivers.

However, a major problem in all rivers is that many of the more insidious types of pollution, for which no-one can easily be blamed (eg. eutrophication and sediment inputs), are not sufficiently damaging to the wider public interest to be under statutory control. Improvements in this area must be voluntary and can be hard and expensive to achieve. Some statutory bodies have set up initiatives to encourage good practice by providing incentives, eg. the pioneering EA Land Care project which has been launched in the catchment of the Hampshire Avon. In addition, Government agencies run a number of Agri-environment-subsidised schemes (eg. Environmentally Sensitive Area payments, Countryside Stewardship, the Countryside Premium Scheme) to encourage the adoption of environmentally-friendly farming in particular areas.

## Role of non-statutory conservation groups

Many non-statutory groups are active in some form of river conservation. Most of these could be loosely defined as pressure groups which represent public and private interests (eg. angling organisations, such as the Anglers' Conservation Association, Salmon and Trout Association, Atlantic Salmon Trust, local fishery associations and river-protection societies, and general conservation organisations, such as the Wildlife Trusts, Friends of the Earth and the Royal Society for the Protection of Birds). They raise public awareness of important issues and so influence the statutory organisations and Government. By concentrating on single issues they can often meet a specific conservation goal which could not be achieved by a public body, whose policy must achieve a balance between conservation and the needs of developers.

A major recent development has been the establishment of numerous non-statutory co-ordinating groups whose roles are to implement river conservation and rehabilitation work. These groups can take various forms. Some are fishery-led (eg. the Tweed Foundation or the West Galloway Fisheries Trust) or have a significant fisheries input (eg. the West Country Rivers Trust or the Wye Foundation). Others may be initiated by more community-based concerns (eg. the Local Government-funded Pang Valley Countryside Project) or even by major conservation organisations (eg. Worldwide Fund for Nature's Wild Rivers Initiative in Scotland).

The work of these bodies can overlap with some of the functions of statutory bodies or be additional to them. A major part of their role has been to seek new forms of funding unavailable to statutory bodies but they may also be more successful in achieving specific objectives than a statutory body which has to satisfy a range of numerous objectives.

Finally, a major force in the conservation and management of rivers is, of course, the landowners. Ultimately, whatever the roles of the regulating bodies, it is landowners' actions and the uses to which they put their rivers and adjacent land that are the most important determinants of river conservation.

## Conservation actions

The biggest issue in river conservation is getting remedial work done on the ground. The challenge is to establish the most effective co-operation and co-ordination between diverse river-users at the lowest possible cost. River conservation work involves distinct elements which we think should be performed by different types of co-ordinating bodies.

- Water quality and quantity are fundamental requirements of freshwater life and should continue to be looked after by statutory bodies such as the EA and the SEPA, operating to the highest professional standards.

- Statutory bodies involved in river- and land-use management need to collaborate closely and form a joint policy on river quality (diffuse pollution, land-use effects and land drainage), with firm, attainable objectives. Current duplication of schemes should be eliminated. Policies should be objective-led rather than directed at furthering the interests of the agency or department.

- Agricultural subsidy policies should recognise margins of watercourses as having a high environmental priority and be altered to provide funding for the agreed conservation policy on individual rivers. The subsidies on offer from current incentive schemes are frequently much less than those available for conventional farming, even from the same bodies.

- The restoration of riverine habitats that have been degraded by dredging and intensive land use is a priority for the 21st century. Again, statutory bodies need to agree a long-term strategy as to how past habitat damage should be rectified. Long-term catchment management plans being drawn up by the EA go some way towards this but more agreement is needed on what must be done in conservation terms.

- In addition to implementation of habitat restoration by statutory bodies, improvements by riparian owners and river trusts within the agreed framework should be encouraged.

- The widespread establishment of trusts of river-users may be the most successful way of establishing local co-operation and management. Concerned river-users are more likely to achieve their goals because they have better-defined objectives and are more cost-efficient.

- Also, river conservation is likely to be adopted on a large scale only if there are users who have an interest in maintaining, and are paying for, the conservation value. This is already being demonstrated by the recently established river trusts, which were all initially promoted by fisheries interests.

## Sources and references

1. Hynes, H. B. N. (1972) *The Ecology of Running Waters*. University Press, Liverpool.

2. Holmes, N. T. H. (1983) *Classification of British Rivers According to Their Flora*. The Nature Conservancy Council, Peterborough.

3. Ward, J. & Browning, D. (1997) *Acid Rain – a Perspective*. Institute of Energy, London.

4. Anon. (1994) *The Tweed Foundation: 1994 Progress Review and Report*. The Tweed Foundation, Melrose.

5. Giles, N. & Summers, D. W. (1996) *Helping Fish in Lowland Streams*. Game Conservancy Limited, Fordingbridge, Hampshire.

6. Egglishaw, H. J. (1985) Afforestation and fisheries. In: Alabaster, J. S. (Ed.) *Habitat Modification and Freshwater Fisheries*. Butterworths, Sevenoaks, Kent. 236–44.

7. Newborn, D. & Booth, F. (1992) The ecological impact of moorland drainage. *The Game Conservancy Review of 1991*, 23: 106–9.

8. Mills, D. H. (1989) *Ecology and Management of Atlantic Salmon*. Chapman & Hall, London.

9. Pearce, F. (1997) Sheep dips poison river life. *New Scientist* (11 January): 4.

10. Brookes, A. & Sheilds, F. D. (1996) Perpectives on river channel restoration. In: Brookes, A. & Sheilds, F. D. (Eds) *River Channel Restoration*. John Wiley & Sons Ltd, Chichester. 1–19.

11. Purseglove, J. (1988) *Taming the Flood*. Oxford University Press, Oxford.

12. Keller, E. A. (1975) Channelisation: a search for a better way. *Geology*, 3: 246–8.

13. Anon. (1992) *The Influence of Agriculture on the Quality of Natural Waters in England and Wales*. Water Quality Series. National Rivers Authority, Bristol.

14. Anon. (1995) *Understanding Riverbank Erosion*. National Rivers Authority, Northumbria & Yorkshire Region, Leeds.

15. Hunt, I. D. (1996) *High & Dry. The Impacts of Over-abstraction of Water on Wildlife*. The Biodiversity Challenge Group, c/o RSPB, Sandy, Beds.

16. Anon. (1997) *Wildlife and Freshwater: An Agenda for Sustainable Management*. English Nature, Peterborough.

# 3. Game conservation issues

Involving, as it does, an active role by man, game management by its very nature is more controversial than a simple nature protection approach would be. Apart from the ethics of taking quarry species for sport, there are a few areas where the management of game is misunderstood. The Game Conservancy Trust will continue to explore these areas in a factual and scientific manner, and will develop an approach that supports wildlife conservation in its widest sense.

# 3.1 Game and wildlife conservation

A beetle bank dividing a large cereal field

It is a common view, held by many people living in the countryside, that on estates and farms where gamebird conservation is integrated with forestry and agriculture, many species benefit and the landscape and wildlife are richer. The reasons are sympathetic habitat management, habitat creation and a reduction in game-predators. Woodland planting and coppicing, maintaining hedgerows, using chick-food-friendly insecticides on cereal crops in June, planting cover crops for holding and driving birds in the winter, feeding tonnes of grain to pheasants in the winter, regularly maintaining a patchwork habitat of heather structures by burning, maintaining stream banks for brown trout and controlling corvids and foxes all play a role. Over the last 20 years, much of our research has focused on quantifying the effects of game management on the wider flora and fauna.

## Farmland

### Field boundaries

Field boundaries are often the principal nesting sites of partridges and pheasants. Many boundaries have been maintained and managed for this purpose while others were being destroyed to increase field sizes and accommodate large machinery.

The essential element of nesting cover is the raised bank of tussocky, perennial grasses and wildflowers at the base of a hedge, wall, fence line or ditch. If properly maintained, the perennial grassy cover prevents colonisation by aggressive, annual arable weeds, such as cleavers and barren brome, which can otherwise easily spread into adjacent crops. Many farmers respond to these weeds by increasing the amounts of herbicide used at crop edges or by spraying hedge bottoms, with disastrous consequences for wildlife. By maintaining nesting cover, the loss of weed flora and subsequent conservation damage are avoided. Research to prevent the degradation of perennial grassy hedge bottoms and to promote the use of selective herbicides to control problem weeds has been led by game conservation scientists[1].

Grassy nesting banks are also chosen as over-wintering cover by a range of important beneficial predatory insects and spiders[2]. In spring, they emerge from this cover and move back into arable crops. Many studies have now clearly demonstrated their importance in eating aphids and other crop pests, helping to prevent pest damage and reducing the need for insecticides. Partridge nesting banks have also been shown to be good nesting sites for species such as yellowhammers and lesser whitethroats[3].

## Beetle banks

Our research on hedgebanks led us to develop 'beetle banks'. These are strips of grass on a raised earth bank designed to be run across large tracts of arable land and not to interfere with farm machinery. They avoid the direct costs of planting and maintaining a new hedgerow and also the indirect costs resulting from the reduced efficiency of large machines operating in small, irregularly shaped fields. Beetle banks quickly become excellent over-wintering sites for aphid-eating beetles and spiders. Up to 1,500 predators per

*The thick grass bank at the base of a hedge provides nesting cover for yellowhammers and lesser whitethroats*

*Butterfly numbers per kilometre along two types of cereal headland on a Hampshire farm in 1987. Three times as many butterflies were seen on conservation headlands compared with normal ones.*

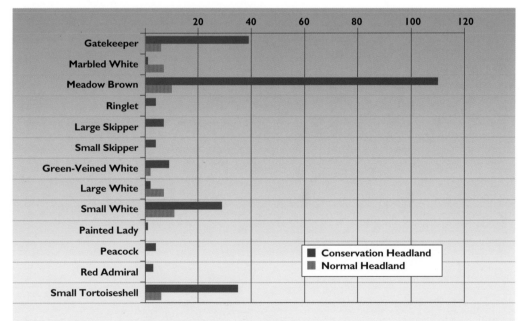

square metre in the second winter after establishment have been found in beetle banks[4] and so far grey partridges, red-legged partridges, skylarks and harvest mice have nested in them.

## Cereal-field margins and conservation headlands

As the near ubiquitous use of herbicides and insecticides on modern cereals causes poor gamebird chick survival, we have experimented with cereal-field headlands (the outermost six metres of the crop). By spraying these areas only with selective products, we create insect and weed-rich strips that provide food for wild gamebird chicks and thereby improve their rates of survival[5]. These 'conservation headlands', as we have called them, also benefit other, often endangered, species of farmland wildlife[6].

## Beneficial effects on wildlife

We have shown that butterfly numbers along field margins with conservation headlands are much higher than on fully sprayed headlands[7]. Research on butterfly behaviour indicated that it is the broad-leaved weeds, such as field pansy, which act as the nectar sources that are missing on fully sprayed fields. Conservation headlands also act as a no-spray buffer, protecting the hedge bottom from pesticide drift and, as a consequence, helping the hedgerow flowers and butterflies. In the 1980s we conducted annual butterfly counts and found that the abundance of satyrid butterflies remained stable or increased on farms using conservation headlands while, on nearby nature reserves, numbers of these same butterfly species were declining.

Vertebrates also do well near conservation headlands. We radio-tracked wood mice and found that they spent as much as 46% of their time for-

A six metre wide conservation headland around a cereal crop

A gatekeeper butterfly in a conservation headland

**Presence of rare weed species found in a survey of conservation headlands in 18 arable farms in 1987.**

| Scientific name | Common name | Number of farms |
| --- | --- | --- |
| Anthemis arvensis | Corn chamomile | 1 |
| Apera interrupta | Dense-flowered silky bent | 1 |
| Euphorbia exigua | Dwarf spurge | 7 |
| Fumaria micrantha | Dense-flowered fumitory | 4 |
| Galeopsis angustifolia | Narrow-leaved hemp nettle | 1 |
| Kicksia elatine | Sharp-leaved fluellin | 5 |
| Kicksia spuria | Round-leaved fluellin | 5 |
| Legousia hybrida | Venus' looking-glass | 10 |
| Lithospermum arvense | Corn gromwell | 2 |
| Papaver argemone | Long-headed prickly poppy | 4 |
| Papaver hybridum | Round-headed prickly poppy | 5 |
| Petroselinum segetum | Corn caraway | 2 |
| Ranunculus arvensis | Corn buttercup | 1 |
| Scandix pecten-veneris | Shepherd's needle | 1 |
| Silene noctiflora | Night-flowering catchfly | 5 |
| Stachys arvensis | Field woundwort | 1 |
| Valerianella dentata | Narrow-fruited cornsalad | 2 |

aging within conservation headlands, even though these headlands comprised, on average, only 6% of the area of their home range[8].

Many insects are natural enemies of cereal pests and they also benefit from conservation headlands. Our work has shown how economically important species of hoverfly use the nectar and pollen of flowering weeds, such as charlock and mayweed, found in conservation headlands[9] and how we can increase the numbers of these important predators in cereal crops by the use of conservation headlands. Generalist predators, such as ground beetles, were better fed (a higher proportion of beetles had full stomachs) and female beetles produced more eggs in conservation headlands

than individuals in fully sprayed headlands[10].

Many of Britain's rarest plants are arable annual wildflowers. Many of these once widespread and abundant flowers are now extremely rare. Of the 25 species of arable wildflowers listed by the Botanical Society of the British Isles as uncommon or rare, 19 were found in conservation headlands where farmers interested in game conservation used less herbicide to control broad-leaved weeds. Our research has now enabled us to formulate management plans for such species as shepherd's needle (*Scandix pecten-veneris*), pheasant's eye (*Adonis annua*), mousetail (*Myosurus minimus*) and corn buttercup (*Ranunculus arvensis*)[11].

## Set-aside and Wild Bird Cover Option

These days set-aside offers possibilities for creating tailor-made habitats around the farm, benefiting arable game species and wildlife alike. Under the various non-rotational schemes, the option of leaving areas of grassland uncut, especially at field edges, resulted from our work to improve nesting cover. The Wild Bird Cover Option on set-aside has evolved from gamebird conservation ideas designed to create cover in the winter (food and shelter) and brood cover in the summer. Mixtures of two crop groups can be sown in the autumn and the spring to create the correct species composition and structure to provide game and wildlife with the resources they need at critical times of the year. Mixtures using cereals (triticale, a cross between wheat and rye, is particularly useful where rabbits are a problem) with an insect-rich 'contaminant', such as quinoa, can reproduce the beneficial conditions we strive to achieve with conservation headlands.

In winter we use mixtures based on kale to provide cover, mixed with linseed, quinoa or a cereal to provide the mixture of two crop groups. If left for a second year, the plants will set seed and provide a winter larder for flocks of finches and buntings, many species of which have shown alarming rates of decline on farmland in the last 25 years. Non-residual herbicides, and even a little nitrogen fertiliser, are allowed on Wild Bird Cover. Such practices are generally not allowed in the set-aside schemes of other EU member states, making Britain's scheme the envy of Europe. In a recent survey, members of the Trust, because of their interest in game, were found to be 20 times more likely than non-members to take up these wildlife-friendly set-aside management options. Much of Britain's scheme was based on research initiated by us for the conservation of game[12].

# Woodlands

Pheasants provide an important motivation for landowners to create, sympathetically manage and retain small farm woodlands. Estimates of the extent of pheasant shooting and its influence on woodland management vary. Helen Piddington of the Department of Land Economy, University of Cambridge, published a report in 1980 which estimated that shooting took place on 58% of agricultural properties, increasing to 88% of properties more than 400 hectares in size[13]. She also reported that 33% of owners had retained small woods, belts or spinneys or had planted them for game purposes. One in five owners had chosen species of trees for new plantings with pheasants in mind.

In a report to the Standing Conference on Countryside Sports in 1983, members of the Country Landowners Association were asked what were their main incentives for planting or managing small woodlands[14]. Two-thirds stated game conservation as a main reason for retaining existing woodland and over half claimed game as a main reason for planting new woodlands. Game interests were second only to landscape quality as an incentive for woodland management and were usually of more importance than either timber or wildlife generally.

In 1988 we sent a questionnaire to 400 contributors to our National Game-Bag Census, asking for details of their woodland management to encourage pheasants. From 150 replies, 81% had conducted some woodland management for pheasants and over 30% had either planted woodland, felled and replanted or coppiced it for game management. Applicants to the Forestry Commission for financial aid under the Broad-leaved Woodland Grant Scheme were asked by the Forestry Commission to rank a series of aims for planting new woodlands. Game interest constituted one of the first three objectives in over 60% of cases.

In 1996, the Game Management Project co-ordinated by Graham Cox of the University of Bath compared rates of woodland planting and management between farms according to whether or not they released pheasants[15]. Farms releasing pheasants were three times more likely to plant new woodlands, four times as likely to plant shrubs, seven times as likely to manage rides and nine times as likely to coppice their woodlands.

Woodlands for pheasants differ from plantations for timber. In particular they include large rides (more than 30 metres wide), shrubby woodland edge and an interior with gaps in the canopy (skylighting) to let light onto the woodland floor. These have benefits for other species sharing the woodlands.

## Beneficial effects on wildlife

### Butterflies

Many woodland butterflies, particularly the fritillaries, are declining. This has been attributed, mainly, to a lack of coppicing. Rides and management for pheasants increase the amount of light to the benefit of both pheasants and butterflies. In a large woodland block in Dorset, we recently compared butterfly numbers between different habitat types, two of which were managed for pheasants. Among the habitats we examined were:

- Large woodland rides, 30–50 metres wide, cut for pheasant shooting;

- Mixed conifer and broad-leaves areas with an open canopy and shrub layer managed for pheasants;

*A comparison of the numbers of butterflies found along transects through different habitats in a large woodland block in Dorset in 1986. The top two habitats are managed for pheasants[13].*

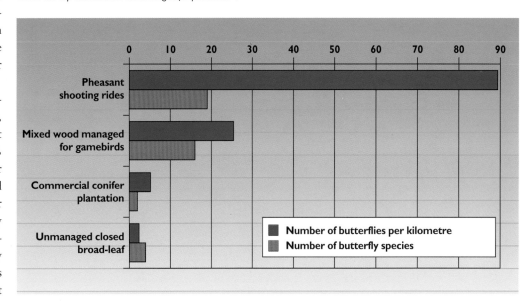

*A pearl-bordered fritillary – a woodland butterfly that benefits from pheasant management*

**Percentage of farmers answering 'Yes' to questions regarding game conservation of their farms.**

| Question | Shoot farms | Non-shoot farms |
|---|---|---|
| Is any special management undertaken to improve conservation on the farm? | 84% | 59% |
| Is farming modified from optimum levels to benefit wildlife on the farm? | 53% | 37% |
| Are timings of operations altered to benefit wildlife on the farm? | 53% | 30% |
| Are selective pesticides used? | 58% | 30% |
| Are field edges left unsprayed? | 66% | 33% |
| Are hedges kept and managed? | 84% | 52% |
| Are winter cover crops planted? | 87% | 0% |

N = 38 farms with shooting and 27 farms without shooting.

Stands of post-thicket conifers;

Unmanaged broad-leaved woodland with neglected hazel coppice and a closed canopy.

We counted butterflies along transects in each habitat throughout one summer and the average number of butterflies seen was recorded. The unmanaged broad-leaves and the conifer plantations contained fewest species and lowest densities. Much higher numbers of butterflies and butterfly species were found along the large rides and in the mixed managed woodland[16].

In the late 1980s strong associations were claimed between the decline of woodland butterflies and the increase in numbers of pheasants reared. When examined scientifically, this relationship proved false. In fact remaining populations of woodland fritillaries were most commonly found in woodlands with populations of pheasants, benefiting from the positive management practices undertaken[17].

*Songbirds*

We also examined the bird communities in 1,200 different woodland plots in Sussex and related these to the structure of the habitat. From these data we found that bird communities could be categorised into distinct groups on the basis of their habitat needs.

The highest numbers of bird species were in mature mixed woodland. In this group were most of the common woodland birds, such as the tits, woodpeckers, nuthatch and tree creeper. However, another group, associated with woodland with open glades and shrubs, included species such as song thrush, spotted flycatcher and some warblers. Pheasants belonged to this second group, so it is apparent that there is a particular range of bird species which benefit from woodland management for pheasants[18].

## Game and nature conservation interests

In some instances there may be a potential conflict of interests between game management and nature conservation. This can arise, for example, where release pens for pheasant and partridge are placed within particularly sensitive and biologically important, semi-natural ancient woodlands. Research has enabled us to produce management guidelines and codes of good practice to prevent such difficulties arising[19].

A questionnaire-survey of farms in Essex (see table opposite), with and without driven game shooting in 1995, found game management strategies on the former which would significantly improve habitats for farmland wildlife. The results of the survey covered 250 shoots comprising more than 10% of agricultural holdings in the county. They clearly revealed that farms having shoots with driven game were twice as likely to moderate their farmland management practices to benefit wildlife than farms without shoots[20].

In summary, in the lowlands, game management has been shown to be an important motivation for managing land more sympathetically than where no game interests are held. The subsequent benefits to non-game species of animals and plants are quantifiable.

## Uplands

Upland habitats cover some 30–35% of the British land surface and support many populations of breeding birds of international conservation importance. British moorland has large breeding populations of golden plover, dunlin and greenshank. British populations of these birds are decreasing. Open moorland dominated by heather is the characteristic upland vegetation of many areas. One of the major uses of heather moorland is for red grouse shooting. Management to increase grouse densities typically includes the control of predation and the rotational burning of heather.

In an analysis of vegetation cover on estates with and without game, made both in the 1940s and the 1980s, it is clear that, where there is an interest in game, the loss of heather has been less[21].

Since 1988, we have been monitoring grouse, their predators and other upland birds on 42 moors throughout much of the north of England and Scotland. On each moor, birds in a square kilometre have been counted at least twice a year for at least five years. These extensive long-term surveys have found that the more grouse on a moor, the more dunlin and golden plover are present.

Golden plovers, like red grouse, are typical moorland birds clearly benefiting from the effects of grouse-moor management. Golden plovers selectively nest on areas of short vegetation, avoiding areas with tall rank heather or thick grass. They consequently benefit from the burning programmes initiated to aid grouse. Meadow pipits were also observed more frequently on moors where the number of grouse shot was high[22].

The control of predation is a feature of grouse management. The culling of foxes and crows on moorland is beneficial to the nesting success of many other ground-nesting birds, although how this relates to their long-term breeding numbers needs to be experimentally tested. Certainly more mountain hares are found on moors where grouse are managed. Many birds of prey, like merlins, peregrines and hen harriers, are well adapted for hunting over open moors. It is therefore particularly important that we resolve the conflict of interests between grouse management and raptor conservation, and find a way of accommodating these birds on upland moors (see particularly *Hen harrier*, page 239).

The alternatives to grouse management on upland moors are intensive grazing (by sheep or deer), afforestation or a system of nature reserves. All agree that neither of the first two options would benefit grouse, or many of the birds that share this unique open habitat, and there is a limit to the potential area of nature reserves.

## Wetlands

Land drainage has always been a key component in agricultural improvement. Indeed field drains were one of the earliest developments of the agricultural revolution. Furthermore, the remaining wetland habitats, especially rivers, have often been

*Damselflies need bank-side vegetation*

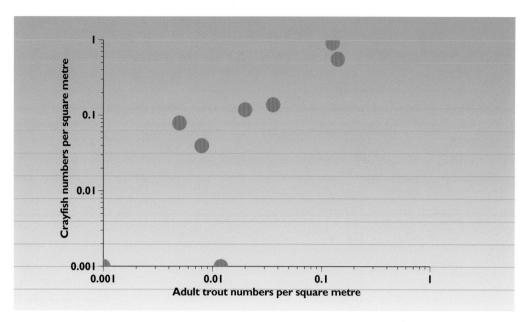

*Trout and crayfish abundance on the River Piddle at Tolpuddle, Dorset. Creating good habitat for trout on this river also benefits crayfish which like similar habitat conditions.*

viewed as mere channels for getting surplus water and other agricultural and urban effluent directly to the sea. As a result, wetlands are scarce and over the long term their quality has deteriorated, even though significant improvements have been made in sewage treatment and pollution control since the Second World War. Land management for waterfowl or snipe, can therefore provide much-needed habitat for other species of waders. Lakes managed for waterfowl, containing artificially created islands or nesting rafts, provide safe nesting havens for ground-nesting birds such as little ringed plover[23].

The game interest, either in salmon and trout or in coarse fish, or indeed in waterfowl, has made an important contribution to habitat creation and the maintenance of wetlands. Although the differing needs of waterfowl and fish often mean that achieving high densities of one usually results in the reduction or exclusion of the other, both groups benefit from improved habitat. So do other species of plants and animals. Thus fishermen and wildfowlers concerned with providing habitats for breeding game will be looking for abundant bank-side vegetation to act as both overhead escape cover and shade for fish and as nesting cover of sufficient height for waterfowl.

Bank-side vegetation is also important for highly valued aquatic animals, such as dragonflies, damselflies, water-voles and otters, and it serves to reduce surface run-off, which may contain pollutants, from adjacent agricultural land. This vegetation also stabilises river banks, which in turn keep streams narrow, fast and deep. Clear, fast streams are important for many aquatic invertebrates, such as mayflies and our native white-clawed crayfish, which seems particularly suited to trout-stream habitats. In a study comparing crayfish densities on stretches of stream, six times as many crayfish were found in areas managed for gamefish compared with those remaining unmanaged[24].

## Sources and references

1. Boatman, N. D. (1993) Selective control of *Bromus sterilis* in field boundaries with fluazifop-P-butyl. *1993 Brighton Crop Protection Conference – Weeds.* 349–55.

2. Sotherton, N. W. (1984) The distribution and abundance of predatory arthropods overwintering on farmland. *Annals of Applied Biology,* 105: 423–9.

3. Stoate, C. S. & Szczur, J. (1994) Nest site selection and territory distribution of yellowhammer (*Emberiza citrinella*) and whitethroat (*Sylvia communis*) in field margins. In: Boatman, N. D. (Ed.) *Field Margins: Integrating Agriculture and Conservation.* British Crop Protection Council, Farnham, Surrey. 129–32.

4. Thomas, M. B., Wratten, S. D. & Sotherton, N. W. (1991) Creation of 'island' habitats in farmland to manipulate populations of beneficial arthropods: predator densities and emigration. *Journal of Applied Ecology,* 28: 906–18.

5. Rands, M. R. W. (1985) Pesticide use on cereals and the survival of grey partridge chicks: A field experiment. *Journal of Applied Ecology*, **22**: 49–54.

6. Sotherton, N. W. (1991) Conservation headlands: A practical combination of intensive cereal farming and conservation. In: Firbank, L. G., Carter, N., Darbyshire, J. F. & Potts, G. R. (Eds) *Ecology of Temperate Cereal Fields*. British Ecological Society Symposium, Blackwell Scientific Publications, Oxford. 373-97.

7. Dover, J. W., Sotherton, N. W. & Gobbett, K. (1990) Reduced pesticide inputs on cereal field margins: the effects on butterfly abundance. *Ecological Entomology*, **15**: 17–24.

8. Tew, T. E., MacDonald, D. W. & Rands, M. R. W. (1992) Herbicide application affects microhabitat use by arable wood mice (*Apodemus sylvaticus*). *Journal of Applied Ecology*, **29**: 532–9.

9. Cowgill, S. E., Wratten, S. D. & Sotherton, N. W. (1993) The effects of weeds on the numbers of hoverfly (Diptera: Syrphidae) adults and the distribution and composition of their eggs in winter wheat. *Annals of Applied Biology*, **123**: 499–515.

10. Chiverton, P. A. & Sotherton, N. W. (1991) The effects on beneficial arthropods of the exclusion of herbicides from cereal crop edges. *Journal of Applied Ecology*, **28**: 1027–40.

11. Wilson, P. J. (1994) Managing field margins for the conservation of the arable flora. In: Boatman, N. D. (Ed.) *Field Margins: Integrating Agriculture and Conservation*. British Crop Protection Council, Farnham, Surrey. 253–8.

12. Sotherton, N. W. (1997) Land use changes and the decline of farmland wildlife: and appraisal of the set-aside approach. *Biological Conservation*, **83**: 259–68.

13. Piddington, H. R. (1981) Land management for shooting and fishing. A study of practice on farms and estates in Great Britain 1971–76. *Occasional Paper of the Department of Land Economy, University of Cambridge*, No. 13.

14. Cobham Resource Consultants (1992) *Countryside Sports: Their Economic and Conservation Significance*. The Standing Conference on Countryside Sports, Reading.

15. Cox, G., Watkins, C. & Winter, M. (1996) *Game Management in England: Implications for Public Access, the Rural Economy and the Environment*. Countryside and Community Research Unit, Cheltenham and Gloucester College, Gloucester.

16. Robertson, P. A., Woodburn, M. I. A. & Hill, D. A. (1988) The effects of woodland management for pheasants on the abundance of butterflies in Dorset, England. *Biological Conservation*, **45**: 159–67.

17. Clarke, S. A. & Robertson, P. A. (1993) The relative effects of woodland management and pheasant predation on survival of the pearl-bordered and small pearl-bordered fritillaries in the south of England. *Biological Conservation*, **65**: 199–203.

18. Robertson, P. A. (1990) *Woodland Management for Pheasants*. Forestry Commission Research Information Note. HMSO, London.

19. Carroll, J. P. & Robertson, P. A. (1997) *Integrated Pheasant Management and Woodland Conservation*. Game Conservancy Limited, Fordingbridge, Hampshire.

20. Howard, N. (1995) *Lowland Game Shooting: Its Significance and Management, and the Farm Income of Farms and Estates in Essex*. Unpublished B.A. thesis, Department of Geography, University of Leicester.

21. Barton, A. F. & Robertson, P. A. (1997) *Land Use Change in the Scottish Uplands, 1945–1990, in Relation to Grouse Shooting Interests*. The Game Conservancy Trust, Fordingbridge, Hampshire.

22. Hudson, P. (1992) *Grouse in Space and Time: The Population Biology of a Managed Gamebird*. Game Conservancy Limited, Fordingbridge, Hampshire.

23. Giles, N. (1992) *Wildlife after Gravel: Twenty Years of Practical Research by The Game Conservancy and ARC*. Game Conservancy Limited, Fordingbridge, Hampshire.

24. Phillips, D. R., Summers, D. W. & Shields, B. A. (1996) *Investigations into the Habitat Use of the White-clawed Crayfish* (Austropotamobius pallipes) *in the River Piddle, Dorset. English Nature's Species Recovery Programme*. The Game Conservancy Trust, Fordingbridge, Hampshire.

# 3.2 The relationship between predator and prey

About 8,000 years ago, during the Mesolithic period, man was a tribal hunter of the forests and northern tundra, perhaps much as the North American Indians were before contact with Europeans changed their life-style irretrievably. At that time, Britain contained a whole suite of mammalian predators adapted to taking a range of different-sized prey animals[1, 8]. These predators, when combined with predatory birds, would certainly have influenced the abundance of many of the prey animals.

However, it is now becoming appreciated that larger predators also regularly kill smaller ones – a phenomenon termed 'intra-guild predation'[9]. This not only affects the abundance of the smaller predators but may in turn take much of the predation pressure off smaller prey. In North America, wolves kill or displace coyotes, which in turn kill or displace foxes – greatly benefiting the waterfowl. Where coyotes have been killed off by livestock farmers, foxes have increased, which has led to increased predation by foxes on nesting ducks[6]. In southern Europe, where there are lynx, there appear to be few foxes[2]. It is also known that foxes kill stoats and martens, though what effect this has on stoat and marten numbers is unknown[4, 5].

Thus, in a primeval ecosystem, such as the Mesolithic one, there was not only a range of predators adapted to different sizes of prey but also a hierarchy of predators whose members interacted. Thus the abundance of any single predator species would have been influenced by the effect of the larger predators in the hierarchy above it as well as by the overall abundance of its prey. The figures on page 66 depict only mammalian predators but we should be aware that predatory birds interact in a similar way and that some of the birds prey on the mammals – eg. eagles kill foxes.

Today, in most of our countryside, this complex food web has become hugely simplified. Man has killed all the large predators and many of the smaller ones have nearly disappeared too, either through changes in habitat or because of trapping. Although we have lost some prey species, eg. the beaver, introduced others, eg. the rabbit, and domesticated yet more, by and large the main prey groups are still in place. Indeed they are more numerous and diverse than they once were[1]. It is the predators which have suffered most.

This has affected all species, benefiting some and disadvantaging others. An obvious effect is that the large deer species no longer have any predators except man. In Britain, man took the place of the wolf and lynx until this century. Now, in recent times, we have reduced our predation and allowed numbers to expand to such an extent that, in some upland areas, over-grazing and browsing by deer are significant problems.

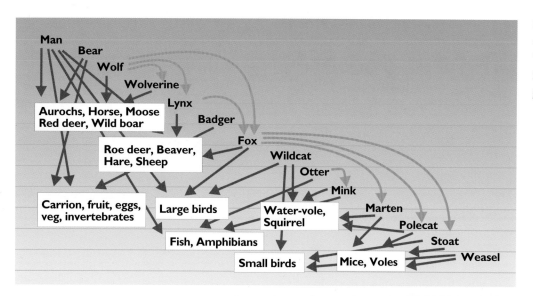

*Probable predator-prey relationships among carnivorous mammals during the Mesolithic period some 8,000 years ago. The main predation impacts are shown in blue and the likely interactions between predators in red. Based on reviews of palaeontological evidence[1] and modern ecological studies[2,3,4,5,6,7].*

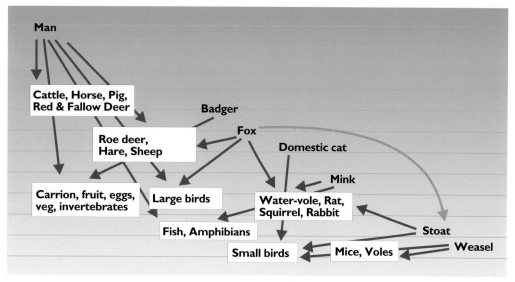

*Predator-prey relationships in lowland Britain today. The large carnivores are gone and otters, polecats, pine martens and wildcats are at present too rare to be significant.*

The consequences of the loss of smaller carnivores are really unknown and clouded by the fact that, in historical times, man has introduced rabbits, rats and domestic cats.

At present, one species of particular importance to farming, game and conservation interests is the fox[10]. The fox remains the only substantial mammalian predator left in good numbers. It seems to us that, in our present landscape, the fox has probably benefited in a number of ways, eg. from the introduction of rabbits and from the absence of larger carnivores, such as lynx and wolf (which, in earlier times, would have reduced its abundance). It follows that fox predation on ground-nesting birds is probably now more severe than it would have been in a primeval system.

There is a lot we can and should do to help the recovery of species such as the polecat or the pine marten but wolves and bears in the English country shires, or even in the Scottish uplands, would be an unreasonable aspiration. Resurrecting the primeval food web can only be a fireside dream.

## Approaches to conservation

We are therefore faced with two approaches to the conservation of predator-prey systems:

- To do as little as possible in the way of management of predators and prey and let the existing animals sort out among themselves which will be the winners and losers;

- To intervene and choose to manage the animals, just as we are prepared to manage the forests and the farms.

It is our contention that it is best to take the latter course for two main reasons:

- We are more likely to produce a more varied community by intervention than if we stand by. Without deer culling, for example, some habitats will tend to be over-grazed and without some fox control we may lose certain populations of ground-nesting birds. There would be a loss of biodiversity overall.

- By allowing man to act as a predator himself (something he has always done), a significant and sustainable wildlife resource can be used.

This provides not only recreation and some income in rural areas but also encourages a substantial investment in habitat conservation not funded by the tax-payer. This is the essence of 'conservation through wise use'.

The relationship between predator and prey has changed but man is still part of the equation. If we choose to opt out, the relationship will shift further in ways we may not want.

## Sources and references

1. Yalden, D. W. (1996) Historical dichotomies in the exploitation of mammals. In: Dunstone, N. & Taylor, V. J. (Eds) *The Exploitation of Mammal Populations*. Chapman & Hall, London. 16–27.

2. Palomares, F., Gaona, P., Ferreras, P. & Delibes, M. (1995) Positive effects on game species of top predators by controlling smaller predator populations: an example with lynx, mongooses, and rabbits. *Conservation Biology*, **9**: 295–305.

3. Strachan, R. & Jefferies, D. J. (1996) *Otter Survey of England 1991–1994*. The Vincent Wildlife Trust, London.

4. Mulder, J. L. (1990) The stoat (*Mustela erminea*) in the Dutch dune region, its local extinction, and a possible cause: the arrival of the fox (*Vulpes vulpes*). *Lutra*, **33**: 1–21.

5. Strachan, R., Jefferies, D. J. & Chanin, P. R. F. (1996) *Pine Marten Survey of England and Wales 1987–1988*. Joint Nature Conservation Committee, Peterborough.

6. Sovada, M. A., Sargeant, A. B. & Grier, J. W. (1995) Differential effects of coyotes and red foxes on duck nest success. *Journal of Wildlife Management*, **59**: 1–9.

7. Pulliainen, E. (1963) Occurrence and habits of the wolverine (*Gulo gulo*) in Finland. *Suomen Riista*, **16**: 109–19.

8. Yalden, D. W. (1991) History of the fauna. In: Corbet, G. B. & Harris, S. (Eds) *The Handbook of British Mammals*. 3rd edition. Blackwell Scientific Publications, Oxford. 7–18.

9. Polis, G. A., Myers, C. A. & Holt, R. D. (1989) The ecology and evolution of intraguild predation. *Annual Review of Ecology and Systematics*, **20**: 297–330.

10. Reynolds, J. C. & Tapper, S. C. (1996) Control of mammalian predators in game management and conservation. *Mammal Review*, **26**: 127–56.

# 3.3 Predation control and conservation

A Larsen trap in use for catching crows

Ever since man has hunted game, he has probably killed and trapped predators for a variety of reasons. Among the mammals, many were taken for their fur but often the primary reason was to protect livestock. Wolves and bears killed cattle, sheep and even people, while others – such as foxes and polecats – killed poultry. As human populations increased and man dominated the landscape, these predators were increasingly regarded as outlaws that needed to be eliminated[1].

In the 18th and 19th centuries landowners became significantly more prosperous as a result of improved agricultural production on their estates and because of other commercial interests. This gave them more leisure time and money to manage the countryside for sport. Furthermore, the development of better firearms, which allowed accurate and rapid shooting, encouraged the development of driven game shooting and large bags. Gamekeepers were employed to ensure that wild gamebirds could be produced in sufficient numbers to maintain these bags. The main aims of these keepers were to stamp out poaching and get rid of all possible predators.

There is little doubt that this 19th century game interest was responsible for the disappearance of some of the raptors and small carnivores from most parts of Britain[2,3]. Other predators, however, withstood this pressure and it was not until the advent of organo-chlorine insecticides that some of their distributions contracted and populations plummeted[2,4]. Currently, most raptors and carnivores are recovering in numbers while some are at an all-time high[5,6].

## Reducing predation pressure

It is our view that game shooting and other sporting interests need not dominate countryside management to such an extent that the conservation of important predators is put in jeopardy. On the whole, we think ecological communities function better with a complex community of predators. We emphatically do *not* advocate a return to the levels of predator removal that were prevalent around the turn of the century.

However, our research has shown that predators, if very abundant, can depress game stocks sufficiently for there to be no possibility of driven wild game shooting[7]. Therefore our objective in game conservation must be to reduce predation pressure on game populations while at the same

In these regions some predators could, as a result, be scarce or absent. We see nothing intrinsically wrong in this, provided it is offset in other regions where the same predators exist in good numbers and their conservation status is secure. However, there are cases where vulnerable and nationally important predators are virtually confined to areas where there is a high game interest and some, such as the hen harrier, also have a significant adverse effect on game stocks. In such cases we need a creative approach whereby agreements are reached between landowners and Government and sustainable numbers of both predator and prey can be achieved. We see no reason why grants, limited culls, target predator densities and other mechanisms should not be used to provide for the long-term interest of the predator population as well as the game.

## Role of predator control in conservation

Although it is clear that predator control is a key component in producing wild game to shoot, we also need to ask whether it contributes to conservation in a wider sense. Evidence here is far from scientifically proven but we do believe that reducing numbers of some of the common generalist predators favours not only certain of the vulnerable prey species but also some rare predators. Pine martens may suffer from fox predation[8] while ground-nesting harriers notably do well on virtually fox-free islands, eg. the Orkneys, Islay, Arran and the Isle of Man.

Of the prey, ground-nesting birds are the most vulnerable. Red grouse, black grouse, capercaillie and grey and red-legged partridges are all game

time enhancing the community of predators in the country as whole. We believe this can be done.

To achieve this goal, we need scientifically sound conservation and sound law. We recognise that national objectives may be different from those of an individual managing his game. In law we need a clear framework which protects both interests but also recognises that the responsibility for any predator control rests with the landowner or his/her authorised representatives. With respect to game, the law should allow control of those predators that cause significant damage provided that the nature of the control does not jeopardise the conservation status of the predators themselves.

The areas of countryside with a high game shooting interest are not evenly distributed across Britain, so it is vital that conservation plans have a regional basis. English Nature's Natural Areas provide an excellent regional scheme for England, although this approach has yet to be extended to other parts of Britain. For some common predators, few restrictions on control are necessary, since the effect on a predator's numbers is only short term and local. For other species a more flexible regional system is required, which balances the need for control (in areas where particular predators are common and having a large impact) with the need for full protection (in regions where these same predators may be rare).

There may be areas where a high game interest predominates, as is currently found, for example, on some upland areas, where contiguous properties are managed principally for grouse.

species whose ranges would contract if predation pressure increased. But waders such as curlew and lapwing are other examples where current levels of predation combined with modern farming may be causing reduced breeding success and dwindling numbers[9].

Crow and magpie control certainly seems to benefit some songbirds, eg. the thrushes and blackbirds, but for others factors such as habitat degradation and pesticides are likely to be of over-riding importance[10]. More research is needed in this area but, on balance, predator control appears to make a significant contribution to the conservation of species other than game. This is underlined by the fact that conservation organisations are finding it increasingly necessary to conduct predator control programmes on nature reserves harbouring vulnerable birds, such as little terns and Sandwich terns (English Nature, Wildfowl and Wetlands Trust, Norfolk Wildlife Trust), capercaillie and avocets (Royal Society for the Protection of Birds).

## Role of habitat management

Finally, it should be remembered that, on most wild game shoots, whether it be a Norfolk partridge beat or a Yorkshire grouse moor, habitat management goes hand in hand with the control of predators. Quite simply, no effort would be made to reduce pesticides on cereals or prevent the over-grazing of heather moorland unless a system of predator control was in place to protect the nesting birds. Habitat management on its own would simply be regarded as a waste of money.

## Sources and references

1. Reynolds, J. C. & Tapper, S. C. (1996) Control of mammalian predators in game management and conservation. *Mammal Review*, **26**: 127–56.

2. Newton, I. (1979) *Population Ecology of Raptors*. T. & A. D. Poyser, Berkhamsted, Hertfordshire.

3. Langley, P. J. W. & Yalden, D. W. (1977) The decline of the rarer carnivores in Great Britain during the nineteenth century. *Mammal Review*, 7: 95–116.

4. Chanin, P. R. F. & Jefferies, D. J. (1978) The decline of the otter *Lutra lutra* L. in Britain: An analysis of the hunting records and discussion of the causes. *Biological Journal of the Linnean Society*, **10**: 305–28.

5. Harris, S., Morris, P., Wray, S. & Yalden, D. (1995) *A Review of British Mammals*. Joint Nature Conservation Committee, Peterborough.

6. Gibbons, D. W., Reid, J. B. & Chapman, R. A. (1993) *The New Atlas of Breeding Birds of Britain and Ireland 1988–1991*. British Trust for Ornithology, T. & A. D. Poyser, London.

7. Tapper, S. C., Potts, G. R. & Brockless, M. (1996) The effect of an experimental reduction in predation pressure on the breeding success and population density of grey partridges (*Perdix perdix*). *Journal of Applied Ecology*, **33**: 965–78.

8. Strachan, R., Jefferies, D. J. & Chanin, P. R. F. (1996) *Pine Marten Survey of England and Wales 1987–1988*. Joint Nature Conservation Committee, Peterborough.

9. Lovegrove, R., Shrubb, M. & Williams, I. (1995) *Silent Fields Gwlad Tawel: The Status of Farmland Birds in Wales*. Royal Society for the Protection of Birds, Sandy, Bedfordshire.

10. Stoate, C. (1995) Does predation management benefit songbirds? *The Game Conservancy Review of 1994*, **26**: 65–6.

# 3.4 Game and wildlife in health and disease

*Dr Phyllis Clapham, Game Research Association pathologist, at work in the 1950s*

Disease is as much a part of animal ecology as predation or habitat quality. However, infectious diseases of wildlife are comparatively rarely studied at wildlife institutes these days. This contrasts with the situation earlier this century when disease was often the primary area of wildlife research. For example, the first studies of red grouse concentrated on disease[1] and much of the early work on the population dynamics of mammals, at the Bureau of Animal Population at Oxford, centred on the possible effects of disease[2]. Indeed, the first full-time paid employee of the Game Research Association was a pathologist, Dr Phyllis Clapham.

This decline in interest stemmed partly from the view that, on an evolutionary time-scale, few animal diseases tend to be a major cause of mortality because it is not always in the evolutionary interests of the disease or parasite to kill its host. Thus it was considered that some diseases evolved to become sublethal but highly infectious, and these diseases tend to depend on healthy hosts to spread infection. Others, such as cholera and malaria, can spread from incapacitated hosts and, as a result, remain highly lethal today.

When myxomatosis was first introduced to rabbits in Britain the initial variant of the virus was highly lethal (virulent) and killed most rabbits very quickly. However, within a decade, this strain had been replaced by a more attenuated (less virulent) form. This form allowed more rabbits to survive but also made them ill for longer, thus increasing the period when they could infect other rabbits[3]. At the same time, surviving rabbits developed immunity and passed on some temporary immunity to their young in their milk. In the end, this resulted in rabbits developing some genetic resistance. Today myxomatosis is endemic but appears to cause only short-term and local changes in rabbit abundance.

Another reason why disease is not frequently studied is that it is often seen as a secondary problem. It is taken as a symptom of something more fundamental, usually caused by human interference, of which there are several kinds:

## Pollution

Exposing animals to pollutants may adversely affect their ability to combat disease although no cases are yet proven. An epidemic of distemper in seals in the North Sea in the late 1980s has been correlated with pollution, which can lower immune responses. However, other factors may have been involved[4] and an expanding seal population, leading to increased densities and a greater likelihood of transmission, is also an explanation.

## Introduced disease

Myxomatosis in rabbits was brought to Europe by a policy of deliberate infection with a virus from the American cottontail[5]. Other diseases have been introduced accidentally by:

- Introduced wild animals. A variety of serious wildlife disease outbreaks has been caused by the introduction of non-native species which have acted as vectors for a disease lethal to the native stock. Viral infections from grey squirrels may have contributed to the disappearance of red squirrels[6]. A fungus from the American signal crayfish is wiping out populations of our native white-clawed crayfish.

- Domesticated animals. The spread of rinderpest across Africa is a classic case where wildlife has been affected by a European disease of domestic cattle[7]. Currently there are concerns that native wildcats are being affected by the distemper virus of feral domestic cats[8], just as African canids are in danger from the canine distemper virus[9].

## Increased population densities

Most animal diseases tend to be density-dependent. In other words, the opportunity for infection increases as numbers rise because transmission becomes easier. For example, the regular outbreaks of strongylosis on grouse moors are a consequence of high population densities[10].

## Conclusion

The wildlife we conserve is no longer part of an environment where animals and disease can evolve with slow change over millennia. Because of change in the physical environment, the mixing of species and change in their densities is now rapid. Disease probably plays a more significant role than it did during earlier epochs. However, whether or not the disease has ultimately been caused by man, the role of wildlife disease needs to be addressed. It is futile to regard disease solely as a symptom of another problem.

# Disease problems of game

Parasites and disease capitalise on high densities of their hosts, which is why disease control is a key feature of farm livestock husbandry. Similarly, though to a much lesser extent, the potential risk of disease increases where game is conserved.

Much of the early game research was on disease. The early work on partridges in the 1930s started with a general concern about the effects of the parasitic roundworm *Trichostrongylus tenuis* on numbers of birds. Since then, we have continued to value research into disease and parasitism, considering both their subclinical effects (poor performance) and clinical effects (illness) in both wild game and hand-reared stock.

Subclinical effects, by definition, often pass unnoticed as their impact is difficult to assess. Much of the research on the population dynamics of red grouse, carried out by the Institute of Terrestrial Ecology in the 1960s and 1970s, ignored the population effects of disease. Later, we were able to show that the subclinical effects of the

parasite *T. tenuis* (the cause of the disease strongylosis) were linked to the cyclic nature of grouse populations[11, 12].

For hand-reared gamebirds, the impact of disease can be particularly acute and, since the Second World War, most gamekeepers who rear birds have employed a variety of techniques to combat disease and parasites. Good husbandry has been, and will remain, paramount for effective disease control. Treatment often relies on medicines developed for the poultry industry.

Today, disease problems are tending to increase. The continuing rise in the number of cases of disease caused by the protozoans *Hexamita* and *Trichomonas*, both in wild and reared gamebirds, demands an epidemiological explanation. Others, such as the protozoan *Histomonas*, the cause of blackhead, have been successfully controlled with the use of the drug dimetridazole *(Emtryl)*[13].

A number of diseases, previously unknown in gamebirds, have appeared recently. These include meningo-encephalitis and inclusion body hepatitis, both highly contagious and fatal. At the same time, other rare conditions have become more common, including coronavirus nephritis, rotavirus and mycoplasmosis (sinusitis and synovitis). Pheasants are now known to be important hosts for *Borrelia burgdorferi*, the bacterium that causes human Lyme disease in areas where ticks are common[14].

At the same time, many medicines traditionally used for disease treatment in reared game are being removed from the market for economic reasons, or because of increased legislation. Bringing in new medicines to replace

them will be expensive and pharmaceutical companies appear unwilling to carry out development for the gamebird market alone as this is not cost effective. Other small-sector livestock industries face similar pressures.

## The future of disease control in game management

For reared gamebirds the first aim should be to reduce the dependence on medicine currently shared by many gamekeepers. This will need more research but simple solutions are possible.

For example, *Hexamita* problems in turkeys in the USA were reduced when the birds were moved from free-range systems and into controlled environments.

Although it should not be inferred that disease is the inevitable consequence of releasing hand-reared gamebirds, some disease problems do result directly from over-stocking and mismanagement. These need to be addressed.

The trade in birds and eggs, and the practice of custom hatching, may also contribute to the spread of pathogens such as the mycoplasmas. While professional game-farmers can and do

help to maintain the health of game by adopting high standards, it may become necessary to regulate the movement of birds and eggs by the use of health certificates and the certification of producers – a scheme possible under the Poultry Trade Directive 90/539.

Other measures might reduce the marketing of caught-up stock, their eggs and progeny. This could force breeders to use over-winter stock which conforms to standards such as those of the Poultry Health Scheme. The poultry industry has adopted a very strict hygiene and management approach to minimise disease problems.

## Poisoning from lead shot

There is now widespread evidence from around the world that spent lead shotgun pellets are causing lead poisoning in some birds. Waterfowl seem to be particularly at risk but there is also evidence of elevated lead levels in some gamebirds in areas of high shooting pressure. In both cases, the problem arises through birds picking up shot, probably instead of grit, and then grinding it up in their gizzards.

In Britain, the overall scale of the problem is far from clear but a voluntary phase-out of lead shot over wetlands important to feeding waterfowl was started. However, the Government has now published a regulation to ban all waterfowl shooting with lead shot. There is an increasingly urgent need for research to quantify the scale of the problem both in terms of incidence and consequent mortality. This is particularly important since many shooters are not convinced that lead poisoning is a real problem.

This in itself would not matter if there were alternative types of shot available at an affordable cost and ballistic performance. In practice, the non-toxic substitutes are either inherently poorer ballistically (eg. steel) or much more expensive (eg. bismuth). Many shooters therefore feel that they are being forced to spend more and/or accept poorer performance without justification.

However, this approach is often inappropriate for game. For example, very strict pathogen-free systems are entirely inappropriate for a gamebird which is to be released into the wild.

## Research and education needs

Routine diagnostic work is now carried out by the Veterinary Laboratories Agency and Scottish Agricultural Colleges and by the 12–20 specialised veterinarians distributed throughout the UK. Accordingly we do not think there is a need for The Game Conservancy Trust to do routine diagnostic work. However, the development of good gamebird husbandry practices, when combined with basic veterinary techniques, will ensure that game animals in the wild and on the rearing field can be cared for without the risk of severe disease outbreaks or resorting to large-scale prophylactic treatments.

Having recruited a Head of Wildlife Epidemiology and Disease, we hope to establish a network of veterinarians competent and willing to deal with gamebird disease. This will be supported by the provision of regular training courses in gamebird disease control.

## Sources and references

1. Lovat, L. (1911) *The Grouse in Health and in Disease*. Smith, Elder & Co., London.

2. Elton, C. (1942) *Voles, Mice and Lemmings: Problems in Population Dynamics*. Oxford University Press, Oxford.

3. Ross, J. (1982) Myxomatosis: the natural evolution of the disease. *Symposia of the Zoological Society of London*, **50**: 77–95.

4. Thompson, P. M. & Hall, A. J. (1993) Seals and epizootics – what factors might affect the severity of mass mortalities? *Mammal Review*, **23**: 149–54.

5. Fenner, F. & Ross, J. (1994) Myxomatosis. In: Thompson, H. V. & King, C. M. (Eds) *The European Rabbit: The History and Biology of a Successful Colonizer*. Oxford University Press, Oxford. 205–40.

6. Duff, J. P., Scott, A. & Keymer, I. F. (1996) Parapox virus infection of the grey squirrel. *Veterinary Record*, 138: 527.

7. Plowright, W. (1982) The effects of rinderpest and rinderpest control on wildlife in Africa. *Symposia of the Zoological Society of London*, **50**: 1–28.

8. McOrist, S. & Kitchener, A. (1994) Current threats to the European wildcat, *Felis sylvestris*, in Scotland. *Ambio*, **23**: 243–5.

9. Ginsberg, J. R. & MacDonald, D. W. (1990) *Foxes, Wolves, Jackals and Dogs: An Action Plan for the Conservation of Canids*. International Union for the Conservation of Nature and Natural Resources, Gland, Switzerland.

10. Hudson, P. (1992) *Grouse in Space and Time: The Population Biology of a Managed Gamebird*. Game Conservancy Limited, Fordingbridge, Hampshire.

11. Potts, G. R., Tapper, S. C. & Hudson, P. J. (1984) Population fluctuations in red grouse: analysis of bag records and a simulation model. *Journal of Animal Ecology*, 53: 21–36.

12. Hudson, P. J. (1986) The effect of the parasitic nematode on the breeding production of red grouse. *Journal of Animal Ecology*, **55**: 85–92

13. Pennycott, T. (1997) Gamebird diseases: The need for more research. *The Game Conservancy Trust Review of 1996*, **28**: 63–5.

14. Kurtenbach, K., Carey, D., Hoodless, A. N., Nuttall, P. A. & Randolph, S. E. (In press) Competence of pheasants as reservoirs for Lyme disease spirochetes. *Journal of Medical Entomology*.

# 3.5 The Allerton project – an example of farming with wildlife conservation

Owned by our partners, The Allerton Research and Educational Trust, the Loddington estate in Leicestershire hosts the Allerton project, our demonstration of how to manage farmland in a way that integrates conservation with profitable arable farming.

The specific project aims are:

- To seek a balance between profitable farming and game conservation which is of benefit to other wildlife and the natural environment.

- To carry out research into the relationship between farming and conservation.

- To use the research results in educating farmers, other conservationists and the wider public.

## The Loddington Estate

The estate is situated around the hamlet of Loddington in eastern Leicestershire. When we took it over we found that management had been min-

**Composition of the Loddington estate.**

| Type of land | Area in hectares |
| --- | --- |
| Arable and set-aside | 254 |
| Permanent pasture | 28 |
| Permanent pasture – let to neighbouring farms | 15 |
| Woodland | 19 |
| Disused railway embankment, two small lakes and several ponds and streams | 9 |

| | |
|---|---|
| ■ | **Woods** |
| ■ | **Ponds & streams** |
| ■ | **Wheat** |
| ■ | **Barley** |
| □ | **Oilseed rape** |
| ■ | **Beans** |
| ■ | **Grass** |
| ■ | **Five-year set-aside** |
| ■ | **Non-rotational set-aside** |

*Distribution of farm crops and main habitats at Loddington in 1991/92 (left) and 1995/96 (right).*

imal and the farming was somewhat run down and 'low-tech', although evidently attractive to wildlife. The composition of the estate is shown in the table on page 79.

Soils on the estate are predominantly heavy clays of the Denchworth and Hanslope series. Soils around the village and the central southern part of the estate are slightly better-drained clay loams. Small areas of ironstone occur to the north and north-east and there are patches of stony or sandy clay loam and clay loam. Annual rainfall is 650 millimetres.

## Farming practice

The farming is mixed arable and sheep. The arable rotation aims to maximise first wheat, which is the most profitable crop. The rotation is:

| | |
|---|---|
| First year | Winter wheat |
| Second year | Winter barley |
| Third year | Oilseed rape |
| Fourth year | Winter wheat |
| Fifth year | Beans |

The soil type is not suited to spring cropping, so most crops are sown in the autumn, thereby taking advantage of the higher-yielding capacity of winter crops. Virtually all the arable land is ploughed before drilling. The grassland is grazed by sheep.

## Habitat management

The programme of habitat improvement began in 1993. To enable the response to be quantified, a number of baseline surveys were carried out in 1992 before management started. Aspects investigated included: soils, woodlands, hedgerows, flora, gamebirds, songbirds, mammals and invertebrates. Since 1992 habitat management has primarily aimed at wild game species, because on most farms these species provide the incentive to undertake conservation work, though much other farmland wildlife also benefits.

### Crop diversity

Large fields have been split into two and the cropping programme has been adjusted so that, wherever possible, identical crops are not grown on adjacent areas. This increased the diversity of crop habitat available to wildlife on all parts of the estate. The two maps *(left)* show the estate in 1991/92, before crop diversity was encouraged, and in 1995/96, when we actively sought to increase it and they demonstrate the impact of the change. Between these years the number of crops grown increased from five to seven, while the number of crop patches on the farm increased from 20 to 43. Although this appears to make farming operations more complicated, it has not proved much more difficult in practice to farm this fragmented field pattern.

### Hedgerows

Hedges are generally trimmed biennially in rotation, usually in January or February. An extensive 5-year programme of hedgerow restoration, including laying, coppicing and gapping-up, is under way, grant-aided by the Countryside Stewardship Scheme.

### Verges

At least 1 metre of perennial grassy vegetation is left undisturbed next to all field boundaries. This serves as nesting cover for birds and over-wintering cover for predatory invertebrates (which help to control crop pests in summer), as well as providing habitat for small mammals, butterflies and other beneficial insects. Verges are only trimmed in alternate years and great care is taken to safeguard them from pesticide and fertiliser drift. Ditch clearing is essential for drainage purposes but this is only carried out once every few years and with minimal damage to ditch-side vegetation.

### Beetle banks

Beetle banks have been established throughout the farm. These are ridges that run across the middle of large fields and are created by ploughing-up from both sides. Sown with tussocky grasses, such as cocksfoot, they provide over-wintering habitat for predators of aphids. These predators protect the crop from aphid pests, so reducing the need for insecticides, which also kill the invertebrate food of young chicks. Beetle banks also provide good nesting cover for gamebirds.

### Conservation headlands

The outermost 6 metres of most cereal fields at Loddington are managed as conservation headlands. They are selectively sprayed to control only the most damaging weeds (wild oats, black-grass, cleavers), while the less harmful species remain as hosts for insects important in the diet of young gamebird chicks. No insecticides are applied to the outer 6 metres of any crop; in the case of cereals this distance is increased to 12 metres in summer.

### Set-aside

A network of strips 20 metres wide has been established throughout the farm. They are sited in field margins or across the centre of large fields. Some incorporate beetle banks. Most of these strips are sown with crop mixtures under the Wild Bird Cover Option in order to provide suitable brood rearing and winter habitat for gamebirds and non-game species. This is one of the most important ways in which habitat is provided and trials are constantly under way to develop improved mixtures.

### Woodlands

Most of the woodlands were planted after the Second World War and had become neglected. However, an extensive programme of thinning, felling and replanting small areas has been carried out. This has improved the long-term timber value, opened up the canopy and increased the herbaceous and shrubby cover. Some woodlands have been extended by new planting, with the emphasis on providing long, shrubby edges to maximise the habitat value for wild game. This work has been grant-aided by the Woodland Grant Scheme and the Farm Woodland Premium Scheme.

### Wetlands

The two small lakes in the centre of the estate had become silted up, polluted and overgrown.

They have been restored by thinning trees (especially at the south side) and dredging to remove silt and pollutants. The sources of pollution have been identified and dealt with. Sluices and weirs have also been rebuilt and banks strengthened. The lakes now have sufficient depth to support brown trout, which were introduced in February 1993. Several other small ponds have also benefited from remedial work. A low-lying area of approximately 3 hectares adjacent to the Eye Brook, formerly in 5-year set-aside, is being converted into a complex of wetland habitats, including wet grassland with seasonal pools and a deeper flight pond, surrounded by willow and hawthorn scrub.

## Gamekeeping

No gamebirds are hand reared for releasing on the estate, so a well-planned programme of predation control is necessary to increase wild game populations and enable them to benefit from the habitat improvements. Most of this predation control is concentrated during the spring and early summer when gamebirds are nesting and at their most vulnerable. Conventional game-keeping techniques are used for foxes, rats, stoats, magpies and crows, which are the principal predators of game and nests. On the estate, as well as on neighbouring ground, foxes are also hunted by the Cottesmore Hunt during the winter.

## Effects on game and wildlife

Of the wild gamebirds the pheasants have shown the most marked improvements in number. Red-legged partridge numbers have also increased. None were recorded in 1992, but there were 119 in autumn 1996 and, in spite of poor weather, still 56 in autumn 1997. The grey partridges

**Increase in wild pheasants and their productivity at Loddington from 1992 to 1997.**

|  | 1992 | 1993 | 1994 | 1995 | 1996 | 1997 |
|---|---|---|---|---|---|---|
| Average brood size | 3.0 | 6.3 | 5.9 | 4.6 | 3.9 | 2.7 |
| Number of broods | 18 | 34 | 45 | 68 | 83 | 71 |
| Number of hens | 35 | 46 | 58 | 80 | 107 | 151 |
| Number of young | 54 | 213 | 266 | 314 | 323 | 195 |
| Total number | 126 | 303 | 383 | 442 | 490 | 420 |

Predation control began in 1993. Bad weather in 1997 resulted in fewer broods and poor chick survival. Data from autumn counts.

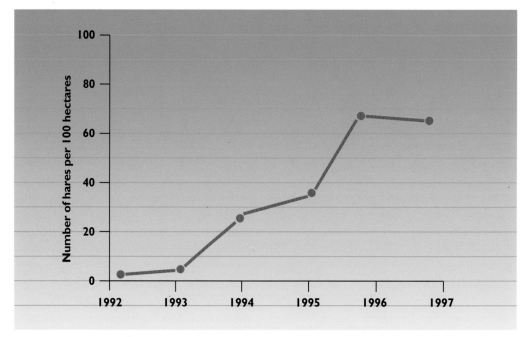

Changes in hare numbers at Loddington from 1992 to 1996, showing peak autumn/winter numbers derived from night-time hare counts.

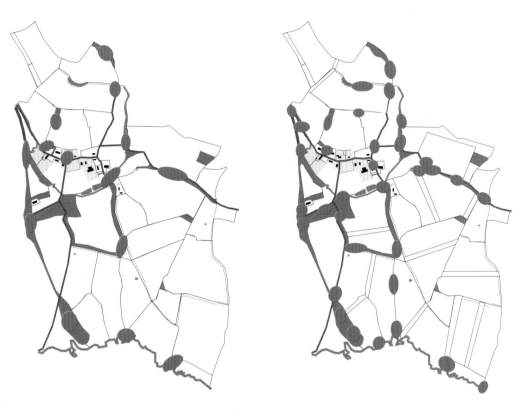

*Song thrush nest*

*Changes in song thrush breeding numbers at Loddington. Territories in 1992 (left) compared with 1995 (right).*

improvement or predation control, or both) remains unclear. We are currently starting experiments to establish the role of each management component.

## Farm economics

### Crop yields

have fared less well. Although in a good year they can produce large broods, the young birds appear to disperse to neighbouring ground during the winter.

The most spectacular increases have been in hare numbers, from less than 10 per 100 hectares before management to over 65 per 100 hectares in only 3 years.

Throughout Britain, farmland songbirds have generally been declining in numbers as a result of intensification. However, at Loddington no species has declined since we started monitoring, in spite of our agricultural improvements. Some species have actually increased. For example, in 1992,

before the project began, the farm held 14 breeding territories of song thrushes. By 1995, the estate supported 35 territories and in 1996 this had increased to 39. Intensive nest searches carried out on Loddington have shown that some species, such as blackbird, dunnock and chaffinch, suffer much less nest predation than they do on nearby farms. Other species, such as whitethroat and yellowhammer, appear to suffer little nest predation everywhere, but they do nest at Loddington in good numbers.

It is becoming apparent that game management helps some species more than others but the exact cause of these increases (habitat

Alongside habitat improvements, the efficiency of the farm has also improved since our stewardship of the estate began. In 1992, the first year before any changes were made, winter wheat yields were 5.56 tonnes per hectare, while for winter barley and oilseed rape they were 5.99 and 2.34 tonnes per hectare respectively. By 1996, wheat yields had improved, averaging over 4 years at 8.12 tonnes per hectare and peaking in 1996 at 10.19 tonnes per hectare. For winter barley the 4-year average was 6.44 tonnes per hectare (1995 peak of 7.41 tonnes per hectare) and for oilseed rape 2.93 tonnes per hectare (1996 peak of 3.62 tonnes per hectare). The average arable gross margin increased from £500 per hectare in 1993 to £803 per hectare in 1996, with the gross margins of wheat (the most valuable crop) increasing from £574 to £983 per hectare.

## Game shooting

Game shooting at Loddington is based entirely on the production of wild game, the aim being to take an appropriate proportion of the autumn stock. In the early years we have deliberately kept this amount small so as to leave sufficient breeding stocks.

Cock pheasants were first shot in the winter of 1993/94, yielding a bag of 53 birds. This has increased annually until the winter of 1996/97 when the bag was 213 cocks. Hares were first shot in the winter of 1995/96 when 45 were shot and this was increased to 90 in 1996/97.

While, on the open market, these numbers would not yield a shooting rental high enough to pay for a gamekeeper, they do show the potential for wild game management on estates where it is appropriate.

## Cost of conservation

It is important that conservation projects of this kind are costed. The largest cost is without doubt the employment of the gamekeeper and the associated expenses of his housing, transport and equipment. However, it would be wrong to attribute all of this to the expense of predator control for game. A large proportion of the gamekeeper's time is spent wardening the estate and managing and improving parts of the hedgerows, woodlands and ponds, as well as controlling farm pests, such as wood pigeons and rabbits, which would otherwise inflict significant crop damage.

We show below the additional costs which impinge on the farm's productivity. These costs vary annually as farm profits and various subsidies change.

### Conservation headlands

In 1994 and 1996 the cost (including the loss of crop yield) of conservation headlands was estimated to be £70–£80 per hectare of headland. This equated in 1994 to a total of £370 for the entire farm, with conservation headlands covering 5.3 hectares (5% of the cereal area). In 1995, conservation headlands covered 11.6 hectares (8% of the cereal area) and the profit foregone amounted to £942; in 1996 they covered 7.4 hectares (15% of the cereal area) and the profit foregone was £617.

### Beetle banks

The cost of creating a beetle bank 500 metres long and 2 metres wide has been estimated at between £22.80 and £30.80, depending on the seed mixture used. Grants are available through the Countryside Stewardship Scheme.

### Set-aside

In 1994 and 1995 a greater proportion of the arable land had to be set aside under the Flexible Scheme rather than the 6-year Rotational Scheme. On many farms, this would be compensated for by positioning the Flexible Set-aside in marginal areas with low yield potential, but we opted to place set-aside strips across fields, so some high-yielding land has been lost. In 1995 the estimated profit foregone because of this amounted to £1,959, half the total 'conservation costs' on the farm. From 1996, this did not apply as the area requirements for the two types of set-aside were fixed at the same level, thus greatly reducing the costs of habitat provision.

### Farm output

The total profit foregone by the farm for the entire conservation programme in 1994 was estimated at £1,865. This equates to £5.60 per hectare over the whole estate, or 5.2% of farm profit. In 1995 it was £3,825 ie. £11.49 per hectare, or 3.6% of estimated farm profit. The increased costs in 1995 were associated with higher gross margins but the cost as a percentage of estimated farm profit was actually reduced. In 1996 the conservation costs fell to £1,782, or 1.8% of the farm profit, largely because there was no extra cost of set-aside. More recently profits have fallen further with consequent increases in the percentage of profit foregone.

## Conclusion

Many see the needs of farmland wildlife and the maintenance of biodiversity as incompatible with profitable farming. In just five years, the Allerton project has demonstrated that this need not be the case. While conservation is not without its costs, these are lower than many people realise and can be easily afforded by those with sufficient interest and incentive. The provision of a harvestable surplus of wild game is an important motivation for many landowners or farmers to undertake such work, provided the costs of the predation control are also taken into account.

# 3.6 Wildlife law and the countryside

We have emphasised that our countryside and wildlife have constantly been subject to the actions of man. Our heritage is not a primeval wilderness resulting from unconscious evolution but has been shaped by our own wishes and for a variety of reasons. Of course, the countryside has not been designed and built in the same way as our cities. Instead, natural processes, such as plant succession and animal survival, have been harnessed by man to achieve his ends. What generations of Britons have done is to create a countryside which is not at some end-point, to be preserved at all costs, but one which re-creates itself over the centuries and evolves with our changing culture and climate.

To conserve the countryside we must preserve the forces that created and continually renew it. To a very large extent these forces are represented by landowners, most of whom take their role of stewardship seriously and are prepared to invest capital into the properties they own. With ownership comes a responsibility and a need to treat the land and its products as a long-term asset to be conserved for succeeding generations. Landowners and their staff tend to know their ground well; they know where the trout spawn, the partridges nest and the woodcock rode in summer. They may need specialist advice on the occurrence and needs of fritillaries or newts but, in the end, they will be the best people to conserve even the small but significant rarities.

## History

Since the Second World War, Government policies of support for farm and forest production have perversely encouraged landowners to turn over most of their ground to these forms of intensive land use, with a consequent loss of valuable wildlife habitat. Only by further Government support, through the establishment of a network of Sites of Special Scientific Interest, have many of these valuable habitats been retained. Thus, paradoxically, conservationists often regard the Government as being the public's protector of wildlife against the selfish commercial interests of landowners. In turn, this often tempts Government (including Local Government) and agencies, usually with public support, to take over many of these management responsibilities themselves[1].

This can have adverse effects. Landowners feel disinherited from what is theirs and become disinclined or nervous about doing anything for themselves. Indeed, they may even be provoked into destroying anything that might in future be designated for protection. These days, if they do feel motivated, they will certainly want a Government grant for conservation work which they would previously have done voluntarily. Thus the agencies find their workload increasing and need yet more funds and staff if they are to discharge their widening responsibilities[1].

## Recommendations

Our plea to the Government is not for *less* money to be spent on conservation but for money to be spent *differently*. Less should be spent on trying to regulate and legislate while more should be spent on research and education, especially on the environmental impacts of various agricultural and countryside schemes, such as set-aside and pyrethroid insecticides. If less money were spent on subsidising intensive forms of land use, less would need to be spent on species and site protection. A sympathetic regional framework should be adopted to ensure that Government policy reflects local character and the aspirations of local inhabitants. The *Character of England* map published by the Countryside Commission (now the Countryside Agency) and English Nature provides a model for this[2].

Although we believe that Government should aim to decrease regulation and encourage more initiative from landowners, there is still a vital place for well-constructed wildlife legislation. Landowners will succeed best with the resident fauna. Where migratory or widely mobile species are involved, they may need encouragement to form associations in order to conserve and manage them. We see the deer management groups and river conservation trusts as models for conserving difficult mobile species such as red deer and salmon.

There are species which significantly damage the landowners' game, agricultural or fishery interests and the Government's role in such cases is to ensure that the wider regional and national conservation interests are also catered for. Many, but not all, of these damaging species are resilient and it is the Government's duty to ensure that the collective action of many landowners does not compromise the conservation status of those which are important and perhaps scarce. Birds of prey on grouse moors are an obvious example[3]. Even in these cases, the future for some of these species would probably be best served by careful management, with Government agreeing a long-term strategy with landowners. This would be preferable to trying to enforce laws that were drafted when ecological circumstances were different and our scientific understanding of the consequences of predation less well understood.

Although the bulk of what we are proposing in this report can be achieved within the existing legal framework, it is our view that the current structure of game and wildlife laws is becoming increasingly cumbersome. If conservation objectives are to be met in the next century, a revision will be necessary.

## Animal welfare

The principal goal of a legal framework should be to support good conservation and wildlife management. Animal welfare is a separate issue. Although aspects of wild animal welfare have clearly been assessed with scientific criteria[4, 5, 6], on the whole, animal welfare remains a matter of ethical debate and moral judgement[7], whereas legislation to conserve wildlife needs to be based on ecological science. It may well be that our animal welfare laws need revision too, but, in so doing, they need to be separated from conservation legislation. Proper animal welfare laws should recognise the major taxonomic differences between animals but should also use different criteria for the separate categories of wild animals, farm livestock and domestic pets. It should be animal welfare laws that set standards, for example, for gamebird rearing and humane spring-traps.

## Existing legal problems with conservation law

Most legislation contains some ambiguity, but existing wildlife legislation suffers from several problems that are structural in nature.

- **Existing legislation consists of a series of overlapping statutes some of which are more than a century old[8].** In general, past legislation has not been repealed, so for example, to determine the legality or otherwise of killing a hare, one would have to refer to the Night Poaching Act (1828), the Game Act (1831), the Ground Game Act (1880), the Hares Preservation Act (1892), the Ground Game Amendment Act (1906), the Forestry Act (1967) and the Wildlife and Countryside Act (1981). If the hare was in Scotland other statutes would also be involved. In some cases, overlaps of this nature actually result in conflicting laws, adding to the confusion.

- **Because it attempts to be specific, the pivotal Wildlife and Countryside Act (1981) contains numerous ambiguities and inconsistencies which make its meaning unclear.** A recent example of this was when we attempted to clarify the legal position over the use of the newly developed Larsen trap to capture

magpies and crows. Our reading of the Act suggested Larsen traps were lawful. However, the then Nature Conservancy Council, acting on the advice of the then Department of Environment, told us that these traps were unlawful. We therefore initiated procedures to obtain a licence for their use. During the course of consultations for this, the Ministry of Agriculture, Fisheries, and Food, advised by Treasury lawyers, stated that, in their view, the use of such traps was in fact legal under the Wildlife and Countryside Act without the need for a licence. The Department of the Environment then changed its view and so we were able to proceed without a licence. However, later it was pointed out by the Royal Society for the Prevention of Cruelty to Animals that the Larsen trap appeared to contravene another part of the same Act and, as a result, an Open General Licence had to be issued in order to avoid any doubt.

- **The Wildlife and Countryside Act (1981) and earlier laws are inflexible, with the result that new laws have to be passed to deal with each new situation as it arises.** Thus, in addition to the Wildlife and Countryside Act (1981), there is the Conservation of Seals Act (1970), the Deer Act (1991), the Protection of Badgers Act (1992) and several others, all of which should arguably have come within the general scope of the Wildlife and Countryside Act itself.

## Our international obligations

- **The Ramsar Convention on Wetlands of International Importance especially as Waterfowl Habitat (1971, 1982, 1987)** aims to stem the progressive encroachment on and loss of wetlands now and in the future. It seeks to promote the wise use of all wetlands within the territories of Contracting Parties, each of which are required to designate at least one site to a list of Wetlands of International Importance. Hunting in wetlands must therefore be compatible with the general requirements of wise use.

- **The Bern Convention on the Conservation of European Wildlife and Natural Habitats (1979)** aims to maintain or adapt the population of wild flora and fauna at levels corresponding to ecological requirements. The conservation of species goes together with the conservation of natural habitats. Contracting Parties are required to regulate hunting and the sale of carcasses to keep populations out of danger.

- **The Bonn Convention on the Conservation of Migratory Species of Wild Animals (1979, 1985, 1988, 1991, 1994)** provides a framework for the conservation of migratory species and their habitats by means of research, protection and the conclusion of international Agreements, as appropriate. One example is the Agreement on the Conservation of African–Eurasian Migratory Waterbirds (1995), which seeks to co-ordinate at the flyway (migration route) level measures to maintain or restore migratory waterbird species to a favourable conservation status. Any use of the birds must be sustainable for the species concerned as well as for the ecological systems that support them.

- **The Birds Directive (Directive 79/409/EEC of the Council of the European Community on the Conservation of Wild Birds)** imposes legal obligations upon member states to maintain or adapt populations of naturally occurring bird species at levels corresponding to ecological requirements, to regulate trade in birds, to limit hunting to species able to sustain exploitation and to prohibit certain methods of capture and killing. In particular, *hunting must not jeopardise conservation efforts, must comply with the principles of wise use and ecologically balanced control of the species concerned* and must be compatible with the maintenance of the populations of the species hunted 'at a satisfactory level'. There is an obligation on member states to see that monitoring, other research and management plans are in place to show compliance with the Directive. Fundamental to the management of populations is the development of management or restoration plans or measures at the species level.

- **The Habitats Directive (Directive 92/43/EEC of the Council of the European Community on the Conservation of Natural Habitats and of Wild Fauna and Flora)** brings European legislation in line with the terms of the Bern Convention, to which Europe has been a party since 1982.

- **The Rio de Janeiro Convention on Biological Diversity (1992)** has as its objectives the conservation of biological diversity and the sustainable use of its components. It obliges contracting parties to develop or adapt national strategies, plans or programmes towards the conservation and sustainable use of biological diversity. In this context, hunting needs to be sustainable and not harm biological diversity.

- **The more recent laws are protectionist in character and do not encourage the development of active conservation strategies which alter with time, place and circumstance.** In the Wildlife and Countryside Act (1981) animals and plants are listed in schedules, each of which imparts a different level of protection. In practice, protection may be of little use in many situations and can even hamper progress. The red squirrel, for example, has continued to lose ground to the grey squirrel in recent years – just as it has done ever since the latter became established in the 1930s – yet the Wildlife and Countryside Act actually prevented the poisoning of grey squirrels in areas where there are reds, even though a means of delivering poison solely to the greys had been found.

- **Species protection is often opposed by field sports interests because it is seen as a one-way process.** This is clearly shown by the cases of the stock dove and the dark-bellied brent goose. Both of these birds were shooting quarry until they became protected because of their decline through reasons unconnected with shooting. Since protection in 1981 (but not because of it) the stock dove population has more than doubled to 240,000 pairs and wintering dark-bellied brent, protected in 1954, have increased ten-fold to 103,300 birds[9]. At the moment, however, Government conservation agencies seem very unwilling to recommend that the species be returned to the quarry list, even though the conservation case for their protection has evaporated. In a future legal framework we should like to see protection extended to quarry species on a temporary basis, when the need arises, and automatic revocation if and when agreed target conservation objectives are reached.

For the above reasons we believe that our existing wildlife legislation, including much of the Wildlife and Countryside Act, will have to be reviewed and replaced if wildlife management and conservation are to remain dynamic processes into the next century. There is no doubt that revising existing legislation will be difficult. In particular, we need to convince people that returning more responsibility to land-managers will result in better conservation, not worse.

There is a strong current of opinion that the fauna and flora belongs to the people and that it should all be protected in law and managed by Government agency[10, 11]. Certainly we agree that our wildlife is a national treasure which needs an all-embracing legal protective framework, but ultimately it has to be conserved by the owners of the land on which it is found. Without their co-operation the future is bleak whatever the statutory framework.

## Sources and references

1. Pennington, M. (1996) *Conservation and the Countryside: By Quango or Market?* Institute of Economic Affairs, Environment Unit, London.

2. Anon. (1996) *The Character of England: Landscape, Wildlife and Natural Features.* Countryside Commission & English Nature, Cheltenham & Peterborough.

3. Redpath, S. & Thirgood, S. (1997) *Birds of Prey and Red Grouse: Report of the Joint Raptor Study.* The Stationery Office, London.

4. Kreeger, T. J., White, P. J., Seal, U. S. & Tester, J. R. (1990) Pathological responses of red foxes to foothold traps. *Journal of Wildlife Management,* **54**: 147–60.

5. White, P. J., Kreeger, T. J., Seal, U. S. & Tester, J. R. (1991) Pathological responses of red foxes to capture in box traps. *Journal of Wildlife Management,* **55**: 75–80.

6. Bateson, P. (1997) *The Behavioural and Physiological Effects of Culling Red Deer. Report to the Council of the National Trust.* University Publications Centre, Cambridge.

7. Scruton, R. (1996) *Animal Rights and Animal Wrongs.* Demos, London.

8. Parkes, C. & Thornley, J. (1994) *Fair Game – The Law of Country Sports and the Protection of Wildlife.* Pelham Books, London.

9. Stone, B. H., Sears, J., Cranswick, P. A., Gregory, R. D., Gibbons, D. W., Rehfisch, M. M., Aebischer, N. J. & Reid, J. B. (1997) Population estimates of birds in Britain and the United Kingdom. *British Birds,* **90**: 1–22.

10. Mabey, R. (1980) *The Common Ground: A Place for Nature in Britain's Future.* Hutchinson, London.

11. Shoard, M. (1987) *This Land is Our Land. The Struggle for Britain's Countryside.* Paladin, London.

# Part 2

# Species

# conservation plans

# 4. Resident small game mammals

In a legal sense, rabbits and hares are both agricultural pests and game, and various Acts of Parliament reflect this. Unlike in continental Europe, where rabbit and hare shooting are held in high esteem, in Britain these animals are an important quarry for a whole range of rural pursuits, including hunting, coursing, falconry and ferreting. Because rabbits and hares eat agricultural crops, their numbers will always need to be controlled but The Game Conservancy Trust believes that it is important to retain their legal status as a game species as well. The fact that these animals are a sporting quarry helps to encourage their conservation where numbers are few or moderate, as well as providing some incentive for pest control where it is needed.

**Brown hare habitat:**
kilometre squares containing
at least 25 hectares of tilled
land or managed grass but no
urban land or major roads.
**Yellow =** area of optimum
brown hare habitat, where
there is at least 25% tilled
ground.
**Dark green =** area of suboptimum habitat with less
than 25% tilled ground.

From ITE Land Cover and OS
Geographic Reference maps

# 4.1 Brown hare
*(Lepus europaeus)*

## History and current status

The brown hare is a farmland animal that thrives best on arable ground. It has always been much less abundant on pasture land[1]. It is thought to have originated in the steppes of central Asia and to have spread westward across Europe as forest was cleared for farming in the Neolithic period. The brown hare, however, did not appear in the British fauna until the Roman era[2].

As brown hares spread into most lowland farming districts they probably displaced the smaller mountain hares *(Lepus timidus)* which formerly inhabited low-ground areas, just as they do in Ireland today. Only in the uplands or in northern forested districts are mountain hares likely to have held their own. Because of predation, and hunting for food, brown hares were probably never very abundant until the 18th and 19th centuries, when the combination of land enclosure, agricultural improvement and predator control allowed populations to rise. On large, well-managed estates, like Holkham in Norfolk, the numbers shot peaked in the late 19th century[1], but the size of the bag at that time may have been related to improvements in firearms and shooting popularity as much as to agricultural changes.

The Ground Game Act (1880) gave tenant farmers the right to kill hares and rabbits on their farms in order to protect their crops. However, during the period of declining farm prices from the late 19th into the early 20th century, this had the perverse effect of encouraging farmers to trap rabbits in large numbers as an alternative crop[3]. In many districts, such as southern Wales and parts of the West Country, brown hares appear to have been trapped out of existence at this time.

Currently hares are a minor shooting quarry and most driven hare shoots are designed to prevent crop damage and to cull a large proportion of the stock[4]. Hares are also an animal of the chase and both hunting with hounds (beagles and harriers) and coursing with greyhounds have a long history. However, these sports kill very small numbers of hares[4] and, indeed, in some places, hares are conserved especially because of the coursing interest.

## Conservation plan

Currently, the total British population of brown hares is estimated at 600,000–800,000 animals

over winter[5], with a distribution favouring arable districts and land which is gamekeepered. On a national scale numbers seem to be stable. Hare populations fluctuate substantially from year to year, not only because of the effect of weather on leveret production and survival but also because of a range of diseases which can reduce autumn numbers. There is, however, no evidence that the new viral disease known as 'European brown hare syndrome' is doing permanent damage to hare numbers.

We have calculated what we believe to be a meaningful objective for the brown hare population, based on what is known of the species. In determining the amount of potential habitat for hares in Britain we have included all kilometre squares containing more than 25 hectares of managed farmland, but excluded all those influenced by cities, towns, large villages and major roads.

Although some of these squares may actually be unsuitable for hares, eg. because of their isolation, they are roughly balanced by others (such as some upland or heavily forested squares) where small numbers do in fact survive. Squares which also contain more than 25% tilled ground have been considered as optimum habitat.

The optimum habitat covers 66,979 square kilometres and the suboptimum habitat 65,494 square kilometres (see map). Assuming that typical figures we have obtained are generally applicable, 5 hares per square kilometre for optimum habitat and 2.5 hares per square kilometre for suboptimum habitat, with no predator control by gamekeepers in either, gives 498,630 hares all told. Gamekeepers using fox control can produce 30 hares per square kilometre on optimum ground and 15 per square kilometre on suboptimum. Lowland keepered ground covers very roughly

16,187 square kilometres (2,000 keepers each with 2,000 acres/810 hectares), so adding the effects of the gamekeepers gives 802,117 hares, which is very close to the national estimate.

Assuming no increase in the amount of keepered ground, we estimate that optimum habitat could be improved to support 40 hares per square kilometre with a gamekeeper and 15 without. For suboptimum land we anticipate 20 hares per square kilometre with a gamekeeper and 7 without. This would set a population of 1.7 million hares as a sensible conservation objective. This target is in line with the Biodiversity Action Plan for this species, which calls for a doubling of spring numbers by the year 2010[6].

In order to achieve this target we need sympathetic farming policies and also recognition of the role that foxes play in governing hare numbers[7]. Changes in the management of fox numbers will affect hares. Hares are best sustained by mixed farming systems which provide them with a diversity of crops at different growth stages, so that short grass or crops are available all year round[8]. Although policies such as set-aside can be used to help species such as hares, the main thrust of Government action within the Common Agricultural Policy (CAP) should be to push for a more environmentally sensitive system of agriculture, especially the encouragement of mixed arable/livestock systems.

## Research needs

There has been a lot of research on hares, especially in continental Europe, and most of their ecology is well known. Key research questions remaining are:

- Do modern arable systems lead to serious food shortages for hares in summer? This could reduce leveret survival, as has been suggested by enclosure experiments in Denmark[9].

- Does the use of herbicides directly or indirectly affect the health or nutritional status of hares?

- Does set-aside benefit hares (as many farmers believe) and how can it and Agri-environment schemes best be managed for hares?

- What conservation measures can be developed to help hares in the suboptimum livestock-rearing and dairy-farmland areas, where hare numbers are low and their distribution is patchy?

## Conservation actions

- The Joint Nature Conservation Committee should continue to push forward with its plans to ensure that mammals in Britain are adequately monitored. Most mammals, unlike birds, are not adequately monitored. As a result, controversy often surrounds their changing fortunes; the brown hare being a case in point.

- Because hares feed on and live in arable crops, the Pesticide Safety Directorate should require pesticide manufacturers to demonstrate a product's safety to hares before its introduction. Any products not meeting this standard should be withdrawn.

- Hares should remain a game species because this encourages their conservation.

- Co-ordinated programmes need to be developed between police and farmers to target and put a stop to poaching gangs. Illegal poaching with lurcher dogs remains a persistent problem in many areas.

- New Agri-environment Measures are needed to encourage more mixed farms (crops and grass) in lowland districts. This should be considered in discussions over reform of the CAP.

## Sources and references

1. Tapper, S. & Parsons, N. (1984) The changing status of the brown hare (*Lepus capensis* L.) in Britain. *Mammal Review*, 14: 57–70.

2. Corbet, G. B. (1986) The relationships and origins of the European lagomorphs. *Mammal Review*, 16: 105–10.

3. Lockley, R. M. (1964) *The Private Life of the Rabbit*. André Deutsch, London.

4. Stoate, C. & Tapper, S. C. (1993) The impact of three hunting methods on brown hare (*Lepus europaeus*) populations in Britain. *Gibier Faune Sauvage*, 10: 229–40.

5. Hutchings, M. R. & Harris, S. (1996) *The Current Status of the Brown Hare* (Lepus europaeus) *in Britain*. Joint Nature Conservation Committee, Peterborough.

6. Anon. (1995) *Biodiversity: The UK Steering Group Report. Volume 2: Action Plans*. HMSO, London.

7. Reynolds, J. C. & Tapper, S. C. (1995) Predation by foxes *Vulpes vulpes* on brown hares *Lepus europaeus* in central southern England, and its potential impact on annual population growth. *Wildlife Biology*, 1: 145–58.

8. Tapper, S. C. & Barnes, R. F. W. (1986) Influence of farming practice on the ecology of the brown hare (*Lepus europaeus*). *Journal of Applied Ecology*, 23: 39–52.

9. Hansen, K. (1997) Effects of cereal production on the population dynamics of the European hare (*Lepus europaeus*). In: Marboutin, E. & Berthos, J.-C. (Eds) XIIth Lagomorph Workshop, Clermont-Ferrand, July 1996. *Gibier Faune Sauvage*, 14: 510–11.

**Mountain hare habitat and distribution:** kilometre squares containing at least 25 hectares of moorland heath. **Blue =** main areas of habitat in which mountain hares occur. **Green =** areas of suitable habitat with no hares.

From ITE Land Cover map and BRC mammal atlas.

# 4.2 Mountain hare
*(Lepus timidus)*

## History and current status

Mountain hares have a very wide, virtually circumpolar distribution extending throughout the tundra regions of the former USSR, northern Europe, Greenland and Iceland, with the closely related Arctic hare (*Lepus arcticus*) in Canada and Alaska[1]. In the Old World their habitat extends southward throughout the boreal zone to the fringes of agricultural land or open grassland. In North America the Arctic hare is restricted by the boreal forest, which is inhabited by the snowshoe hare (*Lepus americanus*). This world-wide pattern of restriction by both habitat and other species of hare explains the distribution of the mountain hare within Britain.

When Britain became separated from Europe in the early Mesolithic period, most land was either tundra or forest and the hares present at that time were certainly mountain hares[2]. Without the later introduction of the brown hare, mountain hares would probably have remained throughout England and Wales, just as they currently do in Ireland. After the introduction of the brown hare in Roman times, mountain hares became restricted to upland regions where they were able to hold their own, feeding on heather and other moorland plants, while the brown hares fed on lowland grasses and agricultural crops. A similar separation occurred on the Isle of Man, where mountain hares appear to have been introduced more recently[3].

It is not clear whether this retreat proceeded smoothly, until mountain hares remained only in the Scottish Highlands, or whether they remained widespread throughout upland England and Wales as well – only to become extinct there much later. Certainly, it is clear that they were found only in the Scottish Highlands by the early 19th century. Towards the middle and end of the 19th century – accompanying the development of grouse shooting and the management of heather for grouse – some landowners released mountain hares. At this time, there were hare populations on many Scottish islands and in the whole of the Southern Uplands, parts of northern Wales and the Peak District[4]. Many of these populations have died out, leaving only the well-established population in the Southern Uplands and a small one in the Peak District, while that in northern Wales has probably died out in the last two decades[5].

## Conservation plan

According to a recent study, the British population of mountain hares numbers approximately 350,000[6]. This estimate was based on average densities and an extrapolation to the available moorland habitat. The bulk of this population is in Scotland, with the Derbyshire population numbering about 500[7]. Within Scotland it is clear that there is a huge variation in density and that there are large areas of apparently suitable upland habitat where these hares have disappeared or are missing[8]. The population is therefore fragmented and patchily distributed within sub-populations. The biggest conservation concern is that these fragments will succumb to a variety of pressures in turn and that the animal's range will shrink substantially. Apart from the animal's intrinsic value, mountain hares often provide an important food base for rarer species, such as the golden eagle[9]. The principal conservation objective for this species should therefore be to maintain its current broad range in the north-western Highlands, Central Highlands and Southern

Uplands in Scotland, and to maintain and, if possible, expand the Derbyshire population.

Mountain hares seem to do best in areas managed for red grouse[10]. Indeed, it is probably the intensive fox control combined with rotational burning that benefits both grouse and hares. However, where grouse suffer from tick-borne louping ill infections, hares may help to sustain high tick numbers and facilitate the transmission of the virus between ticks, thus perpetuating the disease. In such cases hares may have to be controlled if the disease is to be eliminated.

On some grouse moors hares are treated as a crop and are popular with hunters from the Continent who enjoy shooting and eating them. Hare shooting on these areas provides additional income, helping to maintain the gamekeeper's employment and the moorland management. Regular shooting is probably necessary on some moors to prevent numbers from getting too high and damaging the heather.

Research in the late 1960s suggested that such culls could be substantial[11], so it is important to demonstrate that modern practices are sustainable and in line with good management. This too should be a conservation objective and is a requirement under the European Habitats Directive.

## Research needs

Future research on mountain hares should be directed at the following:

- Development of a method for more accurate monitoring of the distribution and abundance of this species.

- Development of optimum management strategies for the species to show that it can continue to be harvested in a sustainable way.

- Determination of whether the Peak District population of hares can be increased by reducing local fox numbers, or lowering grazing pressure, or both. The Peak District mountain hares are the most isolated and vulnerable of our populations and would best be sustained by an increase in extent and density.

## Conservation actions

Agencies should work with landowners in an attempt to ensure that large areas of continuous moorland are maintained in upland areas within the species' range.

- Forestry planting likely to fragment upland areas inhabited by mountain hares should be avoided.

- Moor-owners need to establish clear policies for the management of hares on their grouse moors.

- The Government is required under the European Habitats Directive to monitor game bags of mountain hares and we suggest a formal arrangement is made between Scottish Natural Heritage and The Game Conservancy Trust for doing this.

## Sources and references

1. Baker, A. J., Eger, J. L., Peterson, R. L. & Manning, T. H. (1983) Geographic variation and taxonomy of arctic hares. *Acta Zoologica Fennica*, **174**: 45–8.

2. Corbet, G. B. (1986) The relationships and origins of the European lagomorphs. *Mammal Review*, **16**: 105–10.

3. Fargher, S. E. (1977) The distribution of the brown hare (*Lepus capensis*) and the mountain hare (*Lepus timidus*) in the Isle of Man. *Journal of Zoology, London*, **182** (2): 164–7.

4. Barrett-Hamilton, G. E. H. & Hinton, M. A. C. (1912) *A History of British Mammals*. Gurney & Jackson, London.

5. Arnold, H. R. (1993) *The Atlas of Mammals in Britain*. HMSO, London.

6. Harris, S., Morris, P., Wray, S. & Yalden, D. (1995) *A Review of British Mammals*. Joint Nature Conservation Committee, Peterborough.

7. Yalden, D. W. (1984) The status of the mountain hare, *Lepus timidus*, in the Peak District. *Naturalist*, **109**: 55–9.

8. Watson, A. (1973) Population densities of mountain hares *Lepus timidus* on western Scottish and Irish moors and Scottish hills. *Journal of Zoology, London*, **170**: 151–9.

9. Watson, J., Leitch, A. F. & Rae, S. R. (1993) The diet of golden eagles *Aquila chrysaetos* in Scotland. *Ibis*, **135**: 387–93.

10. Hudson, P. (1992) *Grouse in Space and Time: The Population Biology of a Managed Gamebird*. Game Conservancy Limited, Fordingbridge, Hampshire.

11. Flux, J. E. C. (1970) Life history of the mountain hare (*Lepus timidus scoticus*) in north-east Scotland. *Journal of Zoology, London*, **161**: 75–123.

# 4.3 Rabbit
*(Oryctolagus cuniculus)*

## History and current status

The rabbit is not native to Britain but was introduced by the Normans for food and fur. Its history and ecology have been extensively studied and documented[1]. Rabbits are currently so numerous in some areas that they are commonly believed to have been equally abundant throughout historic times. In fact, evidence suggests that rabbits did not become widespread in the wild until after the mid-18th century. Before this time they were kept in enclosed warrens, where they were fed and protected from poachers and predators by professional warreners. The gradual increase in the wild population since the mid-1700s has been attributed to two factors:

- An increase in agricultural productivity in winter since enclosure;

- The countryside becoming increasingly managed for game, with woodland coverts and a reduced number of predators.

Over the last 300 years the economic value of rabbits for fur, food or sport has varied. This contrasts with their nuisance value as an agricultural pest. During periods of agricultural recession, such as the beginning of the 20th century, many farmers in regions such as southern Wales or the West Country derived their principal income from trapping rabbits[1]. By the late 1930s, and during the Second World War, rabbit control was paramount in reducing agricultural damage and rabbit numbers were substantially suppressed.

Since the myxomatosis epidemic in 1954, which initially wiped out 99% of the British rabbit population[2], the true economic impact of rabbit damage has been fully appreciated and rabbits are now regarded almost universally as a serious agricultural pest. However, apart from forming the staple diet of a range of native predators, their grazing effects can produce unusual plant communities on which many invertebrate species of conservation importance depend[3]. They are also a valuable sporting resource for many country people.

## Conservation plan

There is no need to eliminate the rabbit completely in Britain and a programme leading to its

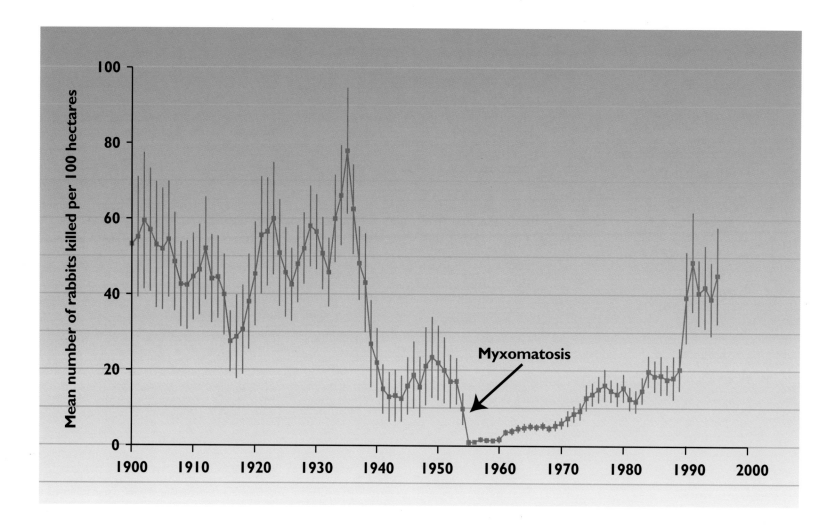

Myxomatosis

extinction, like the one being planned in Australia[4], would certainly be opposed here, not least because the survival of their dependent predators and the maintenance of some grassland ecosystems would be jeopardised. Most predator populations survived the myxomatosis outbreak (although in fewer numbers) by switching to other foods, such as field voles, whose numbers appear to increase in response to a reduction in rabbit numbers. The stoat and the buzzard were the principal predator species affected[3].

Currently, Britain's rabbit population is estimated at 37 million[5]. This compares with a pre-myxomatosis estimate of 100 million and an implied immediate post-myxomatosis level of just one million. Bag records suggest that the numbers killed have substantially increased over the last five years, which may reflect an increase in the rabbit population resulting from dry warm springs and summers and/or set-aside. Populations may eventually be affected by the newly established viral haemorrhagic disease[6]. Unfortunately, this

disease is no longer notifiable, so its current distribution and its future spread will remain largely unknown.

Most farmers, foresters and land-managers believe that current rabbit numbers are too high. They would welcome a return to the levels of the early 1970s, or earlier, when the national population must have been less than 10 million. Under those conditions it was relatively easy to control local numbers except in some downland or sandy-soil situations.

Bag records of rabbits from the National Game-Bag Census for all of Britain. Figures are means with 95% confidence limits.

Effective control today is very labour intensive and almost impossible on a wide scale or in areas where the habitat gives rabbits extensive cover. New methods of control are needed that can be applied over large areas. Apart from the current legal use of poison gas, we do not judge the use of poison to be appropriate for this species, given the inherent dangers of non-target and secondary poisoning.

There is some evidence that predators may help to keep rabbit numbers down[7], so game-keepers and wardens, where they are reducing predators for game or conservation reasons, must also assume responsibility for keeping rabbits in check.

## Research needs

- Novel methods of control other than extensive trapping and poison need to be investigated. Immunocontraception is a promising approach. This works by using pelleted baits that contain a vaccine designed to sterilise the target animal without harming it. This technique, based on triggering an immune response by an animal, could be made rabbit-specific[8].

- More research is required on whether rabbits help to buffer or aggravate predation on other game species.

## Conservation actions

- Predation control programmes for game should include rabbit control to keep numbers in check.

- Grant aid for rabbit control programmes should be considered as part of conservation grant schemes.

## Sources and references

1. Thompson, H. V. (1994) The rabbit in Britain. In: Thompson, H. V. & King, C. M. (Eds) *The European Rabbit: The History and Biology of a Successful Colonizer*. Oxford University Press, Oxford. 64–107.

2. Fenner, F. & Ross, J. (1994) Myxomatosis. In: Thompson, H. V. & King, C. M. (Eds) *The European Rabbit: The History and Biology of a Successful Colonizer*. Oxford University Press, Oxford. 205–40.

3. Sumption, K. J. & Flowerdew, J. R. (1985) The ecological effects of the decline in rabbits (*Oryctolagus cuniculus* L.) due to myxomatosis. *Mammal Review*, **15**: 151–86.

4. Robinson, A. J. & Holland, M. K. (1995) Testing the concept of virally vectored immunosterilisation for the control of wild rabbit and fox populations in Australia. *Australian Veterinary Journal*, **72**: 65–8.

5. Harris, S., Morris, P., Wray, S. & Yalden, D. (1995) *A Review of British Mammals*. Joint Nature Conservation Committee, Peterborough.

6. Trout, R. C. & Chasey, D. (1997) Rabbit viral haemorrhagic disease in Britain. In: Marboutin, E. & Berthos, J.-C. (eds) XXIth Lagomorph Workshop, Clermont-Ferrand, July 1996. *Gibier Faune Sauvage* **14** (3): 541–2.

7. Trout, R. C. & Tittensor, A. M. (1989) Can predators regulate wild rabbit *Oryctolagus cuniculus* population density in England and Wales? *Mammal Review*, **19**: 153–73.

8. Tyndale-Biscoe, C. H. (1994) Virus-vectored immunocontraception of feral mammals. *Reproduction Fertility & Development*, **6**: 281–7.

# 5. Resident large game mammals

Deer have probably never been so abundant in Britain. The disappearance of large predators such as bear, wolf and lynx, as well as much-reduced hunting by man in recent years, has allowed deer populations to expand. Added to this, in the lowlands modern crops provide abundant food for these herbivores all year round. In some regions numbers of deer are excessive and are having a detrimental effect on the flora and the natural regeneration of woodland.

The Game Conservancy Trust regards deer not as pests, but as a significant and often under-utilised game resource. We advise landowners to develop stalking and culling strategies for deer in order to make the best use of this resource and to maintain populations at levels low enough to allow woodland to regenerate and to avoid forestry damage.

**Muntjac habitat and distribution:** kilometre squares containing more than 1 hectare of woodland but no urban or urban fringe.
**Blue =** areas where muntjac appear to be currently established.
**Green =** areas where muntjac are not yet present in significant numbers.

From ITE Land Cover and OS Geographic Reference maps BRC mammal atlas, and Chapman et al. (1994)[1]

# 5.1 Muntjac deer
## (Muntiacus reevesi)

## History and current status

At least five species of muntjac are known, with a distribution from Pakistan to Java and north to mainland China. Two species have been brought to Britain:

- The larger Indian muntjac was brought to Woburn Park in about 1900. This was eliminated in the park but survived as escapes, or as the progeny of escapes, until 1925.

- The smaller Reeves' muntjac was introduced before 1900 and flourished, spreading into surrounding woodlands[1]. In spite of contemporary doubts, it does not hybridise with the Indian species.

The spread of the Reeves' muntjac throughout the Midlands over the last 80 years is shown in the distribution map. Records of small colonies outside the main area suggest human intervention[1].

Owing to their subtropical origin in southern China, muntjac are not seasonal breeders[2]. They produce single fawns every seven months, gestation is 210 days and lactation is six to eight weeks. Mating follows quickly after parturition. Pelage changes (spring and autumn) and, to some extent, antler growth (most adult bucks are in velvet in early summer) have adapted to the British climate[3].

Muntjac are territorial and the social unit is a family group, with young adults being driven off before the arrival of the next fawn[4]. Males make large scrapes and fray on low branches using their tusks, not their antlers. The tusks are the muntjac's primary weapons, showing its primitive ancestry. Both sexes bark like a small dog at intruders, often continuing for many minutes.

Their preferred foods are ivy, bramble, coppice shoots, flowers and seeds of many plants, also fruit, nuts, dead leaves, fungi and market garden produce. They seem to be primarily animals of dense woodland, although analysis of the occurrence of sightings suggest their habitat preferences are very catholic[1].

Little is known so far about predation, parasites and disease, but traffic accidents and loose dogs may kill many every year. Severe winter weather may lead to high mortality.

## Conservation plan

Muntjac have a considerable impact on various human interests. Coppice regeneration is attacked

and may be checked[5]. Young, tender tree seedlings are eaten, sufficient for them to be checked. Damage appears to become severe when muntjac numbers build up in the absence of control. Recent research has shown that browsing on valued plants such as orchids and bluebells can be serious and can also affect the food plants of other woodland species[6].

The British population of muntjac has been estimated at 40,000 animals, increasing at approximately 10% per year. It is simply not known whether this animal will spread into all available habitats or be limited by climate further north and at altitude, nor whether its range will be restricted by roe deer, whose distribution is partially the opposite. However, studies in eastern England suggest that the two do coexist to a large extent. If anything, the muntjac, where numerous, could be restricting the activities and numbers of roe[4].

Control of muntjac is difficult because they inhabit thick cover and rarely stand still to allow a deliberate rifle shot. They are becoming increasingly popular, mainly with trophy hunters from the Continent, and although the carcasses are too small to be of much economic value they are excellent eating.

The main emphasis for this species should lie in discouraging its spread and controlling densities. To this end, the Department of the Environment, Transport and Regions has tried to put a stop to the deliberate spread of the species and, in 1997, added it to Schedule 9 of the Wildlife and Countryside Act (1981), which prevents anyone from releasing them into areas where they are currently absent.

## Research needs

The following areas require investigation:

- New methods of control for muntjac and exploration of techniques such as immuno-contraception.

- Studies on population dynamics in order to predict how numbers are regulated and how control can best be targeted.

## Conservation actions

- Curtailing the spread of this species should be an important conservation objective and Government agencies need to develop with interested parties a control strategy for containing the spread and reducing numbers.

## Sources and references

1. Chapman, N., Harris, S. & Stanford, A. (1994) Reeves' muntjac *Muntiacus reevesi* in Britain: Their history, spread, habitat selection, and role of human intervention in accelerating their dispersal. *Mammal Review*, 24: 113–60.

2. Chapman, D. I., Chapman, N. G. & Dansie, O. (1984) The periods of conception and parturition in feral Reeves' muntjac (*Muntjac reevesi*) in southern England, based upon age of juvenile animals. *Journal of Zoology, London*, 204: 575–8.

3. Chapman, N. G. & Harris, S. (1991) Evidence that the seasonal antler cycle of Reeves' muntjac (*Muntiacus reevesi*) is not associated with reproductive quiescence. *Journal of Reproduction and Fertility*, 92: 361–9.

4. Chapman, N. G., Claydon, K., Claydon, M., Forde, P. G. & Harris, S. (1993) Sympatric populations of muntjac (*Muntiacus reevesi*) and roe deer (*Capreolus capreolus*): a comparative analysis of their ranging behaviour, social organization and activity. *Journal of Zoology, London*, 229: 623–40.

5. Cooke, A. S. & Lakhani, K. H. (1996) Damage to coppice regrowth by muntjac deer *Muntiacus reevesi* and protection with electric fencing. *Biological Conservation*, 75: 231–8.

6. Pollard, E. & Cooke, A. S. (1994) Impact of muntjac deer *Muntiacus reevesi* on egg-laying sites of the white admiral butterfly *Ladoga camilla* in a Cambridgeshire wood. *Biological Conservation*, 70: 189–91.

**Fallow deer habitat and distribution:** lowland kilometre squares (less than 300 metres mean altitude) containing more than 10 hectares of woodland but no urban or urban fringe.

**Blue =** areas where fallow appear to be currently established.

**Green =** areas where fallow are not yet present in significant numbers.

From ITE Land Cover, OS Geographic Reference and Topographic maps and BRC mammal atlas.

# 5.2 Fallow deer
*(Dama dama)*

## History and current status

Although fallow deer were present some 400,000 years ago in Britain, later glaciations restricted them to the Mediterranean basin whence they have been re-introduced to other parts of Europe[1]. There are no reliable records of them being imported into Britain before the Norman Conquest, after which they were kept widely in parks for both food and ornament. They were also preserved in the wild for hunting, eg. in Epping Forest and the New Forest. Indeed, until 1997, the New Forest Buckhounds were the only surviving pack hunting fallow.

The present feral population owes its existence largely to park escapes. Many parks were broken up during the Civil War (1642) and again in the two World Wars[1].

Deer farming became fashionable in the 1980s, some farms keeping fallow in preference to other species. Escapes were inevitable, but are not thought to have made an important impact in comparison with the large number already feral in the countryside.

Fallow exhibit extreme flexibility in most aspects of their social organisation. In high-density populations in large woodlands such as the New Forest, males and females plus young live in separate groups, except during the autumn rut. In lower-density populations in agricultural areas, however, mixed-sex groups regularly occur throughout the winter. In common with other ungulates, group size is flexible and influenced by both habitat and season. Fallow deer also exhibit mating systems ranging from non-territorial defence of harems to the development of clusters of tiny mating territories on leks[2].

The ideal habitat is a mosaic of established broad-leaved woodlands and arable fields. However, fallow make a living in a range of habitats, from commercial conifer plantations to large open agricultural areas with small woodlands. Although primarily grazers, they take a variety of vegetation and, at high densities, may cause considerable damage to forestry and farm crops.

## Conservation plan

The distribution of fallow is general in England, with substantial herds in Wales and southern Scotland. Further north there are local populations arising from park escapes or deliberate releases.

Currently the population size is estimated to be about 100,000, but management of this species outside established park herds is haphazard. This is the most important area that needs to be addressed[3].

## Research needs

A considerable amount of research has been conducted on fallow deer, although much of this has concentrated on deer parks or on wild populations in large contiguous woodlands such as the New Forest[4, 5]. The following remains a priority:

- The ranging behaviour of fallow deer in any environment remains largely unquantified and remains the priority for future research. This is particularly pressing in the case of fallow deer inhabiting agricultural land.

## Conservation actions

- Development and support of regional Deer Management Groups is essential and should be encouraged. Away from large woodlands, fallow populations are probably highly mobile and thus may range over a number of land-holdings.

- Deer Management Groups need to address the significant problems of traffic accidents and poaching in conjunction with local police forces.

- Extension of doe culling seasons, which are currently relatively short, might allow easier population control.

## Sources and references

1. Chapman, D. & Chapman, N. (1975) *Fallow Deer*. Terence Dalton Ltd, Lavenham, Suffolk.

2. Thirgood, S.J., Langbein, J. & Putman, R.J. (1999) Intraspecific variation in ungulate mating strategies: the case of the flexible fallow deer. *Advances in the Study of Behaviour*, **28**: 333-36

3. Harris, S., Morris, P., Wray, S. & Yalden, D. (1995) *A Review of British Mammals*. Joint Nature Conservation Committee, Peterborough.

4. Putman, R. J. (1986) *Grazing in Temperate Ecosystems. Large Herbivores and the Ecology of the New Forest*. Croom Helm, London.

5. Putman, R. J. (1996) *Competition and Resource Partitioning in Temperate Ungulate Assemblies*. Chapman & Hall, London.

**Red deer habitat and distribution:** kilometre squares containing more than 25 hectares of woodland or more than 25 hectares of moorland.

**Blue =** current range of red deer.

**Green =** areas where red deer are not yet present in significant numbers.

From ITE Land Cover map and BRC mammal atlas.

# 5.3 Red deer
*(Cervus elaphus)*

## History and current status

The red deer is Britain's largest native land mammal. Originally a species of the woodland edge, red deer have adapted to an existence in open 'deer forests' of the Scottish Highlands[1,2]. More recently they have colonised commercial conifer plantations where they can attain high population densities[3]. There have been laws to protect red deer since Saxon times and because of conservation, primarily for hunting with hounds but latterly for stalking, they have survived in fluctuating numbers through the Middle Ages to modern times.

The main concentrations are now in the Highlands, south-western Scotland and south-western England, with a wide scatter of local herds in many parts of England and Scotland. They are virtually absent from Wales, although further colonisation of commercial forestry there is possible. Some red deer populations, notably those in the Scottish Highlands and the west of England, may be considered native, although with some injections of other strains. Others owe their origins to escapes from parks or to deliberate introductions[4].

The Scottish herd is estimated to be in the region of 300,000[5]. Between 50,000 and 70,000 red deer are culled every year and in severe winters this may be supplemented by natural mortality. Poaching may add substantially to this figure. No statistics are available for England and Wales.

## Conservation plan

In the Highlands, deer stalking is the primary source of revenue for some sporting estates. Very high local densities of more than 10 deer per square kilometre have been allowed to build up in upland environments and these depend on seasonal movements to low ground in winter. Afforestation and fencing of traditional wintering ground has led to conflicts of interests between forestry and stalking.

Additionally, the impact of red deer on the regeneration of native pinewoods and on heather moorland has increasingly become a conservation issue[6]. Not only does their grazing significantly affect the ground cover but this, in turn, reduces the numbers of insects which form the staple diet of the chicks of many birds, especially gamebirds[6]. Unfortunately, using fencing to protect the trees

from deer can be counter-productive as fence wires are also a major cause of mortality for woodland grouse[7].

In parts of Devon and Somerset, it is argued that local support for stag hunting with hounds allows a large deer herd to be maintained. There is also a greater degree of tolerance to farming damage than would otherwise be the case. Elsewhere deer take a lower place in land management priorities because of the damage they cause to forestry and farm crops.

Both deer stalking on the open hill and stag hunting have an accepted and substantial value to the local economy. Red deer in low-ground forestry tend to have a high reproductive rate and grow to a large size (75% larger than upland animals and with correspondingly bigger antlers). This gives them value in terms of sport (trophy) fees and in the returns from venison. This can justify:

● Designing the forest so that deer stalking for sport or control can be done efficiently;

● Managing the deer herd at a slightly higher density than would be tolerable if they were regarded purely as pests.

However, the price of venison varies and it has been shown by modelling that managing deer at low densities is not incompatible with maintaining revenue from forest stalking[8].

# Research needs

In Britain, less is known about the effects of management on red deer populations than about natural processes of population regulation[2,9]. The management practice that most directly affects deer populations is culling and there is an urgent need for management-orientated research to address the following issues.

- Practical demonstrations are needed to show that lower hind densities are beneficial to the deer herd and to the habitat, as has been shown in theory[8]. Currently, to reduce over-grazing, sporting estates are being asked to increase their hind culls. However, owners are concerned that this may result in fewer stags and a loss in revenue and capital value.

- The effects of population density on dispersal of both stags and hinds requires study. Movement of deer into areas of low density created by heavy culling or movements of mature stags to areas of high hind densities may disrupt current stalking practice.

- The effect of reduction in deer numbers, currently practised on many estates, on vegetation recovery needs investigating.

## Conservation actions

- Deer-managers need to define optimum stocking levels, taking account of conservation needs as well as sporting requirements. Current numbers of red deer are generally too high so vegetation is being damaged and forest regeneration prevented.

- The development of local Deer Management Groups is essential and must be fostered. Red deer are highly mobile and individual populations inevitably cover many separate land ownerships. This system is already in place in much of Scotland.

- Greater control is needed at the point of sale of venison. Using a mandatory tagging system would reduce unacceptable levels of poaching.

## Sources and references

1. Clutton-Brock, T. H., Guinness, F. E. & Albon, S. D. (1982) *Red deer: Behaviour and Ecology of Two Sexes.* Edinburgh University Press, Edinburgh.

2. Clutton-Brock, T. H. & Albon, S. D. (1989) *Red Deer in the Highlands.* BSP Professional Books, Blackwell Scientific Publications, Oxford.

3. Ratcliffe, P. R. (1987) Red deer population changes and the independent assessment of population size. *Symposia of the Zoological Society of London*, 58: 153–65.

4. Staines, B. W. & Ratcliffe, P. R. (1987) Estimating the abundance of red deer (*Cervus elaphus* L.) and roe deer (*Capreolus capreolus* L.) and their current status in Great Britain. *Symposia of the Zoological Society of London*, 58: 131–52.

5. Anon. (1994) *Red Deer and the Natural Heritage: SNH Policy Paper.* Scottish Natural Heritage, Edinburgh.

6. Baines, D. (1996) The implications of grazing and predator management on the habitats and breeding success of black grouse *Tetrao tetrix*. *Journal of Applied Ecology*, 33: 54–62.

7. Baines, D. & Summers, R. W. (1997) Assessments of bird collisions with deer fences in Scottish forests. *Journal of Applied Ecology*, 34: 941–948.

8. Buckland, S. T., Ahmadi, S., Staines, B. W., Gordon, I. J. & Youngson, R. W. (1996) Estimating the minimum population size that allows a given number of mature red deer stags to be culled sustainably. *Journal of Applied Ecology*, 33: 118–30.

9. Mitchell, B., Staines, B. W. & Welch, D. (1977) *Ecology of Red Deer. A Research Review Relevant to their Management in Scotland.* Institute of Terrestrial Ecology, Cambridge.

**Sika deer habitat and distribution:** kilometre squares containing more than 10 hectares of woodland.
**Blue =** areas where sika appear to be currently established.
**Green =** areas where sika are not yet present in significant numbers.

From ITE Land Cover map and BRC mammal atlas.

# 5.4 Sika deer
## (*Cervus nippon*)

## History and current status

Sika originate from the Far East and some 13 different races are recognised, many of them endangered in their native countries. Size varies considerably, from the typical Japanese race with a shoulder height of 65–79 centimetres to the Dybowski sika of Manchuria and Korea which measures about 110 centimetres. Sika are closely related to red deer and can interbreed with them. In habit they keep more to woodland than red deer. Populations which are subject to disturbance become largely nocturnal.

Most sika in Britain are Japanese in origin and were brought first to Ireland in about 1860, to Powerscourt, and thence to a variety of places in England and Scotland. Some were released deliberately, eg. in Kintyre, the New Forest, Dorset and Bowland. The deer at Bowland are thought to have been Manchurian. Others escaped from parks, especially during the two World Wars, and established feral populations.

In recent years the sika has extended its range, especially in Scotland. The distribution map shows how it is now well established from Argyll up to the Great Glen and again north from Inverness to Sutherland. Another colony in Peebles is now expanding northward and eastward[1]. In England sika are to be found in Lancashire and Yorkshire, southern Dorset and the New Forest[1]. In addition, small local populations exist in the vicinity of several of the parks from which they originally escaped.

Further expansion seems likely, especially in the north. Sika appear to favour the wetter, acid-soil areas and avoid chalk downland.

## Conservation plan

Sika present major problems in Britain. Locally they may cause considerable damage to farm and forest crops. Also, and of most ecological significance, they tend to interbreed with red deer[2].

Although no data on population size or the extent of the annual cull has been attempted, the species is now too widespread and numerous to make elimination practicable, even if it were desirable. It is fairly clear however, that the genetic integrity of red deer in Britain is at risk.

A Question of Balance

## Research needs

In view of the species' significance to farming, forestry and red deer management, there is an urgent need for a closer study of its status in Britain. In particular, we need:

- Development of a better methodology for estimating numbers.

- Support for on-going research on hybridisation between sika and red deer.

- Development of a national management strategy using knowledge based on the above.

## Conservation actions

- Government should recognise and support the development of local Deer Management Groups.

- More information should be obtained on current population levels and the impact of culling regimes on sika.

## Sources and references

1. Ratcliffe, P. R. (1987) Distribution and current status of sika deer in Great Britain. *Mammal Review*, **17**: 39–58.

2. Abernethy, K. (1994) The establishment of a hybrid zone between red and sika deer. *Molecular Ecology*, **3**: 551–62.

**Roe deer habitat and distribution:** kilometre squares containing more than 10 hectares of woodland but no urban or urban fringe.
**Blue =** areas where roe are currently established.
**Green =** areas where roe are not yet present in significant numbers.

From ITE Land Cover and OS Geographic Reference maps and BRC mammal atlas.

# 5.5 Roe deer
*(Capreolus capreolus)*

## History and current status

The roe deer is primarily an animal of mixed and small woodland but is capable of adapting to a wide variety of habitats. It has colonised the northern conifer forests and has penetrated many towns, making use of gardens, parks and other open spaces where there is food and cover. It may also be seen well out into open farmland[1].

The roe deer is a native species which has been present in Britain since at least the Mesolithic period. However, probably because of over-hunting, it became extremely scarce in medieval times and by 1700 was considered extinct in southern and central England and all of Wales. It also disappeared in most regions of Scotland except for the northern Highlands. After 1800 there were re-introductions into England and colonies were established in Dorset, Sussex and East Anglia. At the same time, there was a gradual recolonisation of most of northern England and Scotland. Today, roe deer occur in most of southern England, all of northern England and Scotland, and they are continuing to spread into the Midlands and Wales.

The re-introductions were in response to a vogue for hunting which did not last. Since then roe have been undervalued as a sporting quarry and, as numbers built in the first part of the 20th century, shotgun drives and snaring were the accepted legal means of control.

Deer Acts from 1959 onwards imposed close seasons and limitations on the type and calibres of weapons permitted for deer. Roe stalking as a sport was practised by a few enthusiasts from the late 19th century onwards, but has only become more generally recognised as a method of humane control in the last 30 years.

## Conservation plan

The present population of roe deer in Britain is very difficult to estimate. Roe are highly secretive and visual counting of this species is normally too inaccurate to be useful. However, estimates of density suggest that suitable woodland can hold 0.51–0.72 animals per hectare. Using these figures and known culling rates from parts of Scotland, a figure of between 500,000 and 600,000 has been estimated for Britain[2].

If we assume that the bulk of our present roe population is tied to woodland for at least some

of the time we might define as suitable habitat any kilometre square that includes at least 10 hectares of woodland – provided that the square does not also contain a significant portion of urban land. Within the roe's current range there are 30,500 square kilometres of such habitat, which includes 951,000 hectares of woodland altogether. Given a mean density of 0.61 deer per hectare of woodland, this suggests a roe population of 580,000 animals, which is very close to the current best estimate[2].

Outside the animal's current range there are 576,000 hectares of woodland within these parameters, suggesting a potential for a further 351,000 animals. A future roe population of over one million looks quite likely.

We consider it desirable to manage roe deer numbers for several reasons:

- Damage to crops, trees, gardens and woodland habitats is prevented;

- Reduced-density populations of deer are generally healthier and more productive;

- Roe deer venison provides a high-quality valuable game meat;

- Useful, although not substantial, income for landowners can be derived from stalking and venison sales.

It should be remembered that, in Britain, the roe's main woodland predators (such as lynx) no longer exist and man's intervention for this species can be easily justified in ecological terms.

## Research needs

It is clear from the above that, despite a good deal of research right across the roe deer's range in Europe and Asia[3], there are still large gaps in our knowledge which compromise an effective national plan for this animal. The following areas in particular need investigation:

- The development of a better methodology for estimating numbers of this species.

- An understanding of how densities vary in relation to habitat.

- The relationship of productivity, mortality (especially road deaths) and dispersal with both habitat and density.

- The establishment of a more complete, scientifically based, national management strategy using knowledge gained from the above.

## Conservation actions

- Government should recognise that for this and other deer species the best management solution is regular and systematic culling by landowners. Other damage prevention methods can be useful but will never provide an overall satisfactory solution.

- Landowners with significant roe densities should recognise the need to set up appropriate management through stalking rather than relying on the vagaries of emigration and poaching to dispose of surplus young animals.

## Sources and references

1. Prior, R. (1995) *The Roe Deer*. Swan Hill Press, Shrewsbury.

2. Harris, S., Morris, P., Wray, S. & Yalden, D. (1995) *A Review of British Mammals*. Joint Nature Conservation Committee, Peterborough.

3. Danilkin, A. & Hewison, A. J. M. (1995) *Behavioural Ecology of Siberian and European Roe Deer*. Chapman & Hall, London.

# 6 Gamebirds

Britain's small-game populations have suffered from the environmental deterioration brought about by intensive arable farming and livestock rearing, which have reduced botanical diversity, as well as from the increasing impact of a range of predatory species, which have recovered in abundance since the Second World War.

The Game Conservancy Trust recognises that the high levels of game abundance a century ago were partly a reflection of the heavy suppression of predators for the benefit of shooting; this is no longer compatible with our desire for increased biodiversity. Nevertheless, predator control must remain an essential part of the management of game species because it is only if these species retain their game status that landowners will be sufficiently motivated to retain and manage the habitats essential to their well-being. Without such management, they and related species may not merely cease to be exploitable as game; over wide areas they may cease to exist at all.

**Red grouse habitat and distribution:** kilometre squares containing at least 25 hectares of moorland. Included are all three moorland and heath classes. **Blue =** areas where red grouse are present. **Green =** areas where red grouse are absent.

From ITE Land Cover and OS Geographic Reference maps and BTO bird atlas.

# 6.1 Red grouse
## (*Lagopus lagopus scoticus*)

### History and current status

The red grouse is a bird of heather moorland with a range restricted to areas of blanket bog and upland shrub heath. It is a subspecies of the willow grouse (*L. l. lagopus*), whose range extends across the northern latitudes of Europe, Asia and North America. The red grouse differs by not developing white plumage during winter and in having a diet almost exclusively of heather.

Since the mid-1800s, many areas of heather have been managed to produce grouse for shoot-

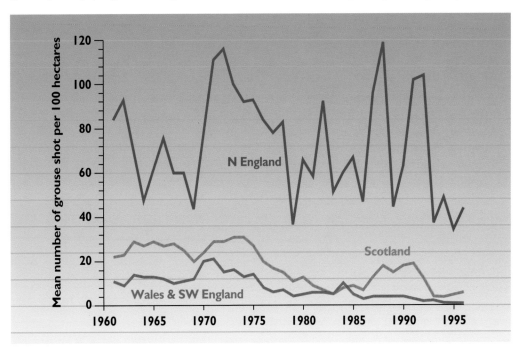

*Changes in grouse shooting bags in Britain. Figures are mean values of all estates contributing to the National Game-Bag Census.*

ing. Indeed, grouse shooting has been one of the major land uses of upland ground and the most important source of income for many estates.

We estimate that the numbers of grouse shot per year between 1911 and 1980 has fallen by 82%. Particularly severe long-term declines occurred after the Second World War and after the mid-1970s in Scotland and Wales. In general, grouse numbers have remained stable on many northern English moors. Numbers have declined seriously in Scotland and grouse are now only present in very low numbers in Wales.

The causes of these declines appear to be multi-factorial and have been reviewed by Hudson[1]. On a national basis, there was a 30% loss of heather between 1950 and 1980, largely due to over-grazing by sheep and conversion to forestry. Increased winter grazing by sheep, and in some

areas by deer, may also be reducing heather quality. However, while heather loss is important, it cannot account for the full extent of the decline in grouse stocks. There is considerable evidence that the populations of many grouse-predators have increased in recent decades, while the area of land covered by the activities of gamekeepers has declined. In particular there is evidence of increases in foxes, crows and raptors in many parts of Scotland and Wales. It seems likely that predation pressure, both by mammals and predatory birds, has increased on many moors. These increases in predator numbers are a significant factor in suppressing grouse numbers, slowing population growth rates and reducing shooting bags on many moors[2].

Approximately one third of grouse moors carry louping ill, a viral disease transmitted between host animals by ticks. The presence of louping ill causes reduced levels of chick survival, with up to 80% of infected chicks dying. As a consequence, chick survival rates average 50% lower on moors with louping ill[3].

The nematode worm *Trichostrongylus tenuis*, the causative agent of the disease strongylosis, is widespread in grouse populations and high levels of infection can cause significant reductions in both breeding success and direct mortality. Research in the north of England has shown that this parasite is largely responsible for the cyclical fluctuations in grouse numbers on moors in this region[4, 5]. The parasite is most prevalent when grouse stocks have been high in the previous year, but it may also reduce breeding success on low-density moors.

## Conservation plan

Current estimates suggest a British breeding red grouse stock of 250,000 pairs. With suitable habitat, breeding densities can reach over 50 pairs per square kilometre. Our conservation plan for this species has two elements:

- To restore the range of the red grouse, although we have no national population target for this species.

- To see national policies implemented that encourage estates to continue providing driven grouse shooting with its associated benefits.

We want to see the range of the grouse extended in areas where the species has been virtually lost (south-western England, Wales and parts of the Lake District). In many cases the first priority will be the restoration of heather-dominant vegetation. This should be achieved through reductions in grazing pressure following reform of agricultural subsidies. Once suitable cover is re-established, appropriate heather management and predator control should be re-introduced.

The main benefits of grouse shooting come indirectly from the management of the heather, namely:

- The reduction of over-grazing, afforestation and invasion by bracken;

- The effects of predator control on other upland species, including livestock;

- The creation of rural employment. If these benefits are to continue then it is necessary to sustain grouse densities on individual estates at a level commensurate with the economic employment of gamekeepers and other staff[6].

Moorland management for grouse often requires external investment and many owners are willing to subsidise their moors in this way. However, such investment is based on the prospect of driven grouse shooting. If grouse numbers are too low to sustain driven shooting, this investment in upland management may cease in many areas. The level at which this could occur varies regionally but is dependent on grouse densities sufficient to allow driven shooting, with a minimum of approximately 20 breeding pairs per square kilometre on moorland managed to ensure a high breeding success. To maintain this density, effective predator control, disease limitation and heather management are essential.

## Research needs

There has been a considerable quantity of research on red grouse. Key questions remaining are:

- How do the effects of predation, dispersal and disease, and habitat, alone and in combination, affect grouse numbers. Experimental studies are needed to understand this fully.

- What are the best methods of eradicating louping ill?

- Can new methods be developed to reduce the frequency and severity of outbreaks of strongylosis, as opposed to local and temporary control effected by using anthelmithics?

- Does grouse moor management increase the overall biodiversity of moorland areas, as we suspect?

## Conservation actions

- In order to limit over-grazing, continued reform of agricultural support for upland areas by statutory authorities and national agencies is urgently needed.

- Re-afforestation needs to be restricted to upland areas adjacent to heather moors.

- Control of predators is necessary for the management of grouse and this should be accepted by conservation agencies and voluntary bodies. National agencies need to ensure that an adequate range of techniques remain available to gamekeepers and others.

## Sources and references

1. Hudson, P. (1992) *Grouse in Space and Time: The Population Biology of a Managed Gamebird*. Game Conservancy Limited, Fordingbridge, Hampshire.

2. Redpath, S. & Thirgood, S. (1997) *Birds of Prey and Red Grouse. Report of the Joint Raptor Study*. The Stationery Office, London.

3. Duncan, J. S., Reid, H. W., Moss, R., Phillips, J. D. P. & Watson, A. (1979) Ticks, louping ill and red grouse on moors in Speyside, Scotland. *Journal of Wildlife Management*, **43**: 500–505.

4. Hudson, P. J., Newborn, D. & Dobson, A. P. (1992) Regulation and stability of a free-living host parasite system – *Trichostrongylus tenuis* in red grouse. I. Monitoring and parasite reduction experiments. *Journal of Animal Ecology*, **61**: 477–86.

5. Dobson, A. P. & Hudson, P. J. (1992) Regulation and stability of a free-living host parasite system – *Trichostrongylus tenuis* in red grouse. II. Population modes. *Journal of Animal Ecology*, **61**: 487–98.

6. McGilvray, J. (1995) *An Economic Study of Grouse Moors*. Game Conservancy Limited, Fordingbridge, Hampshire.

**Black grouse habitat and distribution:** kilometre squares containing either more than 25 hectares of dense shrub heath or a mix of woodland and shrub heath. **Blue =** areas where black grouse are still present. **Green =** areas where black grouse are absent.

From ITE Land Cover map and BTO bird atlas.

# 6.2 Black grouse
*(Tetrao tetrix)*

## History and current status

Black grouse are typically regarded as birds of early successional forest, either coniferous or birch, and of forest-edge habitats. Following reductions in the extent of natural forests, black grouse are now found in structurally similar habitats, such as mosaics of moorland and heathland, early stages of coniferous plantations, rough grazings and traditionally managed meadows.

Black grouse have been declining throughout virtually all their European range over the last century. In Britain, the decline has been considerable over the last 150 years and the population is now mostly confined to Scotland and north-eastern England, with a small number in Wales[1]. Even where the bird remains, numbers are still declining and an analysis of shooting bags suggests a 90–93% decrease in numbers of black grouse shot in Scotland and northern England since 1900[2].

Since 1989, we have recorded a halving of the number of black grouse males on leks. The current estimate of the British population is 6,500 lekking males in spring[3]. However, numbers fluctuate annually in relation to variations in breeding success.

## Conservation plan

A conservation plan for black grouse should aim to stabilise numbers and to prevent further fragmentation of the species' range, particularly in northern England and Wales. It should also encourage the recolonisation of formerly occupied range between isolated populations. We would like to see populations re-established in areas where they have become extinct within the last 20 years, such as Exmoor.

To achieve this, policies for re-instating the mixed land use pattern of low-intensity agricultural land, woodland and moorland edge favoured by black grouse need to be followed. Periods of reduced grazing pressure, by either sheep or red deer, are required to regenerate black grouse moorland and woodland habitats. Reductions in grazing of red deer in native woodland, together with removal of sheep from the moors in winter and from moorland margins in summer, are likely to result in substantial increases in black grouse numbers[4]. Currently, Government grants for sheep reductions are too small relative to others which encourage over grazing.

High breeding densities of black grouse, up to 15 birds per square kilometre, can be obtained in

A Question of Balance

the pre-thicket stage of commercial plantations. However, numbers soon decline – often to zero – following canopy closure at the thicket stage[5]. Sympathetic management of upland plantation forests, involving increases in the amount of permanent open space within the trees and phased clear felling to produce mixed-aged forests, should be to the long-term benefit of black grouse. Although not currently understood, factors determining the distribution and abundance of birds within second generation forests are the focus of current research.

## Research needs

Key questions are:

- What are the impacts of expanding populations of protected predatory species, eg. pine marten and goshawk, on woodland grouse populations?

- What are the best methods of managing second rotation commercial forests for black grouse?

- What ecological requirements and techniques are needed for the re-introduction of black grouse into formerly occupied areas?

- What is the importance of the size of habitat patches and fragmentation in limiting the distribution of black grouse?

## Conservation actions

- In order to reduce current problems of over-grazing and to pay for positive management initiatives, such as heather recovery, Government should re-target sheep subsidy payments to upland farmers. As part of this, more appropriate habitat management prescriptions should be adopted under the Countryside Premium and other national schemes in appropriate Environmentally Sensitive Areas.

- The Forestry Authority, through the Woodland Grant Scheme, should promote the regeneration of native upland forest without resorting to fencing.

- In Scotland, deer management groups should consider further reducing red deer stocks in areas with black grouse.

- Forest-managers should include the needs of black grouse when preparing forest management plans and, where possible, should undertake management trials.

- Two black grouse recovery projects are underway. In the North Pennines, we have a programme to help moor owners manage moorland edge for black grouse; this is a joint project with English Nature, the Royal Society for the Protection of Birds (RSPB) and the Ministry of Defence. On Tayside, a similar project has been started with Scottish Natural Heritage, the RSPB and European funding. Both these should provide models for black grouse management in the future and in other areas.

## Sources and references

1. Gibbons, D. W., Reid, J. B. & Chapman, R. A. (1993) *The New Atlas of Breeding Birds of Britain and Ireland: 1988–1991*. British Trust for Ornithology. T. & A. D. Poyser, London.

2. Hancock, M., Baines, D., Gibbons, D., Etheridge, B. & Shepherd, M. (1999) The status of black grouse in Britain. *Bird Study*, **46**: 1–15.

3. Hudson, P. J. & Baines, D. (1995) The decline of black grouse in Scotland and northern England. *Bird Study*, **42**: 122–31.

4. Baines, D. (1996) The implications of grazing and predator management on the habitats and breeding success of black grouse *Tetrao tetrix*. *Journal of Applied Ecology*, **33**: 54–62.

5. Cayford, J. T. (1990) The distribution and habitat preferences of black grouse in commercial forests in Wales: conservation and management implications. *Transactions of the International Congress of Game Biologists*, **19**: 435–47.

**Capercaillie habitat and distribution:** kilometre squares containing more than 10 hectares of coniferous woodland within the capercaillie's range.
**Blue =** areas of current distribution.
**Green =** areas where capercaillie are absent. Many woodlands, including some of those shown, may not be sufficiently old to have the right ground flora to support capercaillie.

From ITE Land Cover map and BTO bird atlas

# 6.3 Capercaillie
*(Tetrao urogallus)*

## History and current status

The capercaillie is primarily associated with conifer woodlands in Scotland, especially mature Scots pine forests with an understorey of heather, bilberry (*Vaccinium myrtillus*) and cowberry (*Vaccinium vitis-idaea*)[1].

Originally restricted to Scotland, Ireland and northern England, the capercaillie became extinct there in the 18th century following extensive felling of pinewood habitats and a run of cold, wet summers in the 'Little Ice Age'. It was re-introduced into Scotland, by landowners with an interest in shooting, in the mid-19th century and spread to eastern and central Scotland. In recent years, numbers have decreased.

The reasons for the recent reductions in numbers and range are poorly understood, but include habitat deterioration, increased predation, fence collisions and insect shortages in June causing poor chick survival[2]. The Scottish population is only a small proportion of the world population, which is also declining over most of its range in association with losses of extensive mature forest and human disturbance.

When more common, capercaillie were often shot either as trophies or on organised drives, but bags have never been large. Since the recent reduction in numbers there has been a voluntary moratorium by landowners on shooting. However, there is no sign that this has had any effect on the decline.

## Conservation plan

The capercaillie is included in the *UK Red Data Book* as a localised breeding species largely confined to a rare and vulnerable habitat: native pinewood. It is listed as being 'of High UK Conservation Concern' because of its rapid decline (over 63% decrease in distribution by 10-kilometre squares between the two *Atlas* periods, 1968–72 and 1988–91). An Action Plan for this species has been drawn up by the UK Biodiversity Steering Group and we support its objective and most of its recommendations.

The population in Britain was estimated at 20,000–50,000 birds in the mid-1970s to early 1980s, but the most recent estimate was a winter population of 2,200 birds (95% confidence limits 1,500 – 3,200)[3]. The main conservation aim must be to stabilise numbers within the core range in the eastern and central Highlands, and then to increase the population size and expand the range

to other parts of Scotland.

Native pinewoods are considered to be the core habitat for capercaillie and highest densities occur here. Expansion of this habitat, through encouragement of forest regeneration programmes and improvements in habitat quality by reducing numbers of red deer, should be the first priority. The alternative of using deer fencing carries with it the penalty that what is achieved through regeneration can be outweighed by increased mortality of capercaillie following collisions with fences[4, 5]. However the new technique of cladding deer fences with strips of orange flagging can reduce losses by some 70%[6]. Even so, these collisions remain a significant form of mortality.

The Royal Society for the Protection of Birds at its reserve at Abernethy is beginning to show how a combination of habitat management, reduction in deer numbers and predator control can cause a dramatic improvement in capercaillie breeding success. It is likely that, if such measures were more widely applied, the Action Plan objective of restoring numbers to their 1970s' levels could be achieved.

Capercaillie requirements within commercial forests are relatively poorly known[7]. Sympathetic management incorporating the retention of Scots pine, especially some of the older, bigger trees, and management of the canopy to promote a bilberry-rich understorey should be implemented. Further research is urgently needed to identify the requirements of chicks, particularly in spruce forests with little or no bilberry.

## Research needs

Key questions are:

- What are the precise habitat requirements of

capercaillie, especially during the breeding season?

- What is the ecology of capercaillie in commercial and non-native pine plantations? This is particularly important as commercial forests held large numbers of capercaillie in the 1970s.

- As with black grouse, by how much do capercaillie benefit from predation control and what will be the likely effect of increasing numbers of species such as pine marten and goshawk?

## Conservation actions

- The Forestry Authority should encourage the management of existing habitats and the creation of new native pinewoods.

- Landowners and gamekeepers should identify fence lines that regularly kill capercaillie and work towards either removing them or cladding them with plastic flagging to reduce losses. The Forestry Authority now gives grants for this cladding.

- Commercial forestry enterprises should retain native Scots pine and associated ericaceous ground vegetation, especially in the capercaillie's current and former range.

- Red deer over-grazing remains a significant problem. Numbers of red deer need to be reduced to assist natural regeneration of native pine without unnecessary fencing.

- Disturbance at capercaillie leks by bird-watchers needs to be reduced. Landowners and agencies should work together to limit this, perhaps by providing viewing facilities at selected sites.

- Release schemes based on hand-reared birds should be discouraged for the present, but ultimately they may be needed to restock areas where capercaillie have disappeared or where they may be appropriately introduced. In the latter situation the International Union for the Conservation of Nature and Natural Resources (ICUN) guidelines should be followed[8].

## Sources and references

1. Picozzi, N., Catt, D. C. & Moss, R. (1992) Evaluation of capercaillie habitat. *Journal of Applied Ecology*, **29**: 751–62.

2. Moss, R. (1994) Decline of the capercaillie (*Tetrao urogallus*) in Scotland. *Gibier Faune Sauvage*, **11**: 217–22.

3. Catt, D. C., Baines, D., Picozzi, N., Moss, R. & Summers, R.W. (1998) The abundance and distribution of capercaillie *Tetrao urogallus* in Scotland 1992–1994. *Biological Conservation*, **85**: 257–67

4. Catt, D. C., Dugan, D., Green, R. E., Moncreif, R., Moss, R., Picozzi, N., Summers, R. W. & Tyler, G. (1994) Collisions against fences by woodland grouse in Scotland. *Forestry*, **67**: 105–18.

5. Baines, D. & Summers, R. W. (1997) Assessments of bird collisions with deer fences in Scottish forests. *Journal of Applied Ecology*, **34**: 941–8.

6. Andrew, M. & Baines, D. (1997) *The Impact of Deer Fences on Woodland Grouse*. The Game Conservancy Trust, Fordingbridge, Hampshire. Unpublished report to the Royal Society for the Protection of Birds, Scottish Natural Heritage and Millennium Forest for Scotland Trust.

7. Picozzi, N., Moss, R. & Catt, D.C. (1996) Capercaillie diet, habitat and management in a Sitka spruce plantation in Central Scotland. *Forestry*, **69**: 373–88.

8. IUCN (1993) *Draft Guidelines for Re-introductions*. International Union for the Conservation of Nature and Natural Resources, Gland, Switzerland.

**Wild red-legged partridge habitat.**

**Yellow =** optimum habitat, where there is at least 50 hectares per kilometre square of tilled land, less than 10 hectares of woodland and no urban land, villages and major roads; also where the mean daily maximum July temperature exceeds 19°C.

**Green =** suboptimum habitat, which is similar but has between 10 and 50 hectares of tilled land per kilometre square.

From ITE Land Cover, OS Geographic Reference and Met. Office maps.

# 6.4 Red-legged partridge
*(Alectoris rufa)*

## History and current status

The red-legged partridge (redleg) is not native to Britain, but was successfully introduced to East Anglia in about 1770, using stock from France. Although becoming well established by the end of the century, its spread across Britain was slow and its current distribution was not reached until the 1930s. Despite its introduced status, the conservation of the red-legged partridge in Britain is important because the natural range of the species is restricted almost entirely to three European countries (Spain, Portugal and France), where numbers are declining.

As one would expect from its Mediterranean origin, the red-legged partridge thrives on dry, sandy soils and breeds best in areas of high summer temperatures. It has been less susceptible than the grey partridge to the reduction in cereal insects since the 1950s because its chicks consume considerably more seeds and vegetable matter, even shortly after hatching[1]. In the wild, the hen bird commonly lays two clutches, incubating one herself and leaving the other for the cock. Thus each pair has the potential to produce two broods more or less simultaneously[2].

This ability to lay two clutches has meant that the redleg also lays more in captivity, making it attractive to rear and release for sporting purposes. Starting in 1963, this practice increased rapidly as it was seen as a means of maintaining a partridge shoot despite the decline of the grey. In the late 1960s, game-farmers discovered that the closely related chukar partridge (*Alectoris chukar*) and chukar/redleg hybrids were nearly twice as prolific in captivity. The first ones were released in 1970 and they quickly became popular throughout lowland Britain. The disadvantage for the conservation of the wild red-legged partridge stock was three-fold:

- Chukars and hybrids bred much less well than pure redlegs in the wild;

- Hybridisation threatened the genetic purity of the wild stock;

- High levels of releasing induced an unsustainable shooting rate of wild redlegs[3].

Out of concern for the wild red-legged partridge, the releasing of chukars and chukar/red-

A Question of Balance

leg hybrids was prohibited in 1992 and, since then, the breeding success of wild red-legged partridges has improved[4]. Releases of pure red-legged partridges are estimated at about two million birds a year.

The current status of the *wild* red-legged partridge in Britain is difficult to assess because of the scale of releasing. Nevertheless, it seems that there has been a marked decline, at least since 1985. The British population size is estimated to lie between 90,000 and 250,000 pairs.

## Conservation plan

Because of its dislike of cold, wet conditions, the wild red-legged partridge is restricted to lowland areas in the eastern parts of Britain (although the pattern is being obscured somewhat in recent times by the large-scale releasing that is taking place). On keepered ground it increases in abundance even more substantially than the grey partridge[5].

In calculating potential habitat for wild red-legged partridges, we included all kilometre squares containing more than 10 hectares of tilled farmland and less than 50 hectares of woodland and excluded those influenced by cities, towns, large villages and major roads. We imposed the additional condition that the mean maximum daily temperature in July should be at least 19°C, to reflect the bird's warmth-loving tendencies. We considered as optimum habitat such squares that contained at least 50% of tilled land.

The total area thus defined occupies 38,000 square kilometres of the UK, of which 33,000 square kilometres may be considered optimum. Under modern agriculture, around four pairs per square kilometre would be expected on optimum ground and two pairs per square kilometre on suboptimum ground, doubled if the land is keepered[5]. Approximately 6% of this suboptimum land is currently keepered, yielding a predicted 159,000 pairs. This is about midway within the current estimated range of population size.

Suitable habitat management alone could raise densities to eight pairs per square kilometre on optimum and four pairs per square kilometre on suboptimum land; keepering, because of its synergistic effect, would triple these figures. Based on the same keepering assumption as before, a realistic conservation target for red-legged partridges would be a total of 335,000 pairs. This would represent about 10% of the world total.

## Research needs

Red-legged partridges have attracted a lot of research attention, so much of their ecology is known. Some of the main questions remaining are:

- Does the releasing of reared redlegs indirectly affect the wild stocks of either species of partridge?

- What impact, if any, do raptors have on wild redleg stocks?

## Conservation actions

In broad terms this species will benefit from the same conservation actions as for the grey partridge.

- As an alternative to put-and-take redleg shooting, shoot-managers could place more emphasis on improving habitat and predator management to increase the production of wild birds.

- Landowners should continue to ensure that any stocks of redlegs which they release are pure *Alectoris rufa* in origin. They should not release them on heather moors.

## Sources and references

1. Green, R. E., Rands, M. R. W. & Moreby, S. J. (1987) Species differences in diet and the development of seed digestion in partridge chicks *Perdix perdix* and *Alectoris rufa*. *Ibis*, **129**: 511–4.

2. Green, R. E. (1984) Double nesting of the red-legged partridge *Alectoris rufa*. *Ibis*, **126**: 332–46.

3. Potts, G. R. (1988) The impact of releasing hybrid partridges on wild red-legged populations. *The Game Conservancy Review of 1987*, **20**: 81–5.

4. Anon. (1996) Grey partridge: Still out in the cold but getting warmer. *The Game Conservancy Trust Review of 1995*, **27**: 31–2.

5. Potts, G. R. (1980) The effects of modern agriculture, nest predation and game management on the population ecology of partridges (*Perdix perdix* and *Alectoris rufa*). *Advances in Ecological Research*, **11**: 1–82.

**Grey partridge habitat.**

**Yellow =** optimum habitat, where there is at least 50 hectares per kilometre square of tilled land, less than 10 hectares of woodland, and no urban land, villages or main roads.

**Green =** suboptimum habitat, which is similar but has between 10 and 50 hectares of tilled land per kilometre square.

From ITE Land Cover and OS Geographic Reference maps

# 6.5 Grey partridge
(*Perdix perdix*)

## History and current status

The grey partridge was originally a bird of temperate steppe grasslands. It has adapted readily to open arable landscapes and, accordingly, vastly expanded its range as agricultural development spread westwards across Europe over the last eight millennia. After the last Ice Age, the grey partridge arrived naturally in Britain. The combination of land enclosure, increased cultivation and intensive predator control in the 18th and especially the 19th century boosted its numbers considerably and it became the most popular sporting quarry of the last century. Bag records show that the largest numbers were shot between 1870 and 1930, during which period around two million grey partridges were killed annually[1].

The same bag records indicate that, after the Second World War, the numbers of grey partridges dropped by 80% in 40 years. Our research has established three main causes for the decline[2, 3, 4].

- Chick survival rates fell from an average of 45% to under 30% between 1952 and 1962. In the first weeks of life, grey partridge chicks feed almost exclusively on insects to obtain the proteins needed for rapid growth. The introduction of herbicides in the early 1950s eliminated many crop weeds that were insect food plants and, by the 1980s, the number of chick food insects in cereals had fallen by at least 75%. Although the drop in chick survival rates was partially compensated by lower over-winter losses, it reduced autumn stocks sufficiently to upset the economics of game management.

- Many gamekeepers either lost their jobs or turned towards pheasant rearing, resulting in less predator control and an increase in predation during the nesting season, leading to more hen and nest losses.

- In some areas the situation was exacerbated by the removal of grassy nesting cover as fields were enlarged by removing hedgerows and field boundaries.

These findings have been confirmed by separate experiments showing that, where predators are controlled, chick food insects restored and nesting cover replanted, grey partridge density increases[5, 6, 7].

Although practised on a few estates, implementation of such measures is too localised to have an overall impact on the current national status of the species, which is listed in the *UK Red Data Book* and has been placed on the short list of the UK Biodiversity Action Plan.

Nowadays, in most areas, grey partridges are seldom shot because of their low numbers. Nevertheless, there remain a few wild partridge estates, particularly in northern Norfolk, where careful management maintains sufficiently high stocks for sport and where the bird thrives. The total British population of grey partridges is currently estimated at around 145,000 spring pairs, the bulk of which are on the arable lowlands of eastern Britain.

## Conservation plan

In calculating the potential habitat for grey partridges, we included all kilometre squares containing more than 10 hectares of tilled farmland and less than 10 hectares of woodland and excluded those influenced by urban areas, large villages and major roads. This should give a reasonable approximation to the open arable habitat where the bird was common in the past, as well as taking in fringe upland habitat on the edge of cultivated ground that also supports this species. Again using the past as a guide, we considered as optimum habitat all squares containing at least 50% of tilled land in which the woodland area does not exceed 10 hectares.

The total area thus defined occupies 78,000 square kilometres, of which 36,000 square kilometres may be considered optimum. Under modern agriculture, around four pairs per square kilometre would be expected on optimum ground and two pairs per square kilometre on suboptimum ground, doubled if the land is keepered[3].

Approximately 6% of the suboptimum land is keepered, yielding a predicted 242,000 pairs. Current estimates are only about 60% of this, which may be explained partially by the fact that small isolated fragments of habitat may be unable to sustain partridges in the longer term.

Suitable habitat management alone could raise densities to eight pairs per square kilometre on optimum land and four pairs per square kilometre on suboptimum land. Keepering, because of its synergistic effect, could triple these[3]. Based on the same keepering assumption as before, we would anticipate a potential population total of 511,000 pairs, which would still be less than half the national stock at the turn of the century.

The nesting cover and insect-rich brood-rearing habitats needed to reach this target are typical of low-intensity, mixed arable agriculture. Set-aside options help by replicating these habitats, but widespread adoption of appropriate management practices requires Government backing for extensification. This should include encouragement for mixed arable farming, undersowing and restrictions on chemical inputs[8], as in the pilot Arable Stewardship Scheme.

It should also be recognised that the grey partridge is an open-country bird which does not survive well in farmland that is wooded. This is almost certainly because it becomes increasingly vulnerable to predation by raptors in such situations. Conservation plans to double the amount of woodland in England will therefore have a detrimental effect on this bird. If this proposal were to be applied evenly, the habitat available to the grey partridge would be reduced by some 20%. In our view, therefore, new woodland should be primarily created in areas with existing woodlands and not in Natural Areas that have an open character.

Many game-managers mistakenly believe that the release of reared grey partridges can help to conserve wild stocks. In practice this is not the case. Released birds are relatively poor performers in the wild and they can depress total productivity. We therefore prefer to see grey partridge releasing only on areas which do not offer prime wild partridge habitat.

## Research needs

Like the redleg, grey partridges have attracted a lot of research attention. Key questions remaining are:

- Does pheasant releasing indirectly affect wild grey partridge numbers?

- What, if any, is the impact of raptors on partridge stocks and is predation in winter (by foxes as well as raptors) relatively unimportant for this bird, as our research in Sussex has suggested?

- Can supplementary feeding in spring and summer increase partridge productivity?

## Conservation actions

- The Pesticide Safety Directorate should recommend the banning of broad-spectrum insecticides from field margins (outer 12 metres) between 15 March and 1 September. The use of organo-phosphate insecticides should be discouraged on any part of the field after 1 May, and the use of selective products, such as pirimicarb, should be encouraged.

- Under EEC Regulation 2078/92, we would like to see grant aid for conservation headlands as well as support for the undersowing of spring cereals with legumes and grasses. We are pleased that these are now being assessed as part of the new pilot Arable Stewardship Scheme.

- The character of areas of open farmland should be retained and not altered by misguided encouragement of new woodland.

- Payments for arable reversion in Environmentally Sensitive Areas (ESAs) should be restricted to fields likely to develop into chalk downland. Extensive agriculture needs to be promoted throughout the ESAs.

- Farmers should adopt the Wild Bird Cover Option under the Flexible Set-aside Scheme as the best way at present to provide grey partridge chick habitat.

- In spite of increased costs to shoot-managers, we will encourage those wishing to manage grey partridges for shooting to rely on wild birds (not hand-reared ones) in areas where the habitat is suitable.

## Sources and references

1. Tapper, S. C. (1992) *Game Heritage: An Ecological Review from Shooting and Gamekeeping Records*. Game Conservancy Limited, Fordingbridge, Hampshire.

2. Potts, G. R. (1980) The effects of modern agriculture, nest predation and game management on the population ecology of partridges (*Perdix perdix* and *Alectoris rufa*). *Advances in Ecological Research*, **11**: 1–82.

3. Potts, G. R. (1986) *The Partridge. Pesticides, Predation and Conservation*. Collins, London.

4. Potts, G. R. & Aebischer, N. J. (1995) Population dynamics of the grey partridge *Perdix perdix* 1793–1993: monitoring, modelling and management. *Ibis*, **137**, Supplement 1: 29–37.

5. Tapper, S. C., Potts, G. R. & Brockless, M. (1996) The effect of an experimental reduction in predation pressure on the breeding success and population density of grey partridges (*Perdix perdix*). *Journal of Applied Ecology*, **33**: 965–78.

6. Sotherton, N. W., Robertson, P. A. & Dowell, S. D. (1993) Manipulating pesticide use to increase the production of wild game birds in Britain. In: Church, K. E. & Dailey, T. V. (Eds) *Quail. III National Quail Symposium*. Kansas Department of Wildlife and Parks, Pratt. 92–101.

7. Rands, M. R. W. (1987) Hedgerow management for the conservation of partridges *Perdix perdix* and *Alectoris rufa*. *Biological Conservation*, **40**: 127–39.

8. Potts, G. R. (1997) Cereal farming, pesticides and grey partridges. In: Pain, D. J. & Pienkowski, M. W. (Eds) *Farming and Birds in Europe*. Academic Press, London. 150–77.

**Pheasant habitat.**

**Yellow =** optimum habitat for wild birds, where there is at least between 30 and 80 hectares of tilled land per kilometre square, less than 50 hectares of wood or 40 hectares of managed grass and no urban land or major roads.

**Green =** suboptimum habitat, capable of supporting wild pheasants with either more intensive game management or, in some areas, continued supplement of the population through rearing; these are all kilometre squares that are not urban or moorland and do not contain more than 80 hectares of woodland or grass, or 95 hectares of tilled land.

From ITE Land Cover and OS Geographic Reference maps

# 6.6 Pheasant
## (*Phasianus colchicus*)

### History and current status

The pheasant is not native to Britain, but has a long history of residence here. There is some debate over the success of various possible introductions dating back to the Romans, but it is generally agreed that pheasants were common by the 15th century[1]. The pheasant, although often thought to be a bird of woodlands, is really a species of woodland edge and agricultural land[2]. In areas where woodlands are not common, shrubby wetlands provide suitable habitat[3]. Despite its introduced status, the conservation of the pheasant is important because of its long history of

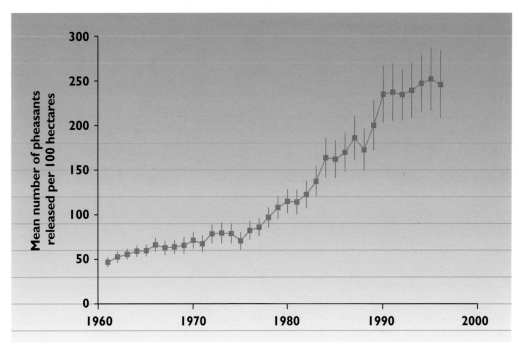

*Mean number of pheasants released in Britain each year by contributors to the National Game-Bag Census.*

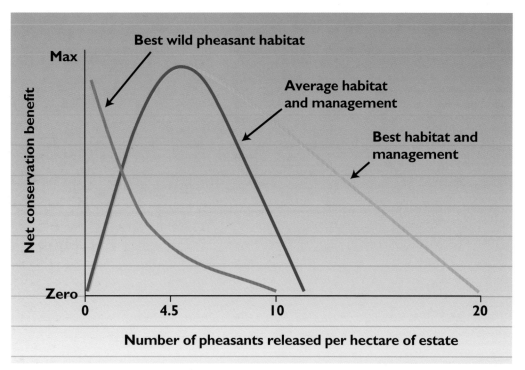

Max

Best wild pheasant habitat

Net conservation benefit

Average habitat
and management

Best habitat and
management

Zero

0    4.5    10    20

**Number of pheasants released per hectare of estate**

*Descriptive model showing the relationship between conservation benefit and pheasant releasing density. The average release density on pheasant estates in Britain is 4.5 birds per hectare. At this level, there is an economic incentive to undertake habitat management. Above 10 birds per hectare, this benefit declines significantly. In areas where wild pheasants flourish, there is little or no benefit from releasing.*

naturalisation and importance as a symbol of our traditional countryside.

During the 20th century the pheasant has become an increasingly important gamebird. Lowland game bags at the turn of the century suggest that the pheasant then comprised about 15% of the bag (the main gamebird then being the grey partridge), whereas in the 1980s it had increased to more than 55% of the bag. The higher figure translates to rough estimates of 12 million pheasants currently shot each year[4]. However, the bag, and probably the population, of truly *wild* pheasants has not increased or has even declined over time. Recent estimates suggest that about eight million pheasants each autumn are derived from birds which have bred in the wild. The change in the number of pheasants harvested is a direct result of increases in rearing. Estimates of around 20 million released each year have been made. In 1900, the average bag of pheasants was approximately 25 per 100 hectares, rising to almost 150 per 100 hectares in the 1980s[4]. The present percentage of wild-bred pheasants in the harvest is difficult to estimate but may be as low as 10%.

It is difficult to separate geographical areas with truly viable wild stocks from areas where the population is mostly supported by rearing. At present, pockets of wild pheasants occur in arable areas of East Anglia, Kent, central-southern England, north-eastern England and some lowlands of Scotland. Because the pheasant is so adaptable within rather wide constraints, many other areas may be capable of supporting low-density populations. This, along with stocking, accounts for the much wider distribution found in recent nationwide bird surveys compared with that given here.

## Conservation plan

Since the advent of driven game shooting in the 19th century, pheasants, and latterly, to a much lesser extent, partridges, have been hand-reared by gamekeepers to increase the size of the shooting bag. In many parts of Britain this rearing continues to supplement birds produced in the wild. In other areas it has come to be the main source of game, largely because present-day land use no longer allows viable populations of wild game to survive.

The current relative cheapness of the hand-reared bird is a by-product of the poultry industry after the Second World War. In Victorian and Edwardian days pheasant eggs had to be incubated and chicks raised with a small army of broody hens. This involved large rearing fields and an associated staff who looked after the stock and had to prepare a protein-rich diet for the chicks by hand daily. Hand-reared game was then an expensive option only possible on large estates with wealthy owners. For most shoots in that era the employment of a gamekeeper to control predators and look after the wild game was the best, and indeed only, viable option. Today, with a modernised poultry industry, the economics have reversed. The transfer of poultry technology to the rearing field (the use of incubators, brooder units

and high-protein pelleted food) now allows a single man to rear many more birds than his predecessors, so favouring the hand-reared bird.

These developments have undoubtedly benefited the sport of shooting and made it more accessible to a wider group of people. We need, however, to examine whether hand-rearing significantly contributes to the conservation of either wild game or other species.

Our research shows that, with care, hand-rearing can benefit wild game in three ways:

- It supplements wild stocks and increases wild production[5];

- It encourages the creation and management of habitat which helps wildlife in general[6];

- It provides the economic basis for retaining gamekeepers who can, to varying extents, control predation on wild stock, where it would otherwise be uneconomic.

However, these benefits are not self-evident and too many hand-reared gamebirds can be detrimental to wild stocks, other species and the habitat.

Our research suggests that in average circumstances, releasing up to 10–12 pheasants per hectare of estate will not cause significant conservation problems. However, it would be wrong to say this is a threshold above which releasing causes damage. In suitable habitats, releases of over 12 birds per hectare may be appropriate. But a release density in excess of 20 birds per hectare is likely to cause negative ecological effects in most cases (see figure on page 152). Symptoms of over-stocking are identifiable as follows[7]:

- The gamekeeper has little or no time to attend to predation control during the nesting season;

- The breeding success of the wild stock of pheasants and partridges is poor;

which contained more than 50 hectares of woodland, between 30 and 80 hectares of arable, and less than 40 hectares of managed grassland, and excluded urban areas. This resulted in an area of 40,484 square kilometres. These criteria highlight the regions (see map on page 150) which have the best potential for supporting wild pheasants with a shootable surplus. There are many more areas which can only support pheasants if they are constantly restocked with reared birds, or could only support wild populations if land manage-ment was changed significantly.

On the 6% of this optimum land that is keep-ered and well managed, we could expect 100 hens per square kilometre to produce about five fledged young each per year. On the rest of this optimum ground we might have 10 hens per square kilometre producing only 2.5 chicks per year. This suggests a total annual wild production of 2.2 million young pheasants. Without management for shooting and the constant replenishment of the breeding popu-lation by hand-reared birds, we anticipate that pheasant numbers would decline dramatically.

We would like to see a twin approach to pheas-ant management in Britain:

- In optimum habitats, we feel most effort should go into the management and conservation of wild pheasant stocks through good habitat management and gamekeeping.

- In suboptimum habitats, the hand-rearing and release of pheasants can provide not only shoot-ing but also a range of conservation benefits. We discourage releasing high densities of pheasants because the conservation benefits are not great and it promotes a strictly put-and-take shooting strategy. We are against the rearing and release of pheasants at densities so

- Released birds may show signs of poor health;

- Crop damage is noticeable near release-pen sites;

- Soil erosion appears around release pens;

- If release pens are insufficient in size, vegetation trampling within them becomes obvious.

Many of these symptoms can be relieved with good husbandry, such as increasing release pen size (eg. a maximum of 700 birds per hectare of pen), but as stocking rates increase this becomes progressively more difficult.

Concentrations of reared game attract predators, so adequate protection and some predator control is usually required. In the main the predators involved are common and control inflicts no per-manent harm on their populations. However, some protected species, such as goshawks, buzzards, tawny owls and pine martens can take reared pheasants in or near release pens.

Rearing does provide significant conservation benefits for other wildlife. Woodlands are planted, improved, coppiced and maintained as a conse-quence of pheasant rearing. The nature of these woodlands, with their wide rides, skylights, a berry-rich shrub layer and a surrounding hedge, suits many songbird and butterfly species. We therefore believe that significant restrictions on rearing would have a net negative effect on pheasants and on the conservation of the countryside in general. In many areas this effect could be substantial.

In calculating the potential habitat for truly wild pheasants, we included all kilometre squares

high that there is a net loss in conservation terms and where the high numbers risk disease outbreaks among reared and wild birds

## Research needs

Extensive rearing and shooting complicates our understanding of the wild species. Key questions are:

- What is the trend in number and breeding performance of truly wild pheasant populations?

- What are the effects of disease on both wild and released pheasants and what can be done to control them?

- To what extent do rearing systems reduce the genetic integrity of wild populations?

- How can gamebird rearing systems be improved to make reared birds more viable and better able to contribute to a successful breeding stock? Can transitional techniques, such as cock-only releasing, improve the potential for producing wild pheasants?

## Conservation actions

- Actions relating to the grey partridge (see page 148) will benefit wild pheasants on areas of farmland where woodland is a significant component, or even in the Fens where reedy dykes provide good habitat.

- Woodland grant schemes now recognise that woodland has value other than commercial forestry and shrubs, hedges and open space should continue to be incorporated into planting schemes.

- Shooters should consider wild pheasants as a premium quarry and, where possible, should improve habitats to increase the survival of stock so that some wild birds will always contribute to the bag.

It is our view that hand-rearing and restocking should, on balance, provide a net conservation benefit both generally and individually. Therefore we make the following recommendations.

- Land-managers should give existing wild game populations priority in management terms. In areas with good wild game potential, shoot-owners should try to maximise the potential of a wild game shoot, albeit perhaps with smaller bags.

- Stocking densities for pheasants should be limited to suit the available habitat.

- Because the welfare of the birds is paramount when hand-rearing, *The Code of Good Game Rearing Practice*[8] should always be followed.

## Sources and references

1. Hill, D. & Robertson, P. (1988) *The Pheasant: Ecology, Management and Conservation*. BSP Professional Books, Blackwell Scientific Publications, Oxford.

2. Robertson, P. A., Woodburn, M. I. A., Neutel, W. & Bealey, C. G. (1993) Effects of land use on breeding pheasant density. *Journal of Applied Ecology*, 30: 465–77.

3. Robertson, P. A., Woodburn, M. I. A. & Hill, D. A. (1993) Factors affecting winter pheasant density in British woodlands. *Journal of Applied Ecology*, 30: 459–64.

4. Tapper, S. C. (1992) *Game Heritage: An Ecological Review from Shooting and Gamekeeping Records*. Game Conservancy Limited, Fordingbridge, Hampshire.

5. Robertson, P. (1997) *A Natural History of the Pheasant*. Swan Hill Press, Shrewsbury.

6. Cox, G., Watkins, C. & Winter, M. (1996) *Game Management in England: Implications for Public Access, the Rural Economy and the Environment*. Countryside and Community Research Unit, Cheltenham and Gloucester College, Gloucester.

7. Carroll, J. P. & Robertson, P. A. (1997) *Integrating Pheasant Management and Woodland Conservation*. Game Conservancy Limited, Fordingbridge, Hampshire.

8. Anon. (1998) *The Code of Good Game Rearing Practice*. British Association for Shooting and Conservation, The Countryside Alliance, The Game Farmers' Association and The Game Conservancy Trust.

# 6.7 Stock dove
## (Columba oenas)

### History and current status

The stock dove and rock dove (*Columba livia*) were not generally separated in the literature until after the mid-19th century. Nevertheless, it seems that stock doves expanded their British distribution northwards and westwards after 1850 until most, if not all, lowland areas of Britain were occupied. The species nests in holes in mature trees and specialises in feeding on the weed and grass seeds associated with arable farming. The use of organo-chlorine-based seed dressings from the early 1950s probably led to widespread poisoning of stock doves, whose population fell by around 90% in the space of 10 years[1]. Such seed dressings were withdrawn in 1962 and numbers have built up steadily since (see figure). This increase hides a contraction in range of 7% between 1968–72 and 1988–91, which was probably the result of a combination of nest site disappearance through Dutch elm disease and local food shortages because of agricultural changes[2]. Despite the contraction in range, the level of abundance in 1988–91, at around 240,000 territories, was twice that in 1968–72. Numbers appear to have stabilised between 1991 and 1995.

### Conservation plan

The British stock dove population is largely resident. It was a traditional quarry species until 1 October 1982, when it was granted protection

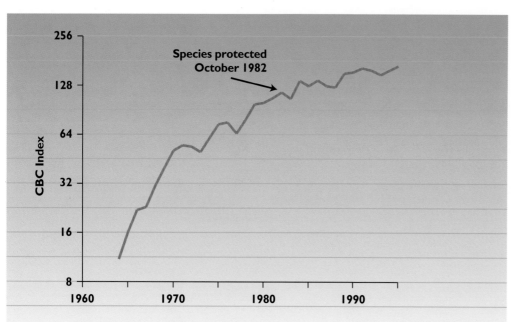

Annual abundance index of stock doves on farmland in Britain from 1964 to 1995. Based on the Common Bird Census of the British Trust for Ornithology.

Clearly, therefore, hunting had no negative impact on this species, either at the level of population size or at that of annual survival[3].

The size of the British stock dove population is currently similar to that of red grouse and considerably larger than those of grey or red-legged partridge. In view of the dove's current excellent conservation status, and of the demonstrable lack of hunting impact on its population, there are no conservation grounds for not restoring it to the quarry list. Indeed, doing so would resolve an existing legislative conflict caused by the fact that, when pigeon-shooters kill birds returning to the roost at dusk, stock doves may be mistaken for wood pigeons. The identification problem may explain why, despite protection, 34% of stock dove recoveries are still reported shot.

## Conservation actions

- The stock dove, which is listed on Schedule 2 Part 1 of the Wildlife and Countryside Act (1981), should be returned to the quarry list.

under the Wildlife and Countryside Act (1981). An analysis of British ringing recoveries found that the change in status resulted in a sharp fall in the proportion of birds that were reported shot or trapped: from 70% to 34%[3]. Nevertheless, there was no matching increase in average annual survival rates of stock doves after 1982. The population growth slowed from an annual rate of 7% in the 10 years preceding the start of legal protection to 5% in the 10 years following it.

## Sources and references

1. O'Connor, R. J. & Mead, C. J. (1984) The stock dove in Britain, 1930–80. *British Birds*, 77:181–201.

2. Gibbons, D. W., Reid, J. B. & Chapman, R. A. (1993) *The New Atlas of Breeding Birds of Britain and Ireland: 1988–1991*. British Trust for Ornithology. T. & A. D. Poyser, London.

3. Aebischer, N. J. (1995) Investigating the effects of hunting on the survival of British pigeons and doves by analysis of ringing recoveries. *Journal of Applied Statistics*, **22**: 923–34.

# 6.8 Wood pigeon
## (*Columba palumbus*)

## History and current status

Although rarely mentioned in the literature of the Middle Ages, the wood pigeon was considered common in wooded and enclosed parts of Britain in the early 1800s, except in the north[1]. By the mid-1800s it had expanded into Scotland, becoming increasingly abundant especially in south-eastern Scotland. By the end of the 19th century it had spread out of woodland into suburban and urban areas and into more open countryside, where it became a serious pest of arable crops. The expansion was probably fuelled by an increase in arable and rotational ley farming, providing food over winter in the form of clover and winter cereals. The species is also likely to have benefited from low predator levels during the heyday of game management in the late 19th century.

It is thought that numbers of wood pigeons continued to increase during the 20th century, as arable farmland became the primary habitat of the species. The population had probably stabilised by the 1950s because, as Murton *et al.* showed, over-winter mortality in the early 1960s was strongly related to clover availability in late win-ter and early spring, thereby regulating breeding numbers in a density-dependent fashion[2]. The decline of ley farming after 1960 reduced the winter food source and bag records for this period suggest that numbers of wood pigeons dropped accordingly[3]. The introduction in the early 1970s of oilseed rape, soon to be grown as a winter crop over much of arable Britain, changed the situation completely because rape provides a ready substitute for clover[4]. Numbers of wood pigeons have risen steadily since at least 1976, according to the Common Bird Census of the British Trust for Ornithology.

The British wood pigeon population is largely resident, whereas the species is mainly migratory in northern and eastern Europe. Because of this, wood pigeons can cause considerable damage to agricultural crops in Britain in late winter and early spring, when alternative sources of food are few. As a result, they are considered a pest and may be shot in Britain all year round under General Licence. The largest bags are obtained in autumn, but shooting in early spring, after winter density dependence has operated, was found to be the most efficient way of keeping numbers under control locally[2]. However, the average survival rate of young birds is now higher than before 1980, probably because winter food is no longer limiting[5].

The peak laying period is May for urban birds and July for rural ones, reflecting food availability. Nest losses can exceed 60% and nowadays, as food shortage in winter no longer seems to be a problem, nest-predation by corvids is probably the single most important factor restricting population growth[6]. The total current British population of wood pigeons is estimated at around 2.5 million pairs.

## Conservation plan

There is a possible conflict between game management and arable farming with respect to the wood pigeon. The planting of game spinneys provides additional nest sites. Game cover and winter feeding of pheasants increases the availability of food, while predation control relaxes what is probably the main limitation nowadays on pigeon population growth. Current levels of shooting are insufficient as a national control method – although they can be effective locally.

## Research needs

Because of the damage that wood pigeons cause to arable crops, there has been, and still is, a considerable amount of research into their ecology by the Ministry of Agriculture, Fisheries, and Food. Conservation questions remaining are:

- To what extent is the potential conflict described above the case?

- What are the costs and benefits to the sportsman and the farmer of a higher quarry density and more pigeon damage?

## Conservation actions

- The Government should maintain the General Licence, under derogation from the EEC Birds Directive, which allows year-round control of wood pigeons as an agricultural pest. The problem of agricultural damage is real and arises through differences in migratory behaviour between British wood pigeons and their European counterparts.

## Sources and references

1. Holloway, S. (1996) *The Historical Atlas of Breeding Birds in Britain and Ireland: 1875–1900*. British Trust for Ornithology. T. & A. D. Poyser, London.

2. Murton, R. K., Westwood, N. J. & Isaacson, A. J. (1974) A study of wood-pigeon shooting: the exploitation of a natural animal population. *Journal of Applied Ecology*, **11**: 61–81.

3. Tapper, S. C. (1992) *Game Heritage: An Ecological Review from Shooting and Gamekeeping Records*. Game Conservancy Limited, Fordingbridge, Hampshire.

4. Inglis, I. R., Isaacson, A. J., Thearle, R. J. P. & Westwood, N. J. (1990) The effects of changing agricultural practice upon wood pigeon *Columba palumbus* numbers. *Ibis*, **132**: 262–72.

5. Aebischer, N. J. (1995) Investigating the effects of hunting on the survival of British pigeons and doves by analysis of ringing recoveries. *Journal of Applied Statistics*, **22**: 923–34.

6. Inglis, I. R., Isaacson, A. J. & Thearle, R. J. P. (1994) Long-term changes in the breeding biology of the wood pigeon *Columba palumbus* in eastern England. *Ecography*, **17**: 182–8.

# 7. Ducks and geese (Anatidae)

Migratory ducks and geese have long been a sporting quarry and in the past many were exploited on a commercial scale. However, the management of migratory species does present a unique set of problems, as they often breed outside Britain and the Europe. Their management therefore has to be subject to international agreement. However, this should not mean that their populations cannot be exploited on a sustainable basis. Indeed, wildfowl shooting can help to recompense farmers for the economic damage caused by some wintering flocks of these birds. Wildfowl shooting also provides an incentive to retain, create and improve breeding and wintering areas for waterbirds and other wetlands species.

The Game Conservancy Trust believes that, where possible, wildfowling should be allowed to continue and in some cases, where populations have recovered from low numbers, we believe the shooting season of some species should be restored. We endorse the Codes of Practice developed for wildfowlers by the British Association for Shooting and Conservation.

# 7.1 Geese

## Current status

Over recent decades geese have flourished and some population increases have been enormous; this includes species such as the native brent, as well as the non-native Canada goose. There are many reasons for this, but species protection and agricultural change are probably the main ones. Indeed the conservation and sporting organ-isations of the 1950s (then the Nature Conservancy, the Wildfowl Trust and the Wildfowlers Association of Great Britain and Ireland) can take a large measure of the credit for the successful outcome of their joint conser-vation efforts, as well as for establishing an increasingly comprehensive counting scheme for monitoring winter numbers[2].

*Counts of wintering numbers of four species of goose. These winter counts (now part of the Wetland Bird Survey) are not population estimates but totals for the UK published by the Wildfowl and Wetlands Trust[1,2]. They are subject to the vagaries of winter weather which can affect both the counting and the movement of birds.*

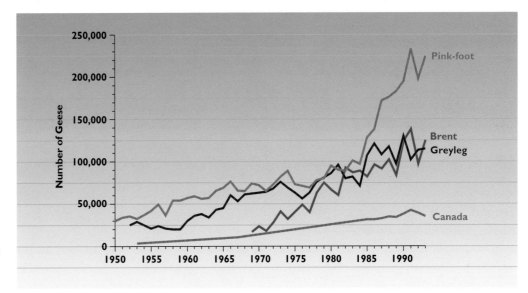

### 7.1.1 Greylag goose
*(Anser anser)*

Greylags are native resident birds consisting of an original stock still present in northern Scotland and stock re-introduced into many parts of England. In 1991 these resident birds totalled about 24,000[3]. In addition, the population is supplemented by a further 100,000 migrants from Iceland each winter. Populations of residents and migrants have increased substantially since the Second World War. Wintering birds tend to rest on inland lakes as well as estuaries and move only short distances to feed, principally on farmland. They prefer agricultural grass but also feed on other crops, such as potatoes.

There is an open season for this species and current levels of exploitation are not restricting the numbers or spread of the resident populations. In recent years numbers of winter migrants seem to have levelled off, but there is no indication of excessive exploitation at the population level. Like the Canada goose, resident birds can cause local problems and similar methods can be used to control both species in the breeding season (see Canada goose 7.1.4).

### 7.1.2 Pink-footed goose
*(Anser brachyrhynchus)*

The pink-foot is one of the most common of the geese wintering in northern England and Scotland, where it rests on sheltered coasts, estuaries and some inland waters. It feeds on salt marshes and nearby farm crops – notably carrots. Some 260,000 wintered in Britain in 1994[4]. This represents the bulk of birds which breed in Iceland and Greenland. Another smaller population, which breeds on Spitsbergen, winters in Denmark and the Netherlands.

This species is a legal quarry and, although concerns have been expressed about the disturbance caused by shooting near havens, the population is clearly flourishing and has increased hugely since the first winter count in 1950/51 estimated 30,000 birds. In conservation terms, Britain is the key wintering area for this bird. It is therefore important that its status and habitats are maintained. Population viability analysis suggests that the pink-foot can withstand current and possibly increased levels of exploitation[5].

Key coastal and estuarine resting areas need to be kept free of disturbance to prevent flocks shifting around unduly, but wildfowlers, landowners and farmers can safely be allowed to continue to shoot flighting and feeding flocks in order to provide sport and offset damage. Bags need to be monitored to ensure they remain at acceptable levels.

### 7.1.3 White-fronted goose
*(Anser albifrons)*

There are two wintering populations of white-fronted goose in Britain:

- The first breeds in Greenland and about half (14,000) winter in Scotland; the remainder winter in Ireland.

- The second, much larger population breeds in the Eurasian tundra and winters in north-western Europe. Those that come to Britain (6,000) tend to frequent English and Welsh sites and represent only a small fraction of the European population.

This is a totally protected bird in Scotland but not in England and Wales.

Wintering birds like to feed on wet rough pastures, although some birds reportedly select improved grassland. In some areas where they associate with the barnacle goose (Islay, Hebrides), farmers receive payments to offset agricultural damage.

### 7.1.4 Canada goose
*(Branta canadensis)*

This North American introduction has expanded ten-fold over the last 40 years. There were estimated to be 61,000 over-wintering in 1991[3] and this number has been increasing at a rate of 8% per year[6]. Although its numbers are low relative to wintering pink-foot, Canadas are resident birds and so even small flocks can cause considerable damage. Furthermore they have become accustomed to human activity and have no hesitation in wintering and breeding in suburban areas. Individual flocks can become a significant nuisance in parks and recreational lakes through fouling and puddling.

There is an open season for Canadas but it is likely that the overall bag is insufficient to exert much control. We do not favour an increase in out-of-season shooting of this species but we think a wider adoption of alternative control techniques would reduce the productivity of local populations in the breeding season. Only in areas with acute problems should flightless flocks of moulting birds be rounded up and culled.

We pioneered the idea of sterilising the first clutches of breeding birds, thus effectively keeping the female on an unproductive nest for most of the breeding season[7,8]. We would like to see an Open General Licence issued for this technique so that it is more widely adopted. Admittedly this would be a long-term measure that largely prevents increase, but if it were integrated with other methods, including winter shooting, many rural

*Grazing barnacle geese*

populations would be effectively controlled[6].

Other methods researched by the Wildfowl and Wetlands Trust, such as altering vegetation height and fencing off nesting areas, can encourage the birds to shift their activity away from areas where they are a nuisance, such as public parks.

## 7.1.5 Barnacle goose (*Branta leucopsis*)

There are two wintering populations of barnacle goose in Britain:

● The first breeds in Spitsbergen and 15,000 (recent counts suggest 20,000) winter at Caerlaverock on the Solway Firth[5].

● The second comes from Greenland and 38,000 (perhaps now 45,000) winter in the Hebrides and on Islay[5]. In the 1996/97 winter there were 31,920 on Islay alone (Sir Charles Morrison, pers. comm.).

Both populations have increased substantially from much lower levels immediately before and after the Second World War. It is possible that, in some localities, wildfowling contributed to keeping numbers low in the past and their recovery may in part be due to the protection now afforded them. However, most of the considerable increase has probably come from improved farming and the greater availability of winter feed. Nevertheless numbers of barnacle goose remain highly localised during both winter and summer.

Their feeding areas are salt marshes and pastures, preferably on fox-free islands. This creates considerable damage to improved grassland, and in certain areas, Scottish Natural Heritage and the European Union provide compensation schemes to farmers at a cost of around £400,000 per year. If the numbers of geese further increase, the cost of compensation is likely to become unacceptably high. In this situation consideration will have to be given to managing barnacle goose numbers. This might include allowing the species to be shot, with appropriate safeguards.

## 7.1.6 Brent goose
### (*Branta bernicla*)

There are two subspecies of this small wintering goose:

- *Branta bernicla bernicla*, the dark-bellied form, comprises the bulk of the wintering birds found along predominantly eastern and southern coasts of Britain. This British population now numbers 125,000[1] birds and represents about half of the total *B. b. bernica* breeding in tundra regions in the north of the former Soviet Union[9].

- *Branta bernicla hrota*, the light-bellied form, consists of a small population (4,000 birds)[9] that winters partly on Holy Island and in Denmark, but breeds in Spitsbergen. It is part of a larger group which breeds in Canada and winters in Ireland.

Brent numbers are now 10 times higher than immediately after the Second World War when numbers were low following the loss, through disease, of their original principal food, eel grass (*Zostera*). Many wintering flocks currently feed inland on winter cereals and oilseed rape.

At present the Ministry of Agriculture, Fisheries, and Food issues some licences to shoot small numbers in order to prevent serious damage to crops. This is seen as back-up to scaring rather than as a method of control. For the dark-bellied subspecies, we think the current licensing scheme should be replaced by an open season. In addition we support the concept of using the Agri-environment Measures to provide inland havens and feeding areas for this species.

The current size of the two subpopulations of brent is clearly satisfactory and we foresee no serious difficulties should numbers increase further, provided farmers and others can shoot them.

## Conservation plan

Goose numbers have generally increased in spite of concerns about the continuing loss of wetlands, coastal mud-flats and salt marshes to a burgeoning coastal leisure industry. To a large extent the increased amount of winter cropping has certainly benefited geese but it has brought with it the problem of agricultural damage[5]. This can be very pronounced as geese are large, their appetite is voracious and a flock of thousands is a real threat to individual farmers. Damage caused by geese can ruin the value of a crop far in excess of the amount they eat. Also 'puddling' at their resting places on wet soils can wreck growing crops. Geese are highly mobile species and can inflict crop damage well away from their resting areas. People involved with protecting flocks of birds may not be sympathetic to the frustrations of farmers some kilometres away.

Given the healthy conservation status of most species, there is no good biological reason why geese should not be harvested, provided the bag is at an optimal sustainable level. However, where the British wintering population is not large we would not support returning a species to the quarry list; it would not be worth setting up a system to regulate what would be a very small bag, eg. for greenland white front.

For other species we believe a regulated harvest would be helpful in reducing damage and lowering the increasing costs of current management schemes. The return of such species to the quarry list would also provide a welcome sporting interest for wildfowlers.

Unlike resident game, where management can, and in the main should, be left to the landowner, migratory geese need to be managed as populations at regional, national and international levels. This may include regulation of the bag. This process has already started for species such as the dark-bellied brent[10].

## Research needs

Geese are an extremely well-studied group of birds. There is extensive information on these species and their numbers are very effectively monitored through midwinter counts maintained by Wetland International's Goose Database.

## Conservation actions

- The broad aim should be to continue to support goose and wetland conservation internationally (something to which the UK is committed through the Ramsar, Bonn and other conventions) as well as delivering this conservation effectively to 'users' of wildfowl at a minimal cost to the tax payer. Appropriate Government agencies, in consultation with conservation and sporting bodies, should therefore continue to build strategic plans for all goose populations resident in and wintering in Britain.

- Geese are a national asset so their conservation can be legitimately supported partially by the Exchequer. Bird-watchers also support such conservation by belonging to bird protection societies. Nevertheless, it needs to be appreciated that consumers also contribute financially: wildfowlers buy licence fees, purchase duck stamps and belong to wildfowling clubs which buy and manage habitats for wintering geese.

- Expenditure for goose conservation involves habitat purchase, lease and management of havens and feeding sites. We believe the emphasis should be on the development of more of these sites, especially feeding areas rented from farmers, who can be contracted to manage them.

- Farmers should be allowed to mitigate crop damage by shooting geese where possible. If they can derive some income from the sale of this shooting so much the better. In many cases the size of the allowable cull must be limited and this can be regulated by licences.

- Compensation should only be paid to farmers in cases where alternative feeding sites cannot be developed, crop damage is severe and, for conservation reasons, it is important to have complete protection. It should be a measure of last resort.

- The Government should continue with negotiations nationally and internationally to obtain agreement on managing the dark-bellied brent goose[10], and should push for its restoration to the quarry list on a regulated basis.

- A higher level of exploitation of some species of goose seems desirable. It would reduce crop damage and increase conservation revenue. It could be effectively regulated and would not compromise the conservation status of any species.

- The Joint Nature Conservation Committee should help other bodies to set up a scheme for monitoring the bags of all geese shot in Britain.

## Sources and references

1. Pollit, M. & Cranswick, P. (1995) Wildfowl counts in the UK. *Wildfowl*, 46: 195–208.

2. Cranswick, P. A., Kirby, J. S., Salmon, D. G., Atkinson-Willes, G. L., Pollitt, M. S. & Owen, M. (1996) A history of wildfowl counts by the Wildfowl & Wetlands Trust. *Wildfowl*, 47: 216–29.

3. Stone, B. H., Sears, J., Cranswick, P. A., Gregory, R. D., Gibbons, D. W., Rehfisch, M. M., Aebischer, N. J. & Reid, J. B. (1997) Population estimates of birds in Britain and the United Kingdom. *British Birds*, 90: 1–22.

4. Fox, A. D., Mitchell, C., Madsen, J. & Boyd, H. (1997) *Anser brachyrhynchus* pink-footed goose. *BWP Update*, 1: 37–48.

5. Anon. (1996) *Wild Geese and Agriculture in Scotland*. Scottish Office Agriculture, Environment and Fisheries Department, Edinburgh.

6. Allan, J. R., Kirby, J. S. & Feare, C. J. (1995) The biology of Canada geese *Branta canadensis* in relation to the management of feral populations. *Wildlife Biology*, 1: 129–43.

7. Wright, R. & Giles, N. (1988) Breeding success of Canada and greylag geese *Branta canadensis* and *Anser anser* on gravel pits. *Bird Study*, 35: 31–6.

8. Wright, R. M. & Phillips, V. E. (1991) Reducing the breeding success of Canada and greylag geese *Branta canadensis* and *Anser anser*, on gravel pits. *Wildfowl*, 42: 42–4.

9. Rose, P. M. (Ed.) (1995) Western Palaearctic and South-West Asia waterfowl census 1994. *IWRB Publication* No. 35. Slimbridge.

10. Van Nugteren, J. (1997) *Dark-bellied brent goose* Branta bernicla bernicla. *Flyway Management Plan*. Ministry of Agriculture, Nature Management and Fisheries, Wageningen, Netherlands.

# 7.2 Ducks

## Current status

The bulk of Britain's ducks breed in the far north, and western Europe serves mostly as a wintering area for these populations. In spite of the fact that agricultural land continues to be drained, and ditches and small wetlands continue to be lost, waterfowl as a group have generally fared well in western Europe since the Second World War. Gravel workings and reservoirs have helped to compensate for the wetland loss and, although there have been shifts in the numbers and range of some species, none have experienced a decline severe enough to cause real concern.

Management of a group like the ducks is, however, inherently more difficult than the gamebirds. Since most species except mallard are migratory, the birds which breed on a landowner's waters in spring and summer and those which are resident in winter during the shooting season are unlikely to be the same. Thus it is entirely appropriate that ducks as a group need to be monitored and conserved on a regional and international basis.

However, owners of wetlands, whether they be private individuals, companies or public bodies, ultimately bear the responsibility for providing the right habitats for waterfowl and we review here what we see as the current issues and required actions for these species.

## 7.2.1 Wigeon (*Anas penelope*)

The wigeon is an important quarry species, especially in coastal areas. Although some birds flight inland to feed on pasture and others occur on large inland waters, undisturbed coastal pasture and salt marsh are the main winter habitat. British wintering birds originate in Iceland, Scandinavia and Siberia and reach an estimated peak population of around 300,000[1]. The north-western European winter population appears to be stable.

This highly gregarious and mobile species is completely herbivorous and prone to human disturbance. In Britain, quiet areas are preferred to areas where human activity is high. Wigeon are susceptible to severe weather and move further south if there are prolonged freezing conditions. Birds breeding west of 80°E winter mainly in north-western Europe, but also in the western Mediterranean, and Britain supports 25% of this western breeding population in winter.

If pits are appropriately restored and managed, gravel extraction can provide extensive new habitat for ducks.

The breeding population in Britain is stable and estimated at 300–500 pairs[2], all confined to the north. Here the favoured habitat is alkaline or neutral upland lakes away from forestry and human disturbance. They require coarse grasses or low shrubs close to the water's edge for nesting. Low duckling survival in some areas may be due to inadequate supplies of invertebrate food.

## 7.2.2 Gadwall (*Anas strepera*)

With a wintering population of some 9,000 birds[1], Britain supports more than half of the north-western European total of this species. Wintering gadwall originate from the Netherlands, Scandinavia and central Europe. Gadwall have expanded their European range and population in recent decades.

The British breeding population, once confined to Norfolk, is about 800 pairs but has been expanding at 4% per year. This has been accompanied by a range expansion within lowland Britain, although this is now thought to have stopped. This was initiated by releases of pinioned and captive-reared stock in the late 19th century and, although winter movements to France and Spain are known to occur, the present British breeding population appears to be largely sedentary.

In Britain, and elsewhere in Europe, the increase in gadwall numbers is attributed in part to the proliferation of flooded gravel pits and similar lowland waters. Gadwall are herbivorous from an early age and require lowland freshwater lakes with abundant water-plants. They avoid water where this vegetation is absent, eg. where there are high fish populations or disturbance is high. Gadwall are highly susceptible to disturbance throughout the year but are particularly secretive during the breeding season.

### 7.2.3 Teal (*Anas crecca*)

In terms of numbers shot, teal is the second most important duck quarry species after mallard. The peak winter population is estimated at over 130,000 birds[2], out of a total north-western European population of some 400,000[3]. Britain supports a larger proportion of the north-western European winter population (38%) than any other country. This population is probably stable[3], even though the numbers wintering in Britain have increased.

The British breeding population is small (1,500–2,600 pairs)[2]. However teal are very secretive and like to remain well hidden in tall reeds so they are very difficult to count and census estimates could be widely inaccurate. The British breeding population may have declined in the past 20 years.

In Britain, breeding teal are found mainly in the northern uplands where they select ponds and lakes away from woodlands. Although widely distributed as a breeding species in southern Britain, breeding densities are very low and associated with undisturbed pools containing abundant emergent vegetation.

Teal ducklings require an abundant supply of aquatic invertebrates but, as adults, they feed on small seeds, such as those of sedges, sometimes taking invertebrates, such as small snails. In winter, teal occur mainly in the lowlands, wherever there is shallow water and a source of food, and concentrate in flocks in estuaries.

Their dependence on the availability of small seeds in shallow water, coupled with their small body size, makes teal vulnerable to severe winter weather. They are therefore highly mobile and travel far in severe weather. In favourable conditions, the British breeding population winters in Britain, but moves south in cold weather. Teal from breeding populations in the Baltic countries and western Siberia move into Britain in winter, particularly in cold weather, but go further south in prolonged freezing conditions.

In mild winters, the proportion of the British breeding population shot in Britain is likely to be relatively high. The fact that shoot bag estimates in Britain[4] and France[5] exceed peak winter population estimates[6] is indicative of the very high mobility of teal through and within these countries, as well as the difficulty of counting these highly secretive birds.

### 7.2.4 Mallard (*Anas platyrhynchos*)

The mallard is the most widely shot of the wildfowl quarry species and the most abundant, in both summer and winter. Most of the birds wintering in Britain are resident breeders, supplemented by small numbers of migrants from Iceland, Scandinavia and the Baltic. Breeding birds appear to be highly sedentary throughout the year, even during cold winter weather. The peak winter mallard population is estimated from wildfowl counts to be 500,000[2].

The number of mallard shot increased during the 1980s[7]. The proportion of reared birds shot is high for this species and the 1980s also saw a substantial increase in the release of reared mallard for shooting, which has since stabilised. Of shoots submitting data to the National Game-Bag Census, 60% regularly shoot mallard and, of these, 14% released reared birds in 1984[7].

Mallard occupy all freshwater habitats, including estuaries, throughout the year, although mountainous areas are generally avoided. This species is not very prone to disturbance and often lives in close proximity to man. It is commonly found in urban areas both during the winter and in the breeding season. However, when regularly hunted, they become very wary.

The breeding population is thought to be about 100,000 pairs[2]. Breeding densities are influenced by the structure of water margins; the creation of small bays in previously featureless lake-sides has been shown to increase the number of breeding birds[8]. The availability of bank-side vegetation as a nesting habitat and the presence of potential nest-predators, eg. foxes, carrion crows and magpies, clearly affect nesting success. Breeding success, and therefore the autumn population of this sedentary species, is determined largely by the weather and availability of aquatic invertebrate food for ducklings soon after hatching[9,10]. Adults are omnivorous, feeding on grain, water-plants and some aquatic invertebrates.

Both breeding and winter populations have remained stable over the past 30 years and have shown little or no response to severe winter weather over this period.

### 7.2.5 Pintail (*Anas acuta*)

This is a very common duck throughout the northern hemisphere and Britain supports a substantial proportion (43%) of the north-western European wintering population[3]. At its yearly peak, Britain may have 25,000–30,000 wintering pintail[2]. Pintail are omnivorous and typically concentrate in a few very large flocks on estuaries and other extensive coastal wetlands. These birds originate in Iceland, Scandinavia, the former USSR and the Baltic countries. As with most other ducks, pintail move further south in severe winter weather, with large flocks occurring as far south as Senegal. The winter population is stable.

In summer Britain supports only a small num-

ber of pintail, confined to their preferred habitat of lowland shallow water in open grassland.

## 7.2.6 Shoveler *(Anas clypeatea)*

Britain is not as important a wintering area for shoveler as it is for other duck species, but the population reaches a peak of about 10,000[2] in November. Most of these birds then move further south to France, the Iberian peninsular and northern Africa, where their diet of planktonic crustaceans and other small invertebrates remains available in estuaries and large areas of shallow fresh water. Shoveler passing through Britain are thought to be from breeding populations in Iceland, Scandinavia and the west of the former USSR. There is no evident trend in numbers in the north-western European population.

In summer the British shoveler population stands at 1,000–1,500 pairs[2]. Shallow, nutrient-rich, open water in open grassland or marsh is the favoured breeding habitat. In Britain the population appears to be stable but, because of the nature of its breeding habitat, it is susceptible to change in water levels and to agricultural activity.

## 7.2.7 Pochard (Aythya ferina)

Pochard wintering in Britain represent 20% of a population breeding in the countries bordering the Baltic. This population increased between the 1940s and 1970s, but the apparent decline over the last decade is not significant[3].

This species has exploited flooded gravel pits and other artificial waters where water-plants are available. Pochard are largely herbivorous and fertile lowland lakes provide suitable habitat in both summer and winter. However, they are considerably more susceptible to disturbance than tufted duck and occupy larger areas of water. The estimated breeding population is 250–400 pairs[2].

## 7.2.8 Tufted duck (Aythya fuligula)

The tufted duck is an important quarry species in central England[7], although it is widespread throughout Britain during the winter. They occur on rivers and in estuaries as well as on fertile lowland ponds and lakes. They are omnivorous throughout the year, can exploit deeper water than pochard and are much less susceptible to human disturbance. Tufted duck commonly occur on lakes in urban areas. Despite this, only 9% of the 750,000 north-western European winter population occur in Britain.

*Midwinter counts of selected species of duck on the Main Lake at the Linford complex of gravel pits in Buckinghamshire, before and after the fish removal operation in 1986. Data from* Wildlife after Gravel *by Nick Giles[8].*

Although some movements to France and Spain are known to occur, British breeding tufted duck are largely sedentary and are joined in winter by birds from Iceland, Scandinavia and the former USSR. As in the rest of its range, the tufted duck population in Britain is now stable or declining slightly, following a substantial increase in the 1970s that was reflected in the bag[1, 7].

The breeding population numbers 7,000–8,000 pairs[2] and is widely distributed on lowland fresh waters, such as lakes and gravel pits, and on sluggish rivers. Despite nesting relatively late in the breeding season, tufted duck are prone to nest predation and often nest successfully only on islands; the presence of islands influences the choice of ponds or lakes as breeding sites. Tall bank-side vegetation is required as a nest site and an abundant supply of aquatic invertebrates, such as chironomids (midge larvae) and gammarids (freshwater shrimps), is essential to duckling survival[11].

## Conservation plan

Many of the general conservation principles applicable to game also apply to the resident waterfowl which do breed in Britain. Protection from predators (crows, mink and fox) and freedom from disturbance, are important for nesting birds, as is adequate nesting cover.

However, there are factors unique to waterfowl. For example, in the late 1980s, we conducted research into competition between fish and ducks, which affects both breeding birds and habitat for wintering populations[8]. Most landowners and conservation bodies have yet to recognise the significance of this and their management of bodies of water takes little account of the results of this work. We believe it should.

Fish compete with ducks for food and, because most of this food is aquatic, fish almost inevitably have the advantage. In spring and summer young ducklings of a range of species feed on

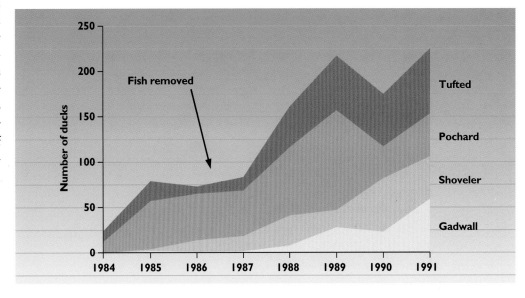

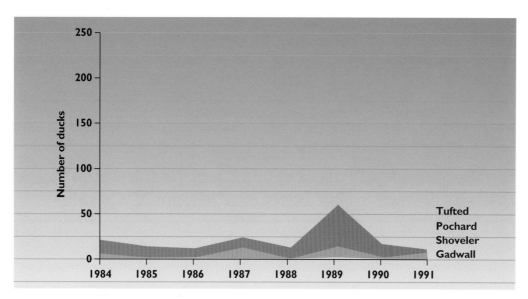

*Midwinter counts of selected species of duck on Black Horse Lake at the Linford complex of gravel pits in Buckinghamshire. This lake was not subject to any fish removal and acted as a control to the experiment on the Main Lake. Data from Wildlife after Gravel by Nick Giles[8].*

invertebrates; emerging midges, for instance, often form the staple diet on many lakes. Bottom-living fish, such as bream, consume huge quantities of these midges in their larval form, while other midwater species, such as perch and roach, intercept the pupae as they swim up through the water to the surface. Where fish are prolific, the effect of their feeding on invertebrate abundance is large. At one of our research sites the bream alone appeared to be eating 7–9% of the larval midges each day[12]. The depleting effect of this over weeks was considerable and we demonstrated this by experimentally removing the fish. As a result midge abundance increased nearly three-fold[13]. There was a consequent increase in duckling survival for both mallard and tufted duck as a ...ult of this fish removal[8].

Fish also eat plants and, when we removed the fish from our experimental gravel pit (17 hectares), its water was transformed from a turbid muddy brown, thick with plankton, to clear water over a stable mud bottom with abundant aquatic plants.

This ecological transformation resulted in a greatly increased number of a whole range of wintering herbivorous waterfowl[8].

This and other work has important management implications for the conservation of waterfowl.

## Research needs

Although the Trust has done considerable research on waterfowl, mainly into the breeding ecology of mallard and tufted duck, and our Advisory Service frequently advises landowners on the manage-ment of small ponds and lakes, our involvement with wildfowl has been limited. We recognise the valuable work done on this group by Wetlands International and the Wildfowl and Wetlands Trust.

## Conservation actions

● More lakes should be developed and managed as havens for ducks. The Government (perhaps through the Countryside Stewardship

Scheme) should further encourage this by grant aid, administered through the country-side agencies and voluntary bodies, such as the county wildlife trusts, and through land-owners. The concept was pioneered for geese by the then Wildfowl Trust in the 1950s.

● Such havens should consist of lakes which are devoted to ducks during summer and winter but which are not subject to other recreational pursuits. Waterfowl management methods include:

(a) Creating appropriate habitat, eg. convoluted gently sloping banks to increase nesting area, islands and other special features, eg. loafing bars (gravel islands where ducks can rest and preen);

(b) Regular extraction of coarse fish;

(c) Control of nest-predators during the breeding season.

# Sources and references

1. Pollit, M. & Cranswick, P. (1995) Wildfowl counts in the UK. *Wildfowl*, **46**: 195–208.

2. Stone, B. H., Sears, J., Cranswick, P. A., Gregory, R. D., Gibbons, D. W., Rehfisch, M. M., Aebischer, N. J. & Reid, J. B. (1997) Population estimates of birds in Britain and the United Kingdom. *British Birds*, **90**: 1–22.

3. Rose, P. M. (Ed.) (1995) Western Palaearctic and South-West Asia waterfowl census 1994. *IWRB Publication* No. 35. Slimbridge.

4. Harradine, J. (1985) Duck shooting in the United Kingdom. *Wildfowl*, **36**: 81–94.

5. Trolliet, B. (1986) Le prélèvement cynégétique de canards en France. Saison 1983–1984. *Bulletin Mensuel de l'Office National de la Chasse*, 64–70.

6. Bertelsen, J. & Simonsen, N. H. (1986) *Documentation on Bird Hunting and the Conservation Status of the Species Involved: Situation in 1986*. Game and Wildlife Administration Report, Kalo Denmark.

7. Tapper, S.C. (1992) *Game Heritage: An Ecological Review from Shooting and Gamekeeping Records*. Game Conservancy Limited, Fordingbridge, Hampshire.

8. Giles, N. (1992) *Wildlife after Gravel: Twenty Years of Practical Research by The Game Conservancy and ARC*. Game Conservancy Limited, Fordingbridge.

9. Hill, D. A. (1984). Population regulation in the mallard (*Anas platyrhynchos*). *Journal of Animal Ecology*, **53**: 191–202.

10. Hill, D., Wright, R. & Street, M. (1987) Survival of mallard ducklings *Anas platyrhynchos* and competition with fish for invertebrates on a flooded gravel quarry in England. *Ibis*, **29**: 159–67.

11. Giles, N. (1990) Effects of increasing larval chironomid densities on the underwater feeding success of downy tufted ducks *Aythya fuligula*. *Wildfowl*, **41**: 90–105.

12. Giles, N., Street, M. & Wright, R. M. (1990) Diet composition and prey preference for tench *Tinca tinca* (L) commom bream *Abramis brama* (L) and perch *Perca fluviatilis* (L) and roach *Rutilis rutilis* (L) in two contrasting gravel pit lakes: potential trophic overlap with wildfowl. *Journal of Fish Biology*, **37**: 945–57.

13. Giles, N., Wright, R. M. & Shoesmith, E. A. (1995) The effects of perch, *Perca fluviatilis* L., and bronze bream, *Abramis brama* L., on insect emergence and bensthis invertebrate abundance in experimental ponds. *Fisheries Management and Ecology*, **2**: 17–25.

# 8 Wading birds

Woodcock and snipe are currently the only waders that are shot in significant numbers in Britain. Although the UK breeding populations of these birds are not large, and their numbers may have suffered in the face of agricultural modernisation, the numbers of migratory wintering birds are huge by comparison.

The Game Conservancy Trust sees no reason to restrict the shooting of woodcock and snipe as there is no evidence that current levels of shooting are having any impact on breeding stocks. On the contrary, we think a sporting interest in these birds is likely to encourage farmers and landowners to preserve the breeding habitat.

**Snipe habitat.**

**Green =** kilometre squares containing more than 0.5 hectares of bog or 10 hectares of heath grass, and squares containing 25 hectares of managed grassland, 0.5 hectares of river and with an average slope of less than 5%.

From ITE Land Cover and OS Topographic Reference maps

# 8.1 Snipe
*(Gallinago gallinago)*

## History and current status

Snipe breed locally throughout Britain but the highest densities of birds are found on wet lowland grass that is subject to periodic flooding. They prefer peaty (but not acid) soils and are virtually absent from coastal grazing marshes with clay or silt soils. Most upland bogs support breeding snipe, albeit at relatively low densities, and the species' current distribution is biased towards northern England and Scotland[1]. Breeding success is often poor because a high proportion of nests is lost to predators and many nests and chicks are trampled by livestock[2,3].

An abundant supply of earthworms and insect larvae, which constitute the snipe's principal foods, is important in spring. Periodic flooding of pastures in winter ensures that the soil remains saturated during early spring, keeping the invertebrates near the soil surface and making the soil soft enough for the birds to probe.

Snipe numbers in Britain are believed to have declined gradually during the 19th century and then to have increased until the Second World War, after which they dropped rapidly and have continued to decline steadily since[4]. These shifts in abundance were probably caused by agricultural changes, particularly land drainage for improved pasture and arable. During periods of agricultural recession, such as between the two World Wars, land drains were not maintained and many pastures must have become waterlogged – to the benefit of snipe. Since the Second World War, the drive to improve agricultural production, and an emphasis by the then Regional Water Boards on flood control, destroyed much of this wet meadow land. Today's pastures have usually been reseeded, fertilised and treated with herbicide, producing a sward unsuitable for breeding snipe. Furthermore, modern silage production is more harmful than traditional hay making because the grass is cut earlier in the year, when the snipe are still nesting.

In winter, some of the 20 million to 30 million snipe wintering throughout western Europe come to the British Isles from the former Soviet Union, Scandinavia and Iceland. Many are found in Ireland and the relatively mild southern and western counties of England and Wales[4]. Because of its unpredictable flight the common snipe is still a highly prized winter quarry species, especially in western Britain.

The British breeding population is currently

estimated at about 55,000 pairs[5]. Numbers are believed to still be declining slowly, particularly in southern England. Evidence from recoveries of ringed snipe suggests that shooting in winter is not a problem and that shooting pressure in Britain has declined since the 1950s[6].

## Conservation plan

To map the potential habitat for breeding snipe we need to consider two principal types of terrain:

• Upland boggy ground;

• Lowland wet grassland.

To select the first, we included all kilometre squares with more than 0.5 hectares of bog or 10 hectares of heath-grass. For the second category we included kilometre squares which contained more than 25 hectares of managed grass as well as 0.5 hectares of river, and with an average slope of less than 5%. All squares that were associated with towns and villages were excluded.

The location of these habitats corresponds fairly well with the current distribution of breeding snipe. In the uplands, breeding snipe are wide-spread but tend to occur at low densities, whereas in lowland areas in southern and south-eastern England they are very local, but can be at high densities where they do occur. A typical density of breeding snipe on blanket bog is only about 0.3 pairs per square kilometre[7], while on wet lowland grassland the mean density can range from 0.17 to 45.9 pairs per square kilometre[8,9]. In our analysis, the lowland wet grassland covers only 12,740 square kilometres whereas the bog and heath-grass habitat covers 21,468 square kilometres.

Given the low densities of snipe that seem to exist currently, we feel there are ample opportunities to improve breeding numbers in upland and lowland habitats. In both cases the major improvement needed is a reversal of previous drainage policies. In the uplands, grips (open drainage ditches) need to be blocked, allowing dried-out moorland to retain and expand patches of bog. In the lowlands, river-side meadows should be allowed to retain a higher water table into spring so that wet flushes and moist areas allow snipe to feed on soil invertebrates into summer.

## Research needs

The ecology and basic habitat requirements of snipe are well documented, so new research needs to be management orientated. Key questions remaining are:

- What is the minimum area of habitat likely to entice prospecting birds in spring to nest and how far will birds move from existing populations to colonize suitable new habitat?

- What is the minimum area of suitable habitat likely to be used by a snipe brood?

- To what extent will predator control increase the productivity of snipe?

- How does grouse moor management affect snipe?

## Conservation actions

- The Ministry of Agriculture, Fisheries, and Food and the Environment Agency should explore and promote ways to retain and increase the extant wet grassland sites. The Hampshire Avon Valley Environmentally Sensitive Area has been created specifically to help birds such as snipe. It should therefore be used as a prototype for wider schemes to retain and enhance river-side meadow land.

- Payments under the Countryside Stewardship

Scheme, and other grants for the creation and management of wet grassland, should be scaled in order to encourage farmers to manage significant areas rather than just single fields.

- Farmers creating habitat for snipe should choose areas where soil drainage is already poor and the water table is raised to within 20–30 centimetres of the soil surface during the breeding season (late March to August). Grazing should be postponed until early June and the stocking rate should not exceed 250 cow-days per hectare during summer. This will reduce losses from trampling and ensure that there is sufficient tussocky cover for nesting in the following year. Grass cutting should be left as late as possible.

## Sources and references

1. Gibbons, D. W., Reid, J. B. & Chapman, R. A. (1993) *The New Atlas of Breeding Birds of Britain and Ireland: 1988–1991*. British Trust for Ornithology. T. & A. D. Poyser, London.

2. Mason, C. F. & MacDonald, S. M. (1976) Aspects of the breeding biology of the snipe. *Bird Study*, 23: 33–38.

3. Green, R. E. (1988) Effects of environmental factors on the timing and success of breeding of common snipe *Gallinago gallinago* (Aves: Scolopacidae). *Journal of Applied Ecology*, 25: 79–93.

4. Tapper, S. C. (1992) *Game Heritage: An Ecological Review from Shooting and Gamekeeping Records*. Game Conservancy Limited, Fordingbridge, Hampshire.

5. Stone, B. H., Sears, J., Cranswick, P. A., Gregory, R. D., Gibbons, D. W., Rehfisch, M. M., Aebischer, N. J. & Reid, J. B. (1997) Population estimates of birds in Britain and the United Kingdom. *British Birds*, 90: 1–22.

6. Henderson, I. G., Peach, W. J. & Baillie, S. K. (1993) The hunting of snipe and woodcock in Europe: A ringing recovery analysis. *Research Report No. 115*. British Trust for Ornithology, Thetford, Norfolk.

7. Reed, T. M., Langslow, D. R. & Symonds, F. L. (1983) Breeding waders of the Caithness Flows. *Scottish Birds*, 12: 180–86.

8. Smith, K. W. (1983) The status and distribution of waders breeding on wet lowland grasslands in England and Wales. *Bird Study*, 30: 177–92.

9. Green, R. E. (1985) Estimating the abundance of breeding snipe. *Bird Study*, 32: 141–9.

# 8.2 Woodcock
## (Scolopax rusticola)

*Breeding woodock like open deciduous woodland with dense ground cover.*

## History and current status

The woodcock that spend the winter in Britain are derived both from our own breeding birds and from migrants from Fennoscandia and the former Soviet Union. These immigrants comprise about 90% of the total wintering population[1].

In spring and early summer male birds are conspicuous over woodland when they perform their breeding display flights (roding). Breeding woodcock are currently most abundant in the north of England and the lower-lying areas of Scotland. In the south, the best numbers occur in Kent, Sussex and Surrey.

Their preferred breeding habitat is deciduous or mixed woodland[2] but conifer plantations are used up to the thicket stage, as are large patches of bracken in upland areas. The incidence of breeding is generally higher in large woodlands; those of less than 10 hectares are rarely used[3]. Wide rides and small clearings (1–3 hectares) provide easy access and flight paths in large woodlands. In mature woodland, an understorey of brambles, hazel, holly or bracken is important to provide cover from avian predators[4]. Earthworms are the main food and birds often persist with their winter pattern of nocturnal feeding on nearby grass fields as late as May[5]. Later in the breeding season they select earthworm-rich soils within the woodland, such as those beneath sycamore, ash and oak, and they feed during daylight hours.

The woodcock's breeding distribution has changed little during the 20th century and the bird appears to have always been absent from Devon, Cornwall and southern and western Wales. Although the number of birds breeding in the UK is believed to have declined over the last 20 years[6], woodcock were rare or absent as breeding birds until the mid-19th century, when extensive planting of pheasant coverts was probably responsible for an increase in numbers[7]. The recent decline could be related to the maturing of large conifer forests planted in Scotland, Wales and East Anglia in the 1950s and 1960s.

The conservation status of birds wintering in the UK but breeding elsewhere is not known. Although most woodcock are shot in winter only in small numbers on pheasant days, there are a very small number of specialist shoots in south-western England, south-western Scotland and in Wales.

## Conservation plan

The British population of breeding woodcock is thought to be about 30,000 individuals[6], but this figure could easily be an underestimate due to the difficulty in counting the species.

We were unable to map potential breeding habitat for woodcock as there is no good explanation yet why the bird does not breed in south-western England, where there appears to be plenty of suitable woodland. The density of breeding woodcock in some prime breeding habitat in Britain is 18–23 birds per square kilometre of woodland[5], but far more extensive counts in Fennoscandian forests suggest typical densities of two birds per square kilometre[8].

Apart from reducing summer woodcock mortality, which may be important, improving the breeding numbers must be based on either providing more woodland or improving its quality. The Government's stated objective to double the amount of woodland in Britain by the middle of the 21st century could, if it were achievable, potentially double breeding woodcock numbers – provided the present resident birds can produce enough young. However, although the woodland planting rate has more than trebled in the decade 1985–94 it is still only a tenth of that required to double Britain's woodland in 50 years[9]. The increased woodland area that has been planted over the last decade will, when it matures, only provide habitat for an additional 600 birds. Thus we believe that the main emphasis for the conservation of this species has to be the improvement of habitat quality.

Woodland management for pheasants throughout Britain probably already benefits woodcock because of the promotion of shrubs and maintenance of rides. In large conifer forests, a better mixture of different age stands will ensure that there are always some suitable areas for woodcock. In woodlands that do not currently hold woodcock, the understorey may need to be restored by thinning or by excluding sheep and deer.

## Research needs

The ecology of breeding woodcock in deciduous habitats is well understood. Key questions remaining are:

- What prevents woodcock from breeding in south-western regions of Britain?

- To what extent are conifer plantations of different ages used by breeding woodcock?

- What are the effects of predators on breeding woodcock?

- How important is the availability of suitable feeding areas on farmland in limiting the distribution of breeding woodcock?

- Is the use of molluscicides and fungicides, some of which are poisonous to earthworms and other soil invertebrates, significantly reducing the availability of food for woodcock on arable farmland?

- Woodcock are dependent on earthworms and we need to assess what impact the spreading populations of flatworms, *Artioposthia triangulata* from New Zealand and *Australoplana sanguina* from Australia, are likely to be having on birds like this.

- Overseas, the conservation status of the woodcock in its main breeding range (Fennoscandia and the former Soviet Union) needs to be determined.

## Conservation actions

- Agri-environment Measures to encourage mixed arable and livestock farming practices will benefit woodcock.

## Sources and references

1. Hoodless, A. N. & Coulson, J. C. (1994) Survival rates and movements of British and continental woodcock *Scolopax rusticola* in the British Isles. *Bird Study*, **41**: 48–60.

2. Clausager, I. (1972) Skovsneppen (*Scolopax rusticola*) som ynglefugl i Danmark. *Danske Vildtundersogelser*, **19**: 1–39.

3. Fuller, R. J. (1982) *Bird Habitats in Britain*. T. & A. D. Poyser, Calton, Staffordshire.

4. Hirons, G. & Johnson, T. H. (1987) A quantitative analysis of habitat preferences of woodcock, *Scolopax rusticola*, in the breeding season. *Ibis*, **129**: 371–81.

5. Hirons, G. (1983) A five-year study of the breeding behaviour and biology of the woodcock in England – a first report. In: Kalchreuter, H. (Ed) *Proceedings of the 2nd European Woodcock and Snipe Workshop*. IWRB, Slimbridge. 51–67.

6. Gibbons, D. W., Reid, J. B. & Chapman, R. A. (1993) *The New Atlas of Breeding Birds of Britain and Ireland: 1988–1991*. British Trust for Ornithology. T. & A. D. Poyser, London.

7. Holloway, S. (1996) *The Historical Atlas of Breeding Birds in Britain and Ireland: 1875–1900*. British Trust for Ornithology. T. & A. D. Poyser, London.

8. Hoodless, A. & Saari, L. (1997) Woodcock. *Scolopax rusticola*. In: Hagemeijer, W. &. Blair, M. (Eds) *The European Ornithological Atlas*. Birdlife International, Cambridge.

9. Anon. (1997) *Woodland creation: Needs and opportunities in the English countryside*. Forestry Commission & Countryside Commission, Walgrave, Northampton.

# 9 Gamefish and sportfish

Stocks of wild gamefish have suffered as environmental conditions in river catchments have deteriorated under the pressures of agricultural intensification, pollution, low rainfall and water abstraction. At the same time the popularity of angling continues to increase and many fishery-owners try to satisfy this demand by stocking hatchery-raised fish.

The Game Conservancy Trust advocates increasing stocks of wild fish by making large improvements to river catchments. We believe the adverse effects of modern agriculture and low flows can often be mitigated by habitat improvements. On a small scale we have demonstrated the huge benefits of habitat improvements to wild trout numbers. Our research will continue to demonstrate this approach on a larger scale. To accommodate increased fishing pressure, we will encourage the increased use of catch-and-release fishing as an alternative to the stocking of reared fish into our river systems.

The distribution of British salmon, classified by the status of their stocks and the typical regional land-use problems that affect them.

**Blue river =** healthy salmon stock.

**Red river =** depressed salmon stock.

**Black river =** salmon absent.

**Mauve land =** upland regions.

**Dark green land =** dairy regions.

**Light green land =** upland grazing and forestry.

**Blue land =** areas of acid deposition.

**Yellow land =** arable regions.

**Grey land =** industrial and urban areas.

# 9.1 Atlantic salmon
(*Salmo salar*)

## History and current status

Along the eastern rim of its range, the Atlantic salmon was once widespread and common from the former Soviet Union to Portugal. However, over much of this area, populations have either drastically declined or become extinct[1]. Good stocks only remain in parts of Scandinavia, Ireland and northern and western Britain, but even here there has been an apparent decline in returning adult salmon in many areas during recent decades. In Britain, this decline has been most noticeable among spring-returning fish (springers) that have spent more than two winters at sea, while there has been a relative increase in later-returning one-year-olds (grilse)[2].

The decline in numbers has been partly due to an increase in natural mortality at sea, following

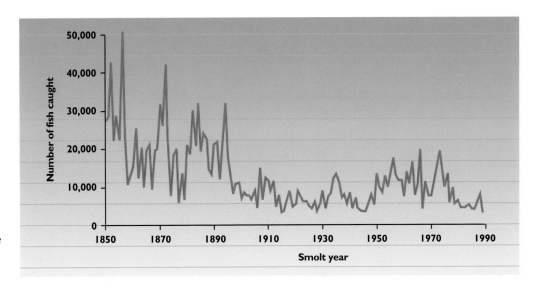

*Long-term changes in salmon catches by River Spey net and coble fishermen, showing successive good and poor periods. N.B. The number of crews declined from seven to two over the period, so catches early on are not directly comparable with later ones. Data: The Crown Estate.*

a period of exceptionally good survival in the 1960s[3]. However, past records show that survival was also low in the late 1940s while there was exceptionally high survival in the 1880s[4]. The widespread swing from spring salmon to grilse has also happened before: catches were dominated by spring salmon in the 18th century, grilse in the early 19th century and spring salmon again in the early 20th century; now grilse are dominant again[2, 5]. Changes identified in the marine environment and other fish stocks over a similar time-scale suggest that this is a result of marine climatic conditions. When viewed in this light, the significance of the recent fluctuations in salmon stocks is less frightening than it may at first appear.

To compound these changes, there are also problems affecting rivers in Britain.

- **Pollution from industrial and urbanised areas.** This wiped out salmon from a major part of their natural range in England and central Scotland, and has been a major problem in the past. Fortunately, this situation is improving and salmon are now returning to rivers such as the Clyde and Tyne.

- **Building of weirs in lowland areas.** In the past, weirs, built to aid milling, factories and water-meadows, obstructed the passage of adult fish moving upstream from the sea and of young fish moving downstream to the sea for the first time (smolts). Although this problem is generally diminishing, hydro-electric developments since the Second World War are once again making it a serious and continuing issue in many formerly high-quality rivers in Scotland[1].

- **Quality of spawning and juvenile habitats.** This varies throughout Britain but can be a major inhibiting factor on salmon numbers. Generally speaking, habitats appear relatively good in most Scottish rivers, but poorer in England and some Welsh rivers. For geological reasons, southern rivers are inherently more silty, their catchments are more intensively used and dense shading by bankside trees is much more common. To complicate matters, as outlined in the section on rivers (page 45), there has also been a general deterioration in habitat quality as land use has become more intensive in recent decades[3]. Currently, as a consequence of the combination of increased mortality at sea and already marginal habitat, many southern rivers have few salmon, with some populations at critically low levels. In general, populations are stronger in Scotland, but some give cause for concern.

There is also widespread public concern over several aspects of salmon conservation.

- **Exploitation.** In the 1960s a drift-net fishery began off western Greenland and in the 1970s a line fishery started near the Faroe Islands. These fisheries catch salmon from British rivers while they are on their oceanic feeding grounds. In addition, with the advent of monofilament nylon nets in the 1960s, other offshore fisheries developed on migration routes, particularly off Ireland and Northumbria[1, 3, 6]. However, in the long term, it is unlikely that these fisheries have increased overall exploitation because there has been a decline in traditional netting over the same period. Furthermore, high-seas fisheries are becoming increasingly subject to restriction – indeed the Greenland and Faroese fisheries have now virtually stopped[7]. British salmon have long been exploited by netsmen. During the 19th century the salmon was principally a commercial species, with net fisheries in most rivers, in estuaries and along the coast[3]. Increasingly, recreational angling has taken over the exploitation and few commercial fisheries now remain. Despite popular assertions, scientific research does not suggest that exploitation in itself is the cause of the long-term changes described above[3,6]. However, at times like the present, when many factors adversely affect salmon populations, exploitation may have a compounding effect.

- **Predation.** Controversy surrounds a number of salmon-predators which have increased in numbers in recent years. Examples are goosanders, mergansers, cormorants, grey seals and even otters[8]. While these predators cannot be implicated as major drivers of change, they can remove substantial numbers of fish. In some rivers, losses of juvenile fish may be balanced by an increased survival of other fish, but losses of smolts and adults are direct losses to the exploitable population.

- **Salmon farms.** While, on the one hand, the dramatic rise in output from salmon farms has rendered much commercial and illegal fishing of wild fish uneconomic, there are worries that interbreeding between wild and cultivated strains may reduce the fitness of wild stocks. There is also concern that salmon farms may affect migration of wild stocks.

- **Industrial fishing.** It is thought that a reduction in food supply, as a consequence of industrial fishing of small species such as sand-eel, may affect salmon survival. However, there is no good evidence that industrial fishing of sand-eel does seriously reduce salmon numbers; in fact the survival rates of sand-eel larvae appear to be a more important factor[9]. Also, growth rates of salmon at sea are currently high in historic terms, suggesting that they are not short of food[4]. Indeed it may be that depletion of stocks of sea fish such as cod, saithe and mackerel have actually increased the food supply for marine salmon.

## Conservation plan

The health of any salmon population depends firstly on the quality of its freshwater habitat. Good salmon rivers must have plenty of clean water and be free from obstructions to migrating salmon. They must also contain silt-free gravel spawning areas. Less obviously, they should also contain the type of habitat which juvenile salmon prefer: ideally fast-flowing water about 20–30 centimetres deep, with large cobbles, debris or weeds among which they can hide[1].

It is cheaper to preserve existing good habitat than to restore badly degraded habitat. Preservation of good habitat should therefore be given top priority. The second most cost-effective conservation measure is to eliminate barriers to salmon migration. Thirdly, degraded habitats in nursery streams should be restored. This is expensive because it involves large areas and therefore it must be viewed in the long term. Strategic plans need to be drawn up and progressively

implemented to spread the costs over time. While some degree of artificial stocking has long been practised on many rivers, the impact of this is generally thought to be minimal[3] and we believe it should be discouraged. A process of education is required to demonstrate the benefits of habitat management and to secure long-term commitment to this form of management.

Because of differences in habitat quality between rivers, factors such as exploitation and the effects of predation must be managed on a river-by-river basis. As recommended by both the Scottish Salmon Strategy Task Force[10] and the former National Rivers Authority[11], we believe that salmon fishing at sea should be discouraged and exploitation limited to within river systems. Even there further controls may be necessary because evidence shows that salmon with different traits (eg. spring running) form substocks within river systems[12]. Apart from this being a sounder form of management, local fisheries which have sole use of a salmon resource also have more incentive to preserve it. For habitat management to be implemented, fisheries must re-invest in the river; therefore fisheries must be as financially viable as possible.

## Research needs

A lot is known about the ecology of salmon in fresh water, but much of their life at sea is still a mystery. Consequently, the above conservation plan accepts that much can be done in fresh water while marine influences must just be accepted. This glaring gap in our understanding must be filled so that those marine processes which are under human influence can be identified and perhaps controlled in future. Key questions are:

- Where do salmon go at sea and by what route(s) do they get there? What do they eat, what is there to eat and what eats them?

- What are the factors determining the age at which a salmon matures and the time of year it will return to the river?

- How can the physical and biological structure of degraded stream habitats be improved for the benefit of salmon?

## Conservation actions

- Salmon fisheries need to be rationalised: marine fisheries should be abolished in favour of in-river fisheries controlled by flexible management regimes that respond to changing climatic conditions and annual variations in marine survival.

- The particular benefits of fishing practises such as catch-and-release need to be appraised in relation to the status of different river stocks.

- Water-quality problems must be overcome and physical barriers must be removed where migration to breeding grounds is obstructed.

- Land use practices adjoining watercourses should take greater considerations of in-stream effects. These include avoiding dredging, reducing conifer planting near streams and the adoption of buffer zones of vegetation.

- Techniques for the restoration of salmon habitat need to be tried, assessed and promoted on a broad basis.

## Sources and references

1. Mills, D. H. (1989) *Ecology and Management of Atlantic Salmon.* Chapman & Hall, London.

2. Anon. (1994) *Run Timing of Salmon. Report of the Salmon Advisory Committee.* Ministry of Agriculture, Fisheries, and Food, London.

3. Shearer, W. M. (1992) *The Atlantic Salmon: Natural History, Exploitation and Future Management.* Fishing News Books, Oxford.

4. Summers, D. W. (1993) Scottish salmon: the relevance of studies of historical catch data. In: Smout, T. C. (Ed.) *Scotland since Prehistory.* Scottish Cultural Press, Aberdeen. 98–112.

5. Summers, D. W. (1995) Long-term changes in the sea-age at maturity and seasonal time of return of salmon, *Salmo salar* L., to Scottish rivers. *Fisheries Management and Ecology*, 2: 147–56.

6. Anon. (1991) *Salmon Net Fisheries.* HMSO, London.

7. Potter, E. C. E. (1996) Estimated increases in returns of salmon to home waters following the suspension of commercial salmon fishing at Faroes and Greenland. In: Mills, D. H. (Ed.) *Enhancement of Spring Salmon.* The Atlantic Salmon Trust, Pitlochry. 67–86.

8. Anon. (1996) The effects of predation on salmon fisheries. *Report of the Salmon Advisory Committee.* Ministry of Agriculture, Fisheries, and Food, London.

9. Anon. (1997) Factors affecting salmon in the sea. *Report of the Salmon Advisory Committee.* Ministry of Agriculture, Fisheries, and Food, London.

10. Anon. (1997) *Report of the Scottish Salmon Strategy Task Force.* Scottish Office Agriculture, Environment and Fisheries Department, Edinburgh.

11. Anon. (1996) *A Strategy for the Management of Salmon in England and Wales.* National Rivers Authority, Bristol.

12. Youngson, A. F. (1997) *Spring Salmon.* The Atlantic Salmon Trust, Pitlochry.

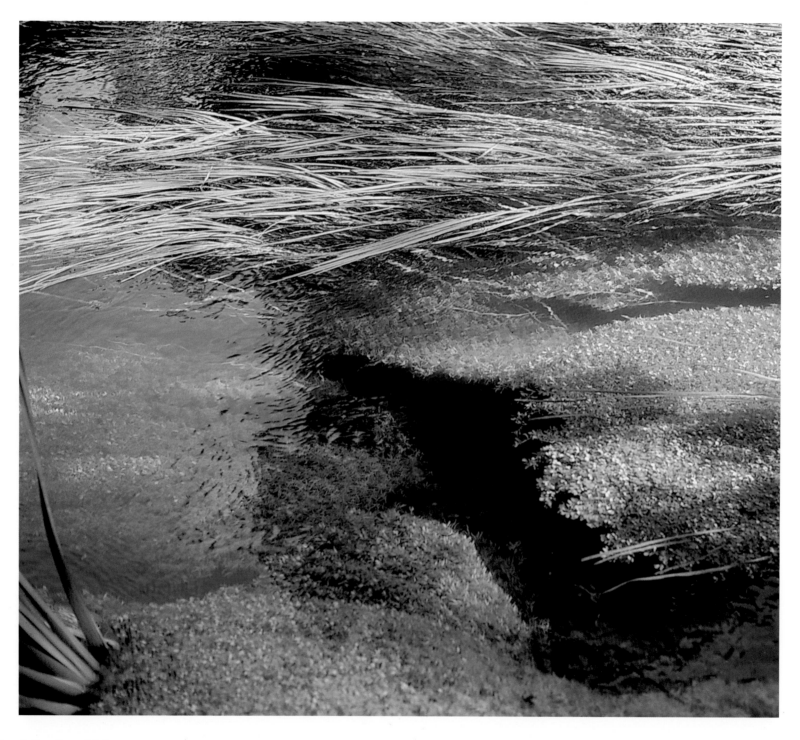

A Question of Balance

# 9.2 Brown trout and sea trout
## (*Salmo trutta*)

## History and current status

The trout is a widespread species and there are probably few river systems where it does not occur in some part. It also exists in a variety of forms which exhibit a range of life-history strategies. While spawning and juvenile fish nearly always need cool, oxygenated streams, as growing adults trout can use streams, rivers, lakes, estuaries and the sea[1].

The two main varieties of trout are:

- Brown trout, which remain in fresh water throughout their lives;

- Sea trout, which spend part of their lives at sea.

Some brown trout live their entire lives in small streams while others migrate from nursery streams to lakes or the lower reaches of large rivers. Sea trout also vary: some remain in coastal and estuarine waters while others become truly marine and may migrate for hundreds of kilometres.

These differences are mainly adaptations to local conditions. Rich environments which can support adult fish, such as chalk streams or fertile lakes, tend to have resident brown trout. Less fertile spate rivers, with good access to the sea, tend to have sea trout.

Sometimes variation leads to local forms, eg. in Lough Melvin, Ireland, there are trout known as 'spotted gillaroo', which feed on bottom-living invertebrates, and silvery 'sonaghen', which feed on plankton[2].

Trout populations have declined during historic times, particularly in lowland England, while the densest populations remain in upland areas of western England, Wales and Scotland. The worst effects of this decline are often masked by the widespread stocking of farm-reared trout[3]. Although some of this decline can be attributed to deteriorating water quality from agricultural run-off, acidification and other effluents, and to loss of water quantity through abstraction, the biggest problem is destruction of habitat. Habitat loss results from a number of factors:

- Increased silt loads clogging spawning gravel;

- Loss of stream structure through dredging;

- Loss of bank-side cover through over-grazing;

- Shading from forestry and lack of management of river-side trees.

Like salmon, sea trout stocks generally seem to have been subject to an increase in natural mortality at sea following an exceptionally good period in the 1950s and 1960s. In some places, eg. north-western Scotland and western Ireland, sea trout numbers have crashed within the last decade and there is concern that these regional crashes may be linked to the rise of salmon farming in these areas[4].

Other problems include the deterioration as a result of acidification of numerous lakes and lochs, or loughs, in Wales and Galloway, and nutrient enrichment in lowland areas throughout the entire British Isles.

In many lowland rivers, stocked trout are more numerous than wild trout. There is concern that this could have a harmful effect on indigenous fish through competition and interbreeding[3].

The demand for trout fishing continues to increase and many rivers do not, and could not, produce enough fish to satisfy this: hence the prevalence of stocking. Although wild trout are capable of withstanding considerable exploitation if environmental conditions are particularly suitable, exploitation often exacerbates the effects of habitat degradation.

## Conservation plan

We think that trout conservation should be based on the creation, management and protection of good habitat. Trout need fast-flowing water over shallow gravel for spawning. Juvenile fish prefer stream margins with abundant cover, where the water is generally less than about 30 centimetres deep. Adult trout prefer pools with cover from draping bank-side vegetation, water-weed, branches and roots or rocks. These features are found in the natural pool-and-riffle sequences that occur in meandering streams[5]. Modern land use often destroys these pool-and-riffle sequences and their related habitats. However, in our research, we have shown that habitat restoration can substantially increase trout numbers.

In areas where trout populations are still fragile, exploitation needs to be controlled. One technique which has proved successful in the USA is catch-and-release angling, rather than killing all fish caught. This is a technique which needs to be encouraged in Britain by overcoming 'cultural' opposition.

While the Environment Agency can regulate the stocking of trout in England and Wales, evasion does occur. It is more important, however, to educate anglers about the value of conserving wild trout and to make them aware of the dangers of indiscriminate stocking.

Many of the factors influencing sea trout numbers may not be subject to control. As described for salmon, changes in the marine environment may have profound effects on sea trout survival. However, those factors which are under human control need to be identified and remedied. This includes managing exploitation in those areas where sea trout are under threat.

## Research needs

The ecology of the trout in fresh water has been widely studied. However, there are several areas where more knowledge would be helpful to their conservation. These include:

- A better understanding of the different habitats required by brown trout at different stages in their life.

- Further studies on the largely unknown marine ecology of sea trout in order to identify possible ways of improving survival at sea.

- Development of more cost-effective and enduring techniques for habitat improvement.

## Conservation actions

- The governing bodies of angling, angling clubs and the fishing press should do more to educate game-fishermen on the habitat needs of wild trout. Only when they learn to recognise good habitat will anglers help to ensure its conservation and creation.

- Government agencies should support the adoption of buffer strips in arable river catchments and the fencing-off of banks in pastoral areas.

- Anglers should consider adopting the catch-and-release approach when fishing rivers with a native wild stock.

- Riparian-owners should avoid stocking domesticated strains of trout where fragile native trout populations exist.

## Guidelines for trout habitat restoration

These are now available in Britain[5,6]. Key features are:

- **Fencing-out livestock.** Thousands of kilometres of streams in Britain have little cover because of bank-side grazing. Simply preventing this grazing will hugely benefit trout.

- **Creating buffer zones.** Wide bands of natural vegetation along river and stream edges protect trout from agricultural run-offs of silt and agro-chemicals.

- **Managing bank-side cover.** River banks need dense ground cover which is cut infrequently. Many fishing clubs destroy this and produce an overly manicured effect which is as bad for trout as it is for other wildlife.

- **Tree thinning.** Too many trees shade-out ground cover, which in turn leads to bank erosion and stream widening. Shading also kills water weeds which provide trout with cover and food.

- **Weed-bed management.** Trout numbers can be improved by cutting weeds to give fast, well-aerated channels between weed beds.

- **Gravel cleaning.** Gravel spawning bars at the tails of pools can be raked or blown clean of silt with a high-pressure water pump.

- **Natural bank protection.** Roots of shrubs and coppiced trees are important in preventing bank erosion.

- **Bank works.** Where banks are eroding through loss of cover, supporting them with logs, boulders and other re-inforcements can stop this process.

- **Channel narrowing.** Dredging, drainage and livestock damage leads to over-wide, slow, shallow streams which support few fish. Narrowing the channel produces faster deeper water that benefits trout.

- **Bank-side covers.** Artificial overhangs of logs create lies for fish in places where natural features have not had time to develop.

- **Midstream cover.** Places for adult trout to hide can be created with anchored logs and other structures.

- **Current deflectors.** These can be used to create variations in current speed and stream depth by deflecting the flow at an angle across the stream.

- **Upstream 'V' weirs.** The pool-and-riffle sequence can be re-created in straightened and dredged streams by making low-profile weirs, each of which will scour out a downstream pool.

The Game Conservancy can provide landowners and fishery-managers with on-site advice and guidance on putting these ideas into practice.

## Sources and references

1. Maitland, P. S. & Campbell, R. N. (1992) *Freshwater Fishes of the British Isles*. HarperCollins, London.

2. Ferguson, A. (1986) Lough Melvin, a unique fish community. *Royal Dublin Society Occasional Papers in Irish Science and Technology*, **1**: 1–17.

3. Giles, N. (1992) Wild trout stocks in the British Isles. *The Game Conservancy Review* of 1991, **23**: 82–5.

4. Anon. (1994) *Problems with Sea Trout and Salmon in the Western Highlands*. The Atlantic Salmon Trust, Pitlochry.

5. Summers, D. W., Giles, N. & Willis, D. J. (1996) Restoration of riverine trout habitats: A guidance manual. *Fisheries Technical Manual 1*. Environment Agency, Bristol.

6. Giles, N. & Summers, D. W. (1996) *Helping Fish in Lowland Streams*. Game Conservancy Limited, Fordingbridge, Hampshire.

**Waters suitable for Arctic char.**

**Red =** kilometre squares containing more than 5 hectares of inland water and adjacent to moorland areas (dark grey) where the topography (>15% slope) suggests that the lakes are likely to be deep.

**Green =** other large water bodies.

From OS Geographic and Topographic Reference maps.

# 9.3 Arctic char
## (Salvelinus alpinus)

### History and current status

Arctic char have the most northerly (circumpolar) distribution of any freshwater fish, with migratory stocks occurring throughout Scandinavia, Iceland, Greenland, Canada and on many Arctic islands. In the far north char may live as long as 40 years, growing slowly, eventually to a large size (1–5 kilograms) and returning many times to their natal stream to spawn. Sea-going stocks often support important ethnic subsistence fisheries in Canada, Iceland and Norway, where fish caught during the autumn run are frozen for winter food[1].

Arctic char in Britain have a very fragmented and localised distribution in large (over five hectares), relatively deep, nutrient-poor, acid or neutral lakes. Locally they can be common. Irish stocks live in shallower, more productive loughs. All British stocks are land-locked, have been isolated since the last Ice Age and thus are non-migratory. The species has a spectacularly colourful spawning livery and often forms reproductively isolated substocks with distinctive behavioural and physical differences[2].

A recent estimate suggests that there are about 200 subpopulations in Scotland, 10 in England and only four in Wales, as well as several in the Irish Republic. Within Scotland, char are fairly common in the Western Isles but rare in Orkney and Shetland (one subpopulation each)[1].

Over the last 200 years several char stocks, including those in Ullswater, Lough Neagh and Loch Leven have become extinct. Lake Windermere char are threatened in the south by increasing enrichment from phosphate-rich sewage effluent. Recent improvements in effluent quality may halt a potential decline. In south-western Scotland Lochs Grannoch, Dungeon, Achray and Venacher may all have lost their char stocks because of acidification[1]. In Loch Doon acidification is advanced and a successful translocation has been undertaken by Scottish Natural Heritage to found a new stock in the nearby Talla reservoir.

### Conservation plan

Stocks of char are small and highly vulnerable. It is therefore important that they are protected from changes in catchment land use and deterioration in water quality. Where extinctions have occurred and water-quality problems can be

*Brown trout and Arctic char*

reversed, a re-introduction or translocation to other suitable waters should be considered.

There has been a recent upsurge in interest in char as an angler's quarry and some surprisingly large fish have been caught. Most of this new interest is based on catch-and-release and seems unlikely to harm char stocks. In fact the growing anglers' interest probably augers well for their conservation.

However, there are threats to lakes containing char, particularly the introduction of other fish species such as pike, ruffe or zander. There have been various initiatives for commercial gill-netting and farming this species, and these proposals need to be appraised for their likely effect on native stocks.

Overall, the conservation plan for this species should be to safeguard existing subpopulations and establish new ones on appropriate man-made waters.

## Research needs

Key research areas are:

- The compilation of a complete inventory of char stocks with site appraisals outlining threats to survival.

- Investigation, using computer modelling, of the sustainable yield from subpopulations where exploitation is contemplated.

## Conservation actions

- Fish farms should be prohibited on cold-water, nutrient-poor sites with char.

- Legislation should be introduced to prevent the introduction of non-native species to lakes with char.

- A detailed and site-specific action plan for the conservation of this species needs to be provided.

- Government Agencies and Non-Governmental Organisations should generate publicity to promote interest in char conservation.

## Sources and references

1. Giles, N. (1994) *Freshwater Fish of the British Isles*. Swan Hill Press, Shrewsbury.

2. Maitland, P. S. & Campbell, R. N. (1992) *Freshwater Fishes of the British Isles*. HarperCollins, London.

**Waters suitable for grayling:** kilometre squares containing more than 0.5 hectares of river, with a mean altitude of less than 300 metres and an average slope of between 1% and 10%.
**Blue =** current distribution of grayling.
**Green =** suitable rivers where grayling are absent.

From OS Topographic map and from Maitland & Campbell (1992)[2]

# 9.4 Grayling
## (*Thymallus thymallus*)

### History and current status

The grayling, with its fatty adipose fin, tends to be grouped with the salmonids but is given separate family status in the Thamallidae. It occupies swift-flowing gravel-bedded streams, which are somewhat slower than traditional trout streams but faster than rivers suited to coarse species, such as barbel and dace. The species occurs in both rain-fed northern rivers and the more even-flowing and productive southern chalk streams. Grayling tend to be prolific where habitat quality is good and have historically been regularly culled on chalk-stream trout fisheries, where they are perceived to compete with trout for available resources[1,2]. While there is no evidence of this harming grayling populations, there is little scientific evidence to support this policy and, increasingly, grayling removals are being abandoned and some introductions taking place. A thriving grayling stock is an indicator of good river quality and the angling interest generated by their presence helps to fund valuable river-management activities that maintain habitat quality for many aquatic animal and plant species.

### Conservation plan

Until we understand more of the ecology of this species there is no merit in drawing up a detailed conservation plan, other than ensuring that river quality and river-side habitats are maintained and improved throughout the middle reaches of river catchments.

### Research needs

Key research areas are:

- Fundamental studies of the population dynamics of this species, including spawning habitat requirements and egg and fry survival.

- An assessment of angling pressure on grayling stocks and how much of this is sustainable.

### Conservation actions

- The sporting value of this species should be promoted and stock should be maintained and developed where possible.

- Introductions to rivers where the species is not already present should be avoided.

### Sources and references

1. Giles, N. (1994) *Freshwater Fish of the British Isles*. Swan Hill Press, Shrewsbury.

2. Maitland, P. S. & Campbell, R. N. (1992) *Freshwater Fishes of the British Isles*. HarperCollins, London.

# 9.5 Pike
*(Esox lucius)*

## History and current status

Pike are classic 'sit-and-wait' predators, capable of fast acceleration after a slow stalking of their prey which may be invertebrates, fish or, less commonly, birds or mammals. An ancient group of fish, pike are represented in the Cromer Forest fossil beds (500,000 years ago) at which time they looked identical to today's species. Eocene sediments in Canada have produced specimens of the very similar *Esox tiemani* of 60 million years ago[1].

In Britain pike are prized by coarse anglers, who pursue them on both running and still waters, but reviled by game-fishing interests because of their undoubted ability to eat significant numbers of wild and stocked brown trout, rainbow trout and Atlantic salmon, as well as Arctic char and other species of conservation priority, such as whitefish. Pike will often constitute 10–15% of overall fish biomass in still waters and slow-flowing rivers but less in fast-flowing streams because of their preference for relatively low-velocity currents.

## Conservation plan

Most management plans concerning pike address their predation impact on fish stocks (usually trout) or, less commonly, waterfowl. Food consumption rates are often over-estimated. A recent realistic annual figure is 0.815 times the pike's body weight to maintain a constant body weight, plus an additional five kilograms for every one kilogram that it puts on as growth. A 9-kilogram pike which grows to 11.5 kilograms in a year therefore needs to eat about 21 kilograms of food in that time (ie. approximately 40 adult trout)[1].

Its preferred prey size is about 10–15% of its body weight, but it can occasionally engulf prey of at least 40% of its body weight. In most habitats, pike can reach a large size (10 kilograms and over) but, in more northerly or unproductive habitats, growth is slower, maturity is attained later and they live longer. Fast growth, as with many fish species, correlates with a short life-span.

Cannibalistic behaviour is very common from an early age and large pike exert a significant degree of population control on smaller individuals. A cull of adult pike often leads to a rapid increase in numbers of juveniles and possibly to increased predation problems[2]. Much depends upon the prey species, habitat type and degree of efficiency with which pike can be removed from a water. Small rivers can be effectively cleared of most pike by electro-fishing, while population control on larger rivers and lakes is much more difficult, time-consuming and, therefore, expensive. The usual approach on large still waters is to use monofilament gill-nets, which endanger non-target species, or large numbers of Fyke nets set in shallow spawning areas early in spring. Fyke nets, which must always be fitted with otter guards, enable species other than pike to be released and are therefore recommended for sites where manpower is sufficient to service them. Even with intensive effort on small fisheries, pike eradication is difficult[3,4].

## Research needs

Research on pike should be of an applied nature and should usually address likely predation effects. It would be valuable to explore the following questions with well-directed experiments:

- Is it ecologically sound and cost effective to cull pike on large lakes (eg. western Irish loughs) in an attempt to improve wild brown trout fishing?

- Do chalk-stream pike constitute a significant threat to Atlantic salmon parr and smolts, both wild and of hatchery origin, and, if so, is culling justified as a salmon conservation measure?

- Does pike removal within waterfowl breeding sanctuaries promote better juvenile bird survival?

- How well do large pike translocated into 'specimen' coarse-angling waters survive and do they contribute significantly to angler's catches?

## Conservation actions

Since pike are common and widespread, no urgent conservation actions are needed other than for wetland-managers in a given area to decide whether they are friend or foe and to act accordingly.

## Sources and references

1. Giles, N. (1994) *Freshwater Fish of the British Isles*. Swan Hill Press, Shrewsbury.

2. Kipling, C. & Frost, W. E. (1970) A study of the mortality, population numbers, yearclass strengths, production and food consumption of the pike *Esox lucius* in Windermere from 1944–1962. *Journal of Animal Ecology*, **39**: 115–57.

3. Mann, R. H. K. (1985) A pike management strategy for a trout fishery. *Journal of Fish Biology*, **27**: 227–34.

4. Wright, R. M. (1992) Alternative strategies for pike, *Esox lucius* L., management. In: Lucas, M. C., Diak, I. & Laird, L. (Eds) *Interactions between Fisheries and the Environment*. Institute of Fisheries Management. 159–64.

# 10 Predatory mammals

Britain's predatory mammals tend to be secretive and nocturnal and so not only do they seem to be rarer than they actually are, but they are also difficult to study and their status is often uncertain. Most have been perceived by gamekeepers and farmers as enemies of livestock and game and, by the turn of the last century, it seemed that a range of smaller carnivores were set to follow the larger ones into extinction. Since then, however, the housing of poultry and the significant reduction in numbers of gamekeepers has given all species a reprieve. All have substantially increased, although some have yet to regain all of their former range.

The Game Conservancy Trust would like to see these animals widespread again, but we would want land-occupiers to be given appropriate powers of control where damage is appreciable and where the conservation status of the predator will not be harmed.

# 10.1 Fox
## (*Vulpes vulpes*)

### History and current status

The fox is indigenous to all of mainland Britain and Ireland, where its fortunes have essentially been determined by man's activities. Factors resulting in high numbers include:

- Man's alteration of the habitat and thus of the fox's prey species;

- The elimination of natural predators (eg. the wolf, lynx and golden eagle[1]);

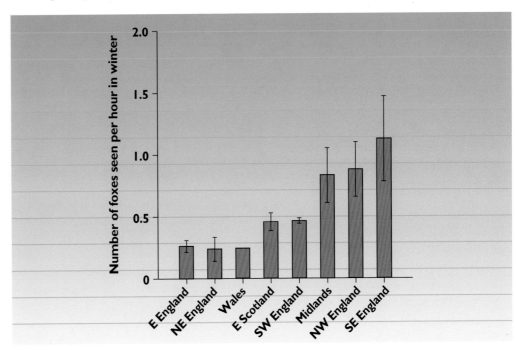

**Right:** *The numbers of foxes seen per hour by gamekeepers directly relates to fox abundance in the region. It is clear that foxes can be more than twice as numerous in some regions than in others.*

- The introduction of new prey species, such as the rabbit and pheasant[2];

- The provision of other new food resources, as in suburban areas.

More directly, man has sought in different circumstances to limit fox abundance through culling and to conserve populations for sport hunting.

In recent historic times, there have been major changes in these factors and there is no reason to believe that fox numbers are currently stable. In addition, there have been recent increases in range: to Anglesey, Holy Island and, at least temporally to the Isle of Man[3] and to parts of East Anglia, parts of the Pennines and eastern Scotland, where they were once very scarce[1,4].

The best estimate of the current British fox population is 240,000 adults in spring, to which a production of 425,000 cubs is added annually[5]. For the population to remain stable, 425,000 foxes must therefore die each year[6]. In both rural and urban areas, mortality caused by man predominates[7,8]. Gamekeepers probably kill 70,000–80,000[4] and fox-hunts a further 16,000[9] annually. Additional culling by other interest groups is difficult to quantify. In urban areas, where 14% of foxes live[5], road traffic is the chief cause of death[7].

The number of foxes killed per square kilometre by gamekeepers has increased steadily during the past 35 years in all regions of Britain. This may be a result of changes in control methods, although ancillary data suggests that, in many regions, it reflects an actual increase in fox abundance[2].

## Conservation plan

Foxes have a large impact on small game species as well as on other vulnerable prey, such as ground-nesting birds. For species like the grey partridge, the main predation is on nesting hens, which lowers production and affects autumn numbers and subsequently breeding stocks. For the brown hare, the main predation is probably on leverets and may be sufficient to keep numbers of adults permanently low. Wild gamebird management for driven shooting – pheasant, partridge or grouse – would be impossible without reducing fox predation. Foxes can also be a real threat to colonial nesting birds, and nature reserve wardens have found fox control essential to prevent the destruction of nesting eider duck and common tern, for example.

The fox is a versatile and robust species which performs well under all British conditions. Management aims to limit fox predation on target species. Since no effective non-lethal means of limiting predation on an extensive basis has yet been developed, practical management depends on culling methods.

Fox-destruction societies and fox-hunts co-ordinate fox management over large regions. The former were once supported by state subsidies, but these now apply only in Scotland. Fox-hunts are self-financing. Otherwise fox control is carried out and paid for privately on individual properties. Some interest groups (eg. neighbouring farmers, conservationists) may benefit from the effects of such control without directly contributing to it.

We have (unpublished) evidence that many independent control efforts within a region can result in regional limitation of fox abundance, although this may not be the primary or conscious aim. This is probably the case in Norfolk, parts of northern England and upland parts of eastern Scotland.

Access to a range of methods, each efficient in different circumstances, is necessary to limit fox numbers effectively in situations requiring it. There is widespread disagreement within and between European countries about the acceptability (on grounds of humaneness) of different culling methods. Moves to standardise legislation and to address animal welfare questions may result in the outlawing of some methods without the provision of suitable alternatives.

## Research needs

Key research areas are:

- Development of reliable methods of estimating and monitoring fox abundance in different regions of Britain.

- Further determination of the role of historical and present-day culling on fox abundance in different regions.

- Determination of the efficiency of different culling methods and the extent to which they are alternatives.

- Determination of the effectiveness of different culling strategies in achieving the aims of different interest groups.

- Exploration and development of both lethal and less conventional non-lethal methods, such as conditioned taste aversion and immunocontraception, to ensure continuous improvement of control methods in terms of efficiency, effectiveness and humaneness.

## Conservation actions

- There is pressure to standardise laws across the EU and progressively to outlaw less humane control methods. This must be balanced by the need to keep fox control economically feasible for all groups, whether they are farmers, landowners or nature reserve wardens. At present we believe this means retaining all methods of control currently legal in Britain.

- Statutory conservation agencies must recognise that the faunal character of many natural areas in Britain may depend on current and/or previous levels of fox control and that there could be a loss of species diversity if fox numbers are allowed to increase unchecked.

## Sources and references

1. Reynolds, J. C. & Tapper, S. C. (1996) Control of mammalian predators in game management and conservation. *Mammal Review*, **1**: 127–56.

2. Reynolds, J. C. & Tapper, S. C. (1993) Are foxes on the increase? *The Game Conservancy Review of 1992*, **25**: 94–6.

3. MacDonald, D. W. & Halliwell, E. C. *(1994)* The rapid spread of red foxes, *Vulpes vulpes*, on the Isle-of-Man. *Global Ecology and Biogeography Letters*, **4**: 9–16.

4. Tapper, S. C. (1992) *Game Heritage: An Ecological Review from Shooting and Gamekeeping Records*. Game Conservancy Limited, Fordingbridge, Hampshire.

5. Harris, S., Morris, P., Wray, S. & Yalden, D. (1995) *A Review of British Mammals*. Joint Nature Conservation Committee, Peterborough.

6. Lloyd, H. G. & Jensen, B. (1976) Annual turnover of fox populations in Europe. *Zentralblatt fur Veterinarmedizin B*, **23**: 580–9.

7. Harris, S. & Smith, G. C. (1987) Demography of two urban fox (*Vulpes vulpes*) populations. *Journal of Applied Ecology*, **24**: 75–86.

8. Reynolds, J. C. & Tapper, S. C. (1995) The ecology of the red fox *Vulpes vulpes* in relation to small game in rural southern England. *Wildlife Biology*, **1**: 105–19.

9. MacDonald, D. W. & Johnson, P. J. (1996) The impact of sport hunting: a case study. In: Taylor, V. J. & Dunstone, N. (Eds) *The Exploitation of Mammal Populations*. Chapman & Hall, London. 160–207.

# 10.2 Stoat
(*Mustela erminea*)

## History and current status

Stoats are indigenous predators, feeding on rabbits, birds and rodents[1,2]. They are larger than weasels, so the prey they kill is consequently bigger. Rabbits are their main prey but ground-nesting birds also figure to a large extent in their diet and, since stoats are competent climbers, hedgerow and tree-nesting species such as wood pigeons are often killed too. Stoats also take gamebird eggs and they are important predators of nesting partridges[3], pheasants and grouse. Apart from shooting, tunnel-trapping with kill-traps is currently the only form of systematic control.

In spite of intensive predator control during the 19th century, this species managed to hold onto its range and it continues to be more or less ubiquitous in most habitats[4].

Stoat abundance seems to be linked in part to rabbit numbers and stoats showed a substantial drop after the myxomatosis epidemic[5]. Currently, the best estimate of the stoat population is 462,000[6]. However, this is based on rather limited information and cannot be taken as very reliable.

## Conservation plan

Stoats are common and under no particular threat. Given that they are known to be significant predators of ground-nesting birds, and that the national stoat population is unlikely to be seriously affected by local predator control, we believe that current control practices must continue where necessary.

Should rabbit numbers be substantially reduced in future we would expect stoat numbers to decline too. However, given that stoats survived a 99% reduction in rabbits at the time of myxomatosis, this need not be a matter for major concern. There is also evidence that stoats suffer intra-guild predation by foxes and we might expect to find that stoat numbers have declined as foxes have increased[7].

## Research needs

There has been a substantial amount of research on this species in New Zealand[8] and Sweden[9], but in both these countries stoats depend on different prey species. The following areas of study need to be addressed:

- Whether secondary poisoning by rodenticides is a serious problem in Britain needs to be checked. Stoats in New Zealand are vulnerable[10], and there is now some evidence that stoats and weasels in Britain are also being contaminated[11].

- Potential methods of monitoring the abundance of all mammals are currently being appraised by the Joint Nature Conservation Committee and we believe that the stoat is one of a number of species where there is a clear need to set up a scheme which can monitor changes over time and between regions.

- The effects of intra-guild predation between different carnivores needs fundamental study, for both the stoat and other species.

## Conservation actions

We feel that no special conservation actions are needed for this species.

## Sources and references

1. Day, M. G. (1968) Food habits of British stoats (Mustela erminea) and weasels (Mustela nivalis). Journal of Zoology, London, 155: 485–97.

2. Tapper, S. (1976) The diet of weasels, Mustela nivalis and stoats, Mustela erminea during early summer, in relation to predation on gamebirds. Journal of Zoology, London, 179: 219–24.

3. Tapper, S. C., Green, R. E. & Rands, M. R. W. (1982) Effects of mammalian predators on partridge populations. Mammal Review, 12: 159–67.

4. Arnold, H. R. (1993) The Atlas of Mammals in Britain. HMSO, London.

5. Tapper, S. C. (1992) Game Heritage: An Ecological Review from Shooting and Gamekeeping Records. Game Conservancy Limited, Fordingbridge, Hampshire.

6. Harris, S., Morris, P., Wray, S. & Yalden, D. (1995) A Review of British Mammals. Joint Nature Conservation Committee, Peterborough.

7. Mulder, J. L. (1990) The stoat (Mustela erminea) in the Dutch dune region, its local extinction, and a possible cause: the arrival of the fox (Vulpes vulpes). Lutra, 33: 1–21.

8. King, C. M. & Moody, J. E. (1982) The biology of the stoat (Mustela erminea) in the National Parks of New Zealand. I. General introduction. New Zealand Journal of Zoology, 9: 49–56.

9. Erlinge, S. (1983) Demography and dynamics of a stoat Mustela erminea population in a diverse community of vertebrates. Journal of Animal Ecology, 52: 705–26.

10. Alterio, N. (1996) Secondary poisoning of stoats (Mustela erminea), feral ferrets (Mustela furo), and feral house cats (Felis catus) by the anticoagulant poison, brodifacoum. New Zealand Journal of Zoology, 23: 331–8.

11. McDonald, R. A., Harris, S., Turnbull, G., Brown, P. & Fletcher, M. (1998) Anticoagulant rodenticides in stoats (Mustela erminea L.) and weasels (M. nivalis L.) in England. Environmental Pollution, 103: 17-23.

# 10.3 Weasel
## (*Mustela nivalis*)

## History and current status

The weasel is our smallest carnivore and an indigenous species, inhabiting areas where small mammals are common. Although weasels prey on small birds, and have occasionally been found to take gamebird chicks[1], they are essentially vole specialists: in woodland they rely on bank voles[2] and in grassy areas on field voles[3]. The small birds that they take are commonly nestlings and generally they eat more birds when voles are scarce[3,4].

Numbers are difficult to estimate, but have been tentatively put at 450,000 individuals[5]. Trapping records from gamekeepers suggest that weasels have been declining, although this could be partly because of less trapping effort by keepers[6]. The decline could be due to a shift in the abundance of prey, as well as to the way in which rough pasture and agricultural grass is managed. Field-vole numbers have probably declined with increased levels of livestock in both upland and lowland areas, and with increased rabbit abundance[5]. This would benefit stoats but be detrimental to weasels.

## Conservation plan

We feel that it is unnecessary to set a population target for this species. Legal protection would not improve the abundance of this animal and, since weasels and stoats kill gamebird chicks, such a move would be unwelcome by gamekeepers. However, there are many habitat improvements which, if implemented, would lead to increased numbers of field voles, benefiting not only weasels but also other rodent-predators, such as kestrels and barn owls.

The principal measures which would increase vole abundance are:

- Lowering of livestock levels on unimproved grassland;

- Incentives to widen the bases of hedgerows so that they can support voles;

- A reduced level of rabbit abundance.

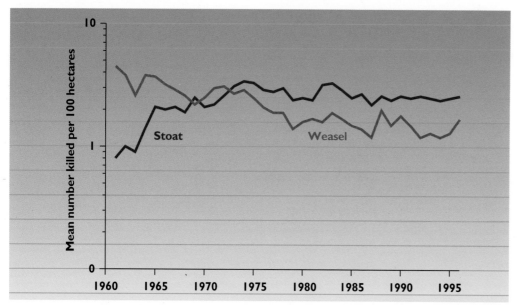

Trend in numbers of weasels and stoats killed by gamekeepers in East Anglia. Data: National Game-Bag Census.

Set-aside can provide added habitat in arable areas, provided grass areas are retained over several years to allow a suitable tussocky vegetation to develop. Farmland features such as grass-field margins and rough grass strips, which are grant-aided through the Countryside Stewardship Scheme in England and *Tir Cymen* (now *Tir Gofal*) in Wales, will provide the habitat for the voles upon which predators such as weasels depend. Newer ideas such as beetle banks, on trial under the pilot Arable Stewardship Scheme, will provide habitat for voles in open arable areas.

## Research needs

- A national scheme for monitoring the abundance of small mustelids is required.

## Conservation actions

We feel that no special conservation actions are needed for this species.

## Sources and references

1. Tapper, S. (1976) The diet of weasels, *Mustela nivalis* and stoats, *Mustela erminea* during early summer, in relation to predation on gamebirds. *Journal of Zoology, London*, **179**: 219–24.

2. King, C.M. (1980) The weasel *Mustela nivalis* and its prey in an English woodland. *Journal of Animal Ecology*, **49**: 127–59.

3. Tapper, S. (1979) The effect of fluctuating vole numbers (*Microtus agrestis*) on a population of weasels (*Mustela nivalis*) on farmland. *Journal of Animal Ecology*, **48**: 603–17.

4. Dunn, E. (1977) Predation by weasels (*Mustela nivalis*) on breeding tits (*Parus* spp.) in relation to density of tits and rodents. *Journal of Animal Ecology*, **46**: 633–51.

5. Harris, S., Morris, P., Wray, S. & Yalden, D. (1995) *A Review of British Mammals*. Joint Nature Conservation Committee, Peterborough.

6. Tapper, S. C. (1992) *Game Heritage: An Ecological Review from Shooting and Gamekeeping Records*. Game Conservancy Limited, Fordingbridge, Hampshire.

# 10.4 American mink
(*Mustela vison*)

## History and current status

Mink are small carnivores of the mustelid family. They are predators, killing a wide variety of principally water-side animals[1] – anything from small frogs and fish to water voles and moorhens[2]. The species in Britain is an American import but is very similar to the European mink (*Mustela lutreola*), which is now extinct here and endangered in continental Europe[3].

The American mink is a very recent introduction. It first became established in the late 1950s, when animals escaped from fur farms in several parts of Britain, but particularly in the south-west[4]. Over the last 30 years the species has been spreading along watercourses into almost all lowland Britain[3,5]. It is also well established along rocky coastlines.

To some extent it can be argued that the mink fits into an ecological niche which is vacant in Britain. On the other hand, in its native North America, the mink is able to prey on the ubiquitous and highly prolific muskrat[6]. Thus, it can equally be argued that the addition of a non-native predator without its natural food base is likely to damage our native fauna severely. Indeed, there is good evidence for this on small offshore islands, where the appearance of mink has been associated with complete nesting failures of colonies of the black-headed gull, common gull, common tern and Arctic tern[7]. Mink are also thought to have been responsible for the disappearance of the moorhen on the Hebridean islands of Lewis and Harris. However, on mainland Britain, populations of moorhen, coot and little grebe – species most likely to have been affected – seem to be holding their own. The most serious effect here seems to be on the water vole and there

*Numbers of mink killed in two regions showing contrasting trends. Data: National Game-Bag Census.*

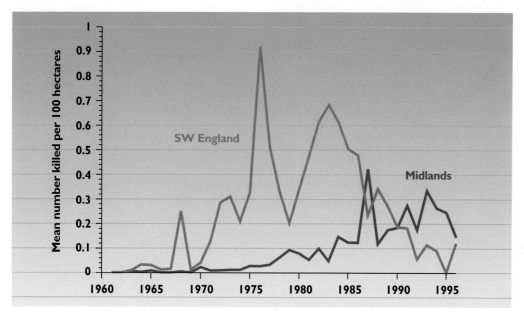

is evidence that these mammals fast disappear from watersheds after mink have arrived[8].

Mink are extensively trapped by gamekeepers and riparian-owners, since there is no doubt that these animals do serious damage to penned gamebirds, waterfowl and fish. Mass kills are frequent and we have evidence of kills of up to 180 in a single night in pens containing some 400 gamebirds.

Unlike some of our native carnivores, and in spite of their recent appearance, mink are now relatively common. There are estimated to be 110,000 in Britain[9].

## Conservation plan

This species is clearly still in a state of flux and regional trends are confusing. In many areas numbers are substantially increasing, but in the south-west of England there has been a noticeable drop in the numbers reported killed by gamekeepers since the mid-1980s. It is probable that this reduction is due to the revival of otter populations in the south-west and that otters are responsible for killing or displacing mink[10].

We believe that landowners, gamekeepers and reserve wardens will have to contend with this species for the forseeable future and any attempt to eradicate them from the mainland is not likely to succeed except locally. However, eradication may be possible on islands of a conservation interest, such as the Isles of Lewis and Harris.

## Research needs

There has been a range of autecological studies of mink but, as yet, little has been done to assess their impact on the native fauna, other than to document their depredations or assoc-iate their appearance with the decline of vulnerable species such as the water vole. In areas where mink are established, studies are needed to assess the on-going impacts on waterfowl, fish and other prey groups. These include:

- The possibility of intra-guild predation between otters and mink.

- A model of population growth and spread in order to determine likely future changes and,

in combination with the points above, to assess the consequences of this for vulnerable species such as water voles.

## Conservation actions

- Gamekeepers should give more attention to mink control in many lowland areas if they are to prevent them raiding pheasant and waterfowl pens and killing large numbers of birds in a single attack.

- River-keepers are advised to use cage-traps and not spring-traps to catch mink on rivers that are frequented by otters. This minimises the likelihood of harming the otters.

- Despatching aggressive animals such as mink caught in cage-traps can be awkward without a firearm. Ministries need to work with interested parties to develop a satisfactory method and protocol for the dispatch of all species likely to be dealt with in this way.

## Sources and references

1. Chanin, P. R. F. & Linn, I. (1980) The diet of feral mink (*Mustela vison*) in southwest Britain. *Journal of Zoology, London*, **192**: 205–23.

2. Wise, M. H., Linn, I. J. & Kennedy, C. R. (1981) A comparison of the feeding biology of mink *Mustela vison* and the otter *Lutra lutra*. *Journal of Zoology, London*, **195**: 181–213.

3. Dunstone, N. (1993) *The Mink*. T. & A. D. Poyser, London.

4. Thompson, H. V. (1964) Wild mink. *Agriculture*, **26**: 564–7.

5. Birks, J. (1986) *Mink*. Mammal Society Series. Anthony Nelson Limited, Oswestry, Shropshire.

6. Errington, P. L. (1943) *An Analysis of Mink Predation upon Muskrats in*

*North-Central United States*. Iowa State College of Agriculture and Mechanic Arts, Ames, Iowa.

7. Craik, C. (1997) Long-term effects of North American mink *Mustela vison* on seabirds in western Scotland. *Bird Study*, **44**: 2–8.

8. Strachan, R. & Jefferies, D. J. (1990) *The Water Vole* Arvicola terrestris *in Britain 1989–1990: Its Distribution and*

*Changing Status*. The Vincent Wildlife Trust, London.

9. Harris, S., Morris, P., Wray, S. & Yalden, D. (1995) *A Review of British Mammals*. Joint Nature Conservation Committee, Peterborough.

10. Strachan, R. & Jefferies, D. J. (1996) *Otter Survey of England 1991–1994*. The Vincent Wildlife Trust, London.

**Polecat habitat and distribution:** defined here as all kilometre squares below 500 metres in elevation except those which are principally urban and suburban or which have more than 75% of pure arable, conifer or moorland. **Blue =** approximate extent of the current distribution. **Green =** areas where polecats are currently absent.

From ITE Land Cover and OS Topographic and Geographic Reference maps, and from J. D. S. Birks (pers. comm.).

# 10.5 Polecat
*(Mustela putorius)*

## History and current status

Polecats are small mustelids closely related to ferrets. Indeed, ferrets appear to be no more than domesticated polecats[1]. So, like the wildcats, native polecats risk hybridisation with feral stocks.

Polecats are generalist predators, preferring low-ground habitats, and on the Continent they appear to favour wet or river-side zones[2, 3]. Polecats will eat any small mammal or bird but in Wales they are known to concentrate on rabbits[4]. They were formerly a widespread species, found in most counties in Britain, but by the beginning of the 20th century the only stronghold left was a small area in western Wales, with very few animals in other parts of Wales and the Welsh border counties.

The demise of the polecat parallels trends in other small carnivores, and in some raptors, which disappeared with the rise of intensive predator control associated with game preservation in the latter half of the 19th century[5]. While it is doubtless true that many polecats were killed by gamekeepers, many others were also killed for their pelts and many would have been taken by rabbit-trappers using gins – particularly in West Country areas.

During the 1950s and 1960s, polecats gradually spread back into most other parts of Wales and they became re-established in parts of the western Midlands[6, 7]. Today the spread continues and animals have turned up as far east as Oxfordshire and Northamptonshire[8]. Other animals have turned up in places not contiguous with this distribution, such as Dorset, Hampshire and Wiltshire, as well as in the apparently well-established populations in Cumbria and Argyll, and this suggests that the natural spread of these animals is being augmented by people releasing polecats without the knowledge of the conservation agencies (J. D. S. Birks, pers. comm.).

Gamekeepers can and still do kill polecats, even though setting traps for them is illegal under the Wildlife and Countryside Act (1981). Shooting them is not. Nevertheless probably most polecats killed by gamekeepers are taken in tunnel-traps set for other mustelids, such as stoats[9]. This is clearly not curtailing the spread of these animals.

There is evidence, however, that some polecats are being killed through secondary poisoning by anticoagulant rodenticides[10] – in a similar fashion to owls[11]. The main agents seem to be second- and third-generation products such as difenacoum. It has already been established that

warfarin-poisoned mice can be lethal to weasels[12] and, of the mustelids, the polecat is likely to be the most vulnerable, because unlike the others, brown rats form a significant component of its diet.

## Conservation plan

The current population of polecats in Britain is estimated at about 15,000 animals, of which 12,500 are in Wales[13]. To estimate the total if polecats spread throughout Britain we have assumed that suitable habitat is represented by all ground which is less than 500 metres in altitude and not more than 75% arable, conifer or moor, and which does not include extensively urbanised areas. If polecats colonise the rest of Britain at densities similar to those in Wales, we might anticipate a total population of some 85,000 animals. How long it might take polecats to spread over the country without assistance is not clear, but at the current rate of progress we might anticipate pioneer animals to be turning up in Kent, Cornwall, Norfolk and Aberdeenshire within two decades. However, it is clear that the pioneering populations in English counties such as Shropshire have a much lower density than the core area in Wales[9].

We think this rate of progress is acceptable in conservation terms and re-introductions are therefore unnecessary and undesirable. Polecats should not be allowed to spread onto offshore islands where they could threaten bird colonies.

We think that protection of this species is unwarranted, given its continued spread and the increasing likelihood of it causing damage to penned game and livestock as its range extends.

## Research needs

It is important to continue the ecological studies of this animal which are currently being conducted by the Vincent Wildlife Trust. These are essential to give us a greater understanding of the species in Britain. Key questions are:

- How serious is the problem of secondary poisoning and how may its impact be reduced?

- What are the likely repercussions of hybridisation with escaped ferrets?

- What are the rates of dispersal of this animal and what is a likely scenario of its future spread?

From the perspective of the other fauna we also need to ask:

- How can we reduce the likely damage to poultry and penned gamebirds? Design changes to conventional pheasant release pens may be needed.

- Are there any prey species that could be seriously affected by the return of polecats? In particular coastal and cliff-nesting birds could be vulnerable. There is already concern about predation on choughs in Pembrokeshire, for example.

## Conservation action

- Cavalier re-introductions into other parts of England and Scotland should be vigorously discouraged by conservation agencies and others.

- The Government needs to keep under review the legal status of polecats and other protected carnivores whose abundance is changing substantially. This is to ensure that the right balance is struck between the conservation needs of the carnivore, the wider conservation interests and the game-managers.

## Sources and references

1. Blandford, P. R. S. & Walton, K. C. (1977) Feral ferret *Mustela furo*. In: Corbet, G.B. & Southern, H. N. (Eds) *The Handbook of British Mammals*. Blackwell Scientific Publications, Oxford. 405–6.

2. Lode, T. (1994) Environmental factors influencing habitat exploitation by the polecat *Mustela putorius* in western France. *Journal of Zoology, London*, **234**: 75–88.

3. Sidorovich, V. E., Jedrzejewska, B. & Jedrzejewski, W. (1996) Winter distribution and abundance of mustelids and beavers in the river valleys of Bialowieza Primeval Forest. *Acta Theriologica*, **41**: 155–70.

4. Walton, K. C. (1977) Polecat *Mustela putorius*. In: Corbet, G.B. & Southern, H. N. (Eds) *The Handbook of British Mammals*. Blackwell Scientific Publications, Oxford. 345–52.

5. Langley, P. J. W. & Yalden, D. W. (1977) The decline of the rarer carnivores in Great Britain during the nineteenth century. *Mammal Review*, **7**: 95–116.

6. Walton, K. C. (1964) The distribution of the polecat (*Putorius putorius*) in England, Wales and Scotland, 1959–62. *Proceedings of the Zoological Society of London*, **143**: 333–6.

7. Walton, K. C. (1968) The distribution of the polecat, *Putorius putorius* in Great Britain, 1963–67. *Journal of Zoology London*, **155**: 237–40.

8. Birks, J. (1993) The return of the polecat. *British Wildlife*, **5**: 16–25.

9. Birks, J. D. S. (1997) A volunteer-based system for sampling variations in the abundance of polecats (*Mustela putorius*). *Journal of Zoology London*, **243**: 857–63.

10. Shore, R. F., Birks, J. D. S., Freestone, P. & Kitchener, A. (1996) Second–generation rodenticides and polecats (*Mustela putorius*) in Britain. *Environmental Pollution*, **91**: 279–82.

11. Newton, I., Wyllie, I. & Freestone, P. (1990) Rodenticides in British barn owls. *Environmental Pollution*, **68**: 101–17.

12. Townsend, M. G., Bunyan, P. J., Odam, E. M., Stanley, P. I. & Wardall, H. P. (1984) Assessment of secondary poisoning hazard of warfarin to least weasels. *Journal of Wildlife Management*, **48**: 628–32.

13. Harris, S., Morris, P., Wray, S. & Yalden, D. (1995) *A Review of British Mammals*. Joint Nature Conservation Committee, Peterborough.

**Pine marten habitat and distribution:**

kilometre squares containing more than 25 hectares of woodland but no motorways, A-roads, urban fringe or large villages.

**Blue =** regions where pine martens are currently established.

**Red =** regions of relict populations where the animals' status is uncertain.

**Green =** areas where pine martens are absent.

From ITE Land Cover and OS Geographic Reference maps, and the Vincent Wildlife Trust and JNCC[3,5].

# 10.6 Pine marten
*(Martes martes)*

## History and current status

Pine martens are primarily forest-living carnivores, although in Scotland they are frequently reported on the open hill – perhaps while crossing between woodland blocks. They prey on small mammals and birds (including gamebirds) and to some extent feed on berries and fruit. In some parts of Scotland, carrion from deer grallochs forms an important component of the diet[1]. Martens are fur-bearers and used to be trapped for their pelts. Although pelt quality in Britain would not have been good compared with that of animals from boreal regions, trapping for fur, as well as predator control to protect game, was almost certainly responsible for the disappearance of martens in most of England in the 18th and 19th centuries[2]. Since the Second World War they have been spreading back into north-eastern Scotland[3] and have been re-introduced successfully into Galloway[4].

Pine martens were given partial protection under the Wildlife and Countryside Act (1981) Schedule 6, which allowed them to be shot but not trapped. This was later extended to give them complete protection by adding the species to Schedule 5 in 1988.

The status of the English and Welsh populations is problematic and, although sightings and other signs are reported from the relict areas[5,6], they are very infrequent – suggesting that, at the very least, the martens there must be very secretive and sparsely distributed[6]. This contrasts with the newly established Galloway population, which also consists of only a small number of animals (about 30), but which nevertheless leaves regular evidence of its presence and has proved relatively easy to live-trap and study[7].

At present the British population is tentatively put at 3,650 adults with the bulk of these in Scotland[8]. The Welsh and English populations may be as low as 50 and 100 individuals respectively.

## Conservation plan

Some people wish to see this species regain its former 18th-century distribution. However, contiguous woodland areas in England are few and, although the south is well wooded, the amount of woodland not intersected by motorways or directly adjacent to urban areas is limited. It may be that martens are already present in the best of the suitably forested regions of Britain.

## Research needs

Re-introductions, even for still-existing members of the fauna, need to be well researched and appraised with care. Even when the re-establishment of a species may be possible and desirable for reasons of faunal diversity, it may conflict with current land use and other conservation objectives. It is imperative, therefore, that adequate environmental impact studies are carried out and that there is an extended period of consultation prior to any re-introduction. So far, Government agencies and voluntary bodies have treated the proposal to extend the range of the pine marten by selective re-introductions with exemplary caution.

The following studies have already been undertaken:

- Ecology of martens in Galloway[7];

- Suitability of various English localities for re-introductions and their probability of success[7];

- Status of the existing English and Welsh relict stock[6];

- Practical problems that gamekeepers face from predation by martens in pheasant release pens[9].

The main requirement now is an assessment of the impact that pine martens could have on potential prey animals in areas where they might be re-introduced. This is the subject of current research and a report of its findings is due shortly. Key questions which will need to be answered prior to any re-introduction include:

- Why are the English and Welsh populations faring so poorly?

In our analysis of potential habitat, there are 20,560 square kilometres which contain more than 25 hectares of woodland and which are not adjacent to motorways, major roads and towns. Taking a density of 0.4 animals per square kilometre within these suitable regions as an optimistic attainable density[7], this suggests a potential British population of just over 8,000 animals. It is possible, however, that southern English counties could prove to have better habitats in terms of prey abundance than many Scottish areas and the species might reach a higher density than 0.4 per square kilometre.

The existing marten populations do not seem capable of spreading rapidly. Indeed the relicts appear to have dwindled rather than increased[5], despite a likely reduction in mortality through gamekeeping. The Galloway stock, although well established and successful, has, in 15 years, spread to cover an area with only an 11-kilometre radius. Given this, it is argued that re-introductions are the only realistic way to help the species regain its former distribution.

- What will be the likely impact of martens on sensitive prey species (eg. red squirrel, dormouse, black grouse, woodcock, wood lark and nightjar) and what would be the effect on these if martens returned to areas where they have been absent for over 200 years?

- What interests would be affected by a widening marten distribution? Game and livestock interests are the most likely to be affected.

Other questions which need research, but to which answers are not essential prior to a re-introduction, are:

- What can be done to improve habitat quality for martens, particularly in areas of intensive forestry?

- What levels of mortality can marten populations withstand, particularly from road traffic?

- To what extent do larger, more successful carnivores, such as foxes, affect marten populations?

## Conservation actions

- If the relict English and Welsh populations of marten are still viable, conservation agencies need to mount a major conservation initiative to improve their status.

- Pheasant release and rearing pens are vulnerable to marten attack. For release pens, Scottish Natural Heritage and Vincent Wildlife Trust recommend closing all ground-level pop-holes at night, removing or cutting back all overhanging trees and using an electric wire on the top netting fringe[9,10].

- Martens are vulnerable to snares set for foxes. Gamekeepers in marten areas need to ensure all snares have stops which leave a hole at least five centimetres in diameter. Fox snares should be set relatively high (25 centimetres).

- If martens become more numerous and widespread some animals will inevitably be killed in traps and snares set by gamekeepers for legitimate species, such as fox, mink and stoat. With the relevant authorities we will develop a Code of Predator Control Practice to help gamekeepers reduce non-target captures in tunnel-traps and snares. These, if complied with, should be used by a keeper in his defence should he unintentionally kill a protected species such as a marten.

- Support for re-introductions by landowners is likely to depend on whether or not, at some future date when specified conservation objectives have been achieved, the Department of the Environment, Transport and Regions is prepared to countenance licensed control of martens shown to be doing significant damage.

## Sources and references

1. Balharry, D. (1993) Social organisation of marten: an inflexible system? *Symposia of the Zoological Society of London*, 65: 321–45.

2. Langley, P. J. W. & Yalden, D. W. (1977) The decline of the rarer carnivores in Great Britain during the nineteenth century. *Mammal Review*, 7: 95–116.

3. Velander, K.A. (1983) *Pine Marten Survey of Scotland, England and Wales*. The Vincent Wildlife Trust, London.

4. Shaw, G. & Livingstone, J. (1992) The pine marten: its reintroduction and subsequent history in the Galloway Forest Park. *Transactions of the Dumfriesshire and Galloway Natural History and Antiquarian Society*, 3rd series, 67: 1–7.

5. Strachan, R., Jefferies, D.J. & Chanin, P. R. F. (1996) *Pine Marten Survey of England and Wales 1987–1988*. Joint Nature Conservation Committee, Peterborough.

xz6. Messenger, J.E., Birks, J. D. S. & Jefferies. D. J. (1997) What is the status of the pine marten in England and Wales? *British Wildlife*, 8: 273-279.

7. Bright, P. W. & Smithson, T. J. (1997) *Species Recovery Programme for the Pine Marten: 1995–96*. Unpublished report to People's Trust for Endangered Species and English Nature.

8. Harris, S., Morris, P., Wray, S. & Yalden, D. (1995) *A Review of British Mammals*. Joint Nature Conservation Committee, Peterborough.

9. Balharry, E. A. & MacDonald, D. W. (1996) *A Cost Effective Method for Protecting Livestock against Marten Predation*. Scottish Natural Heritage, Edinburgh.

10. Balharry, E. (1998) *How to exclude pine martens from game and poultry pens and an introduction to the species in Scotland*. The Vincent Wildlife Trust, London

# 10.7 Badger
## (*Meles meles*)

## History and current status

An indigenous woodland omnivore, the badger likes the patchwork of grass and wood created by livestock farming[1]. Its principal food is earthworms, which it hunts mainly over mown grassland or permanent pasture[2, 3]. However, badgers can be significant predators of vertebrate prey, and experimental studies at Oxford University suggest that their predation may severely limit hedgehog densities in some areas[4]. Badgers are much less numerous in areas where there is little or no grass, such as moorland or intensive arable farmland[5].

The badger has probably always been widespread, although numbers were severely reduced by gamekeeping during the last century. The increase in numbers in the years after the Second World War largely reflects the reduction of such control[6].

Population estimates for this species are good and, for the mid-1980s, were put at 250,000[5]. Numbers have increased substantially since then and are currently thought to be approximately 75% higher, although a formal estimate of present numbers has yet to be made[7].

## Conservation plan

Increased public awareness and special protection have contributed to the increase in badger numbers since the Second World War. Although the animal's abundance now no longer seems to justify the high degree of protection afforded to it, the persistence of badger digging in certain areas and the difficulties of convicting offenders suggest that the law needs to remain tight for this species. However, a large animal with a substantial appetite and propensity for excavation is bound to cause problems for landowners and farmers where it is common[8].

Existing arrangements, set out in the Badgers Act (1992), make provision for badgers to be killed and for setts to be destroyed if such problems are serious and intractable. The main shortcoming of the present situation is the reluctance of officials to issue licences quickly. Generally, we feel that killing badgers is a more effective and humane way of dealing with nuisance animals than attempting translocations – although this may be desirable in some instances in urban and suburban areas.

The persistent problem of cross-infection with bovine tuberculosis (TB) between cattle and badgers has been with us since the early 1970s and the rigorous culling programme at that time, although ruthless, did appear to be working. However, public concern over the conservation and welfare of badgers led to a significant reduction in the scale of culling. At present, TB incidence in cattle in south-western England is higher than at any time since the 1960s. A pre-emptive culling policy had been in operation since 1994[1], but this has been curtailed. Current knowledge of bovine TB in cattle and badgers has recently been reviewed and past policies re-appraised[9]. As a result, a new experimental approach to the problem has started.

It is our view that, if culling badgers proves to be justified on animal health grounds, then where possible the responsibility for carrying out these actions should be given back to the farmers themselves through licensing arrangements.

Although badgers regularly take the nests of ground-nesting birds, and sometimes adult birds, our Salisbury Plain experiment demonstrated that, at least in some areas, badger control was not necessary to increase grey partridge stocks substantially[10].

## Research needs

The following areas need to be addressed:

- The impact of high densities of badgers on ground-nesting gamebirds and songbirds needs to be quantified.

- Development of a TB vaccine for badgers is likely to be the best long-term solution to the bovine TB problem and should be given high priority. Meanwhile, any strategies, including culling or other methods, should be carried out on an experimental basis with controls. We are pleased that this is the approach suggested by the recent review[9], and that the Government is carrying it through.

- Conditioned taste aversion could be an appropriate way of dealing with some badger problems, eg. in dealing with predation on gamebird nests.

## Conservation actions

- Government ministries and conservation agencies need to relax existing licensing arrangements so that farmers can get a quick and uncomplicated response to their requests for either interfering with setts or killing individual badgers. English Nature's Natural Areas Scheme could be used to define regions where badger numbers are healthy and where numbers are low so that licences could be issued more freely or restricted accordingly.

- However frustrating the process, farmers should persist with making licence applications where they are suffering substantial crop or livestock damage from badgers.

## Sources and references

1. Neal, E. & Cheeseman, C. (1996) *Badgers*. T. & A. D. Poyser, London.

2. Kruuk, H. (1978) Spatial organisation and territorial behaviour of the European badger *Meles meles. Journal of Zoology, London*, 184: 1–19.

3. Kruuk, H. & Parish, T. (1982) Factors affecting population density, group size and territory size of the European badger, *Meles meles. Journal of Zoology, London*, 196: 31–9.

4. Micol, T., Doncaster, C. P. & MacKinlay, L. A. (1994) Correlates of local variation in the abundance of hedgehogs *Erinaceus europaeus. Journal of Animal Ecology*, 63: 851–60.

5. Cresswell, P., Harris, S. & Jefferies, D. J. (1990) *The History, Distribution, Status and Habitat Requirements of the Badger in Britain*. The Nature Conservancy Council, Peterborough.

6. Reason, P., Harris, S. & Cresswell, P. (1993) Estimating the impact of past persecution and habitat changes on the numbers of badgers *Meles meles* in Britain. *Mammal Review*, 23: 1–15.

7. Wilson, G., Harris, S. & McLaren, G. (1997) *Changes in the British Badger Population, 1988 to 1997*. People's Trust for Endangered Species, London.

8. Anon. (1995) *Badgers: Their Effect on Agriculture and the Countryside*. The National Farmers Union, London.

9. Krebs, J., Anderson, R., Clutton-Brock, T., Morrison, I., Young, D. & Donnelly, C. (1997) *Bovine Tuberculosis in Cattle and Badgers*. Ministry of Agriculture, Fisheries, and Food, London.

10. Tapper, S. C., Potts, G. R. & Brockless, M. (1996) The effect of an experimental reduction in predation pressure on the breeding success and population density of grey partridges (*Perdix perdix*). *Journal of Applied Ecology*, 33: 965–78.

**Otter habitat and distribution:** kilometre squares containing more than 2.5 hectares of river, 10 hectares of lake or 0.1 hectares of canal, as well as all coastal and shore habitats.

**Blue =** regions where otters currently exist.

**Green =** areas where otters are currently absent.

From OS Geographic Reference map, BRC mammal atlas and other sources[1].

# 10.8 Otter
*(Lutra lutra)*

## History and current status

Otters have always been sparsely distributed and this scarcity is accentuated by their nocturnal habit and secretive nature. Nevertheless, they have had a wide distribution until recently and, despite often being hunted for sport, for their pelts, or because they were thought to damage fish stocks,

they survived much better in England and Wales than other carnivores, such as martens, polecats or wildcats. They were, however, severely affected by pesticide residues and pollution. Since the late 1950s organo-chlorine seed dressings and, more recently, polychlorinated biphenyls (PCBs), have seeped out of the agricultural and urban environments into English river systems. This appears to have reduced the fertility of female otters and wiped out otters from most of England and southern Wales. Geographically, the link between the otter's disappearance and rivers that drain arable and urban areas is clear enough[1,2].

It is obvious that otters eat substantial numbers of fish. Where salmonids are abundant they typically eat small salmon and trout of about 12 centimetres in length[3,4], but in some months they may also consume substantial amounts of carrion from dead spent salmon[5]. In slower coarse-fish rivers and lakes, otters take small members of the carp family (eg. roach and rudd), as well as eels[3]. Coastal otters in the Shetlands feed principally on bottom-living eel-pout, rockling and butterfish[6].

Although an otter may eat over a kilogram of fish per day, this is unlikely to be sufficient to reduce rod catches seriously[7], because otters tend

of available habitat suggests that this might not be the case, so we should not set our aspirations too high. We have included as suitable habitat only kilometre squares containing either coast, lakes, rivers or canals. This amounts to 1,257,000 hectares of water, 934,000 hectares of which are already within the current otter distribution. Assuming that otters recolonise the vacant waters of England at the same density as elsewhere, we cannot expect a total British population of otters to exceed 10,000 animals. However, we appreciate that this analysis is somewhat simplistic because, for example, otters tend to occur at higher densities in lowland districts than they do in upland catchments[1] and habitat quality and food supply are bound to be important.

Given the limited extent of otter habitat in England, it is imperative that watercourses are made as suitable as possible for recolonising animals. We suggest that a general habitat improvement programme to restore inland fisheries (with wild fish rather than stocked ones) will also benefit otters. Otters need well-vegetated banks[13], so river restoration projects should provide better cover as well as a larger prey base. In this respect a lot can be done by landowners and also, in particular, by the Environment Agency (EA), which should continue to devise and promote such schemes[14]. A considerable amount of the habitat removed in the 1960s and 1970s needs to be replaced.

## Research needs

There has already been a considerable amount of research on this species and, although new knowledge is always welcome, we see no major gaps that would prevent the following conservation actions being successful.

to occur at low densities and forage over many miles of river[8]. Nor is the disturbing effect of anglers on otter ecology considered serious[8].

Otters are very difficult to count and the only estimates are calculated from their known distribution (based on finding otter spraints[9]) and intensive studies where population densities are known. The most recent estimate puts the British population at 7,350 animals, of which the bulk (over 6,000) are in Scotland[10]. The number in England is only about 350.

## Conservation plan

Over the last decade otter numbers appear to have been recovering[1,11] and in some areas signs of otters have substantially increased.

Nevertheless, restoring numbers to pre-decline levels is likely to prove very difficult. The continued presence of PCBs in river systems and the growth of road traffic may cause sufficient mortality and/or loss in productivity to prevent recolonisation of parts of the Midlands or southern England. At the current slow rate of progress a full recovery may not occur in East Anglia until the middle of the next century[1]; even in the south-west only 75% of potential sites are expected to be occupied by the turn of the century. We therefore think that further restocking of otters in vacant catchments is justified[12].

The animal's current restricted distribution suggests that, if most of central England were to be recolonised, the total population of otters could increase substantially. However, our map

## Conservation actions

- Riparian-owners should fence streams and rivers to prevent access by livestock, which destroy banks and remove cover. In many situations grant aid is available for this.

- The Farming and Rural Conservation Agency should continue to use the Countryside Stewardship Scheme and Set-aside to encourage farmers to create river-bank buffer zones in important catchments, thus reducing agricultural run-off and improving bank cover.

- The EA should divert more of its flood control budget into conservation work. EA Thames Region has demonstrated the success of this approach. In this way, river meanders can be re-created, hatches rebuilt and wet meadows and woodlands established.

- The practice of removing all dead and toppled trees from rivers in the name of flood control should cease. These create habitat for fish and otters. This applies particularly to willows, which will often re-root and remain stable. Only trees that genuinely threaten public safety should be taken out.

- Most weed-cutting programmes on southern rivers should probably be reduced and, where they are considered necessary, should be carried out in a way that benefits fish stocks.

- All Fyke nets for eels should be legally required to have otter guards fitted.

## Sources and references

1. Strachan, R. & Jefferies, D. J. (1996) *Otter Survey of England 1991–1994*. The Vincent Wildlife Trust, London.

2. Chanin, P. R. F. & Jefferies, D. J. (1978) The decline of the otter *Lutra lutra* L. in Britain: an analysis of the hunting records and discussion of the causes. *Biological Journal of the Linnaean Society*, **10**: 305–28.

3. Wise, M. H., Linn, I. J. & Kennedy, C. R. (1981) A comparison of the feeding biology of mink *Mustela vison* and the otter *Lutra lutra. Journal of Zoology, London*, **195**: 181–213.

4. Kruuk, H., Carss, D. N., Conroy, J. W. H. & Durbin, L. (1997) Otter (*Lutra lutra* L.) numbers and fish productivity in rivers in north-east Scotland. *Symposia of the Zoological Society of London*: 171–91.

5. Hewson, R. (1995) Use of salmonid carcasses by vertebrate scavengers. *Journal of Zoology, London*, **235**: 53–65.

6. Kruuk, H., Conroy, J. W. H. & Moorhouse, A. (1987) Seasonal reproduction, mortality and food of otters (*Lutra lutra* L.) in Shetland. *Symposia of the Zoological Society of London*, **58**: 263–78.

7. Jefferies, D. J. (1987) The effects of angling interests on otters, with particular reference to disturbance. In: Maitland, P. S. & Turner, A. K. (Eds) *Angling and Wildlife in Freshwaters*. Institute of Terrestrial Ecology, Grange-over-Sands. 23–30.

8. Durbin, L. S. (1996) Individual differences in spatial utilization of a river-system by otters *Lutra lutra. Acta Theriologica*, **41**: 137–47.

9. Conroy, J. W. H. & French, D. D. (1987) The use of spraints to monitor populations of otters (*Lutra lutra*). *Symposia of the Zoological Society of London*, **58**: 247–62.

10. Harris, S., Morris, P., Wray, S. & Yalden, D. (1995) *A Review of British Mammals*. Joint Nature Conservation Committee, Peterborough.

11. Strachan, R., Birks, J. D. S., Chanin, P. R. F. & Jefferies, D. J. (1990) *Otter survey of England*. Report of the Nature Conservancy Council, Peterborough.

12. Jefferies, D. J., Wayre, P., Jessop, R. M. & Mitchell-Jones, A. J. (1986) Reinforcing the native otter *Lutra lutra* population in East Anglia: an analysis of the behaviour and range development of the first release group. *Mammal Review*, **16**: 65–79.

13. MacDonald, S. M., Mason, C. F. & Coghill, I. S. (1978) The otter and its conservation in the Teme catchment. *Journal of Applied Ecology*, **15**: 373–84.

14. Ward, D., Holmes, N. & José, P. (1994) *The New Rivers and Wildlife Handbook*. Royal Society for the Protection of Birds, Sandy, Bedfordshire.

**Wildcat habitat and distribution:** kilometre squares containing less than 25 hectares of managed grass or tilled land, but excluding all urban and suburban squares. **Blue =** current extent of wildcat range. **Green =** areas where wild-cats are currently absent.

From ITE Land Cover map and BRC mammal atlas.

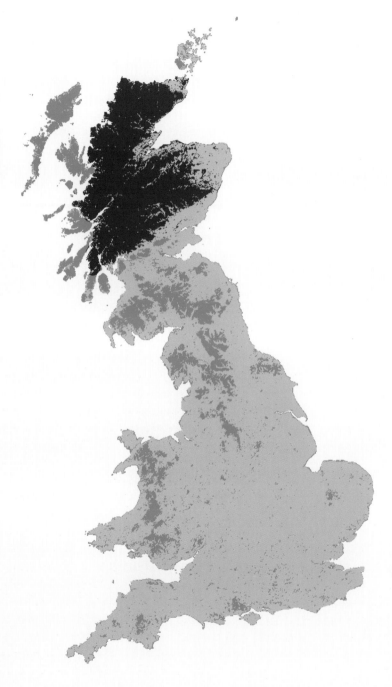

# 10.9 Wildcat
## (Felis sylvestris)

### History and current status

The Scottish wildcat population appears to be one of the most northerly of this species. In Europe the wildcat is found in some forested parts of western Germany and north-eastern France; it is rare in the Massif Central, but occurs regularly from the Pyrenees southwards[1]. It is also found in Italy and wooded parts of the Balkans, and is extensively distributed in Africa. In Britain, it was formerly much more widespread but, even by the late 18th century, it seems to have disappeared from most lowland farming areas[2]. In Europe it is described as an animal of the forest and, although it prefers the woodland edge, the broken patchwork of replanted sections and small fields, it is said to require large contiguous stretches of forest cover to survive. In Scotland it seems less dependent on forest cover, but still needs large tracts of wild country. Small birds and mammals form its staple diet.

Loss of forest to agriculture seems to have been the major reason for the early stages of this retreat into the uplands but later the development of game management for grouse shooting pushed it back until it remained only in the north-western Highlands. During the course of the 20th century the population has gradually expanded to occupy what is apparently all the suitable habitat north of the Central Lowlands[3].

The wildcat is a poorly studied animal, so population estimates are based on the extrapolation of a few known densities to the whole of the inhabited region. The current estimate is 3,500 animals in Scotland[4].

### Conservation plan

Wildcats have been widely killed by gamekeepers on Scottish grouse moors, as well as by upland sheep-farmers who regard them as predators of lambs. The species was only partially protected by the Wildlife and Countryside Act (1981) and full protection was not given until 1988, when it was added to Schedule 5 of the Act. Although protecting animals like the wildcat is undoubtedly popular with the public, it is debatable whether it really has much conservation benefit for a species of this kind. Wildcats had regained their former range north of the Central Lowlands long before protection, and the evidence presented by the then Nature Conservancy Council in 1991 – three years

after the protection order – to support its contention that persecution was a real population threat, was based entirely on a subjective assessment made retrospectively[3]. It is now not known whether this protection has reduced persecution or simply driven it underground, further alienating gamekeepers and increasing their resentment of conservation initiatives.

It is ironic and probably not accidental that the wildcat, within its current range, is most numerous in the eastern Highlands, where game interests are high; in the western Highlands, where game interests are low, it is less numerous[3]. However, the main drawback to such protection is that it diverts attention away from what are probably more significant conservation problems for this species. These are:

- The possibility of disease transmission between domestic cats and wildcats[5];

- Hybridisation with feral cats[6];

- Poor habitat quality of commercial forests[7];

- Separation of the current population from further areas of potential range expansion.

The map and our analysis shows the effect of this separation. Habitat requirements for wildcats are difficult to define precisely but we have assumed here that all areas with more than 25% of either managed grass or tilled land are unsuitable, as are any areas influenced by towns, villages or roads. Given that the area of habitat within the current range contains some 3,500 animals, and assuming that wildcats were to be distributed throughout the same habitats in the Southern Uplands, the Lake District, Pennines, North York Moors and central Wales, we would expect a population of 5,500 animals. This represents a population at low density. To safeguard the species we should aim to substantially improve habitat quality.

## Research needs

An increase in the amount of ecological work on this animal in Scotland would be welcome. However, there have been detailed studies in France[8, 9] and other parts of Europe which are relevant to Britain. Recent work suggests that the anxiety over wildcat hybridisation may be less of a problem than was at first thought and it may occur much less regularly once stable densities of wildcats have been reached[10].

## Conservation actions

- Wildcats share habitat requirements with other game, so they should also benefit from habitat management for species such as black grouse. In particular, regenerating woodland-edge zones, promoting shrub layers within forests and reducing deer numbers will all help wildcats.

## Sources and references

1. Stahl, P. (1992) Le chat sauvage en Europe: les conclusions du colloque international de Nancy. *Bulletin Mensuel de l'Office National de la Chasse*, **174**: 9.

2. Langley, P. J. W. & Yalden, D. W. (1977) The decline of the rarer carnivores in Great Britain during the nineteenth century. *Mammal Review*, 7: 95–116.

3. Easterbee, N., Hepburn, L. V. & Jefferies, D. J. (1991) *Survey of the Status and Distribution of the Wildcat in Scotland, 1983–1987.* Nature Conservancy Council for Scotland, Edinburgh.

4. Harris, S., Morris, P., Wray, S. & Yalden, D. (1995) *A Review of British Mammals.* Joint Nature Conservation Committee, Peterborough.

5. McOrist, S., Bold, R., Jones, T. W., Easterbee, N., Hubbard, A. L. & Jarrett, O. (1991) Some viral and protozool diseases in the European wildcat (*Felis sylvestris*). *Journal of Wildlife Diseases*, 27: 693–6.

6. Hubbard, A.L., McOrist, S., Jones, T.W., Boid, R., Scott, R. & Easterbee, N. (1992) Is survival of European wildcats *Felis silvestris* in Britain threatened by interbreeding with domestic cats? *Biological Conservation*, **61**: 203–8.

7. McOrist, S. & Kitchener, A. (1994) Current threats to the European wildcat, *Felis sylvestris*, in Scotland. *Ambio*, **23**: 243–5.

8. Artois, M. (1985) Utilisation de l'espace et du temps chez le renard (*Vulpes vulpes*) et le chat forestier (*Felis silvestris*) en Lorraine. *Gibier Faune Sauvage*, **3**: 33–57.

9. Stahl, P., Artois, M. & Aubert, M. F. A. (1988) Organisation spatiale et déplacements des chats forestiers adultes (*Felis sylvestris*, Schreber, 1777) en Lorraine. *Revue d'Ecologie (Terre et Vie)*, **43**: 113–32.

10. French, D. D., Corbett, L. K. & Easterbee, N. (1988) Morphological discriminants of Scottish wildcats (*Felis sylvestris*), domestic cats (*F. cattus*), and their hybrids. *Journal of Zoology, London*, **214**: 235–59.

# 11. Predatory birds - the raptors

Britain's birds of prey have become a cause célèbre in conservation, and now that the effects of organo-chlorine pesticides have largely passed, illegal killing by gamekeepers, along with egg collecting, procuring birds for falconry and the use of poison by shepherds, are widely seen as the principal threats to their conservation today. Except on grouse moors, the true effect of many raptors on game has not been adequately studied, but their impact does appear to be much less than that of foxes or carrion crows. For this reason, and because most raptors are less common than many predatory mammals, we believe that legal protection of all raptors should continue. However, on grouse moors, in the absence of foxes and crows, aggregations of breeding hen harriers can have a dramatic affect on grouse production. We think harriers can be managed to overcome this – retaining both harriers and grouse.

The Game Conservancy Trust will continue to study the relationship between raptors and game, and such research should not be taken as a desire to build a case for their control. Where any raptor management is needed we will look for a way that is in the long-term interests of the conservation of raptors as well as game.

**Hen harrier habitat and distribution:** kilometre squares with more than 50% moorland or mire which are also less than 500 metres in altitude (for a fuller explanation see Potts[1]).
**Blue =** approximate current distribution of hen harriers in the breeding season.
**Green =** potential but unoccupied habitat.

From ITE Land Cover, OS Topographic maps and BTO bird atlas.

# 11.1 Hen harrier
*(Circus cyaneus)*

## History and current status

The hen harrier is nationally a rare bird of prey, principally found in remote moorland areas and extensive bog. Globally, however, it is widespread, with an estimated 167,000 nesting females, and not threatened. It nests on the ground in tall vegetation. It hunts small birds (eg. meadow pipits and skylarks) as well as mammals (especially voles) over open ground. Higher numbers of meadow pipits and voles appear to result in higher hen harrier numbers[3]. The female is larger than the male and takes significantly bigger prey, including adult grouse[3]. However, both sexes take grouse chicks when feeding their young in the nest. The hen harrier is at least partially migratory and, in particular, many males move from grouse moors to the lowlands in winter.

The hen harrier was once more widespread in Britain, but there is no good evidence that it has ever been a farmland bird, as it is in France. Perhaps the absence of the common vole (*Microtus arvalis*) in Britain, which is abundant in continental farmland, may be the reason. The gradual loss of lowland heath and drainage of bogs for agriculture could be the cause of the bird's dis-appearance from many English counties in the 18th and early 19th centuries. It was game preservation, however, which finally brought about its near extermination as a breeding bird on the British mainland by around 1900[4]. In Scotland, with a reduction in gamekeeping effort, recolonisation began in the 1930s and the establishment of new forests provided voles and secure nesting sites during the forests' early years. The population continued to expand and increase, although latterly this spread has slowed.

Currently, losses are principally attributed to the illegal destruction of clutches and broods and, to a lesser extent, illegal killing of adult birds on grouse moors. A recent study[5] estimated the number of young harriers reared per female on grouse moors to be only a third of that on other moorland in Scotland. Furthermore, the mortality of female hen harriers on grouse moors is double that on moorland not managed for grouse. The study concluded that gamekeepers destroy nests and kill adults on a significant scale, and suggested that grouse moors are a drain on the harrier population in some areas[5]. The habitat on some grouse moors is highly suited to hen harriers[3], and we would also note that there are large moorland areas, eg. in Wales and south-western England, where harriers do not breed and there are no gamekeepers to blame for their absence.

Illegal killing of harriers continues because harriers are seen as a serious threat to grouse stocks. For the gamekeeper, significant losses of young grouse to any predator mean a direct loss to the shooting bag upon which his job depends. For the moorland-owner, the reduction in grouse numbers to a level that no longer allows driven grouse shooting makes continued investment unsustainable. It has been claimed that losses of grouse to species such as harriers could be absorbed, but this is true to only a limited extent and losses to harriers can be large. Serious reductions in the number of grouse threaten the existence of active grouse management and, in turn, expenditure on improving and maintaining the moorland habitat on which a variable range of species, including hen harriers and many other birds of prey, depend.

*Birds of Prey and Red Grouse*, the report of the Joint Raptor Study, shows that the fears of upland gamekeepers and landowners can be well founded, at least on some moors, and that hen harriers can have an impact on grouse stocks which greatly reduces the potential shooting bag and the future management of moorland[3]. Much of the effect occurs in summer when nesting harriers prey on young grouse to feed their own chicks. This feeding accounted for 37% of the grouse chicks hatched at Langholm (where much of the Joint Raptor Study was carried out). In the absence of raptor predation on grouse in spring and summer, the work at Langholm predicts an increase in the late-summer grouse population of 100% in one year, and of 150% over two years. This predation is aggravated by the semi-colonial nature of nesting harriers, which have a tendency to congregate in favoured areas. On the Langholm moors, the number of hen harriers attempting to

| | km² of suitable habitat | Hen harriers in 1994 | Hen harrier carrying capacity |
|---|---|---|---|
| **Scotland** | 31,544 | 570 | 1,268 |
| **England** | 5,768 | 26 | 232 |
| **Wales** | 2,196 | 27 | 88 |
| **Total** | 39,508 | 623 | 1,588 |

Areas of heather moorland and mire in mainland Britain suitable for breeding harriers. The known numbers of 'pairs' breeding in 1994, and numbers likely to be present in the absence of illegal control. Adapted and updated from Potts[2].

breed increased from two to 20 females in six years[3]. It is a local increase of hen harrier breeding density like this which gamekeepers fear most.

The current British population of hen harriers is estimated to be 686 (± 150) nesting females[6], with the bulk of the population on moorland areas in Scotland[2]. Although there are large differences in the suitability of moorland to support harriers, it is clear that the distribution of breeding birds[1] is less extensive than it might be. There are large areas in England and Wales where harriers are absent but might be expected to occur (see map), amounting to 29% of the potential range.

## Conservation plan

Our goal for this species is to enhance the hen harrier's conservation status by doubling its numbers but, at the same time, managing the increase so that it is spread evenly into areas of suitable habitat. With careful management we think that this can be achieved without causing the demise of driven grouse shooting. In fact, we think that grouse management and hen harriers can coexist. At the same time we want to see an end to all illegal culling.

To achieve this aim, we need to define the conservation goal precisely and ensure that it is realistic. It has been estimated that, if illegal culling and nest destruction on grouse moors were stopped, the harrier population could increase by 13% per year initially until it levelled off (at an unstated level)[5]. This study did not, however, allow for the fact that, during recovery, some grouse moors would become unproductive for grouse, investment would cease and gamekeepers would lose their livelihood. There would then be no fox or crow control and no sympathetic heather management, but there would be conversion of many moors to forest or sheep-walk, which has occurred where grouse interests have been lost elsewhere. The extent to which this might happen is unknown but it would result in a *reduction* of harrier numbers following an initial period of increase, as appears to have happened in Wales.

By reviewing nesting densities of hen harriers throughout their global range and, by applying average densities of birds in areas where there is little or no illegal culling to all of Britain's moorland, including existing grouse moors, it has been estimated that the moorland areas of Britain might support close to 1,600 nesting females (see table)[2].

This is more than double the existing population. We think this is a sensible and achievable conservation goal. Moreover, if this harrier population were distributed throughout the suitable habitat, the birds would be breeding at densities that would not threaten grouse management.

To attain this goal we must set two objectives:

- Since illegal culling and nest destruction is clearly a primary cause of mortality and loss of harrier productivity on grouse moors, it is essential to end it. Harriers have had some protection in law for over a century and full protection since the Wild Bird Protection Act (1954), but this, on its own, has failed to prevent illegal culling. Simply increasing the level of punishment to include custodial sentences will not stop the illegal culling, as conviction rates are likely to remain very low.

  Currently keepers have a strong incentive to get rid of harriers entirely. Frequently they believe a single pair of harriers, if unharmed, could increase to a high density within a few years, which would effectively prevent driven grouse shooting. If, on the other hand, the keeper was required to accommodate only a limited number, or quota, of nesting females and, if there was a means of preventing further increases, then this incentive would be removed and hen harrier numbers overall could increase.

  On the basis of our national goal of 1,600 pairs of harriers, simply dividing the available habitat by this figure suggests one pair per 25 square kilometres of moorland under 500 metres in altitude.

- There are two types of upland moor which currently do not support breeding hen harriers:

(a) Areas adjacent to occupied areas where, with protection, immigrant birds will settle. This category includes some grouse moors, especially in north-western England. We believe that most moorland-managers will accept these immigrants *provided* there is a management option to limit the density to a level that does not significantly damage the grouse stocks.

(b) Areas distant from occupied sites where a more active policy may be required. In these locations there are very few immigrant birds. We suggest stocking these areas with birds that have been specially reared from eggs derived from areas of high harrier density where a lower level of harrier production is desirable. Such operations are widely adopted in conservation plans for raptor species and have been successful for the bald eagle and peregrine falcon in North America, and Montagu's and hen harriers, red kite, osprey and several other species in Europe. The procedures applied are similar to techniques used in the past by falconers and are known as 'hacking'. Essentially, young raptors are reared in aviaries without their parents in locations where one wants them to settle. As they grow, the chicks become imprinted with the locality and eventually form the nucleus of new breeding populations.

There are substantial areas into which harriers could be hacked and, in an analysis of suitable habitat, it has been shown[2] that these areas occur mostly in Wales and south-western England[7].

Our proposals call for the restoration of this species through active management rather than the current uncompromising protection. In Britain,

active management of raptors has already been undertaken under licence; eg. sea eagles, ospreys and red kites have all been re-introduced into areas where they have previously been absent to speed up slow natural rates of range expansion. We want to extend this practice to incorporate a system which limits the nesting density of birds on grouse moors so that the grouse interests, and thus the future of the habitat, can also be protected. We emphasise that we seek an overall *net increase* of more than 100% in hen harrier breeding numbers. The basis for harrier management could involve simply the removal of harrier eggs and, where appropriate, rearing-on the chicks for later release elsewhere[7].

In order to work, such a plan must have the support of grouse moor managers, for whom the ability to manage local harrier nesting density will be critical. At the same time, any management scheme must clearly be seen by conservation agencies, voluntary bodies and the general public to be working for the benefit of harriers. It must therefore contain sufficient checks and controls to ensure that it is not abused. We think a nest management scheme would be best operated by moorland-owners and their staff, and regulated and controlled by Government agency staff. In addition, we would propose that progress should be monitored through a set of regional forums to which representatives of local estates, statutory agencies and Non-Governmental Organisations with a direct interest in birds of prey would be invited.

## Research needs

- Much more needs to be known about the suitability of habitat for hen harriers, both on and off grouse moors, in order to assess the likely ceiling breeding densities in different areas, eg. how many moors would resemble Langholm?

- The role of intra-guild predation in influencing the nesting success of hen harriers needs to be understood more fully. The role of foxes, eagles, and carrion crows in particular may be important.

- Research on the effect of diversionary feeding (supplying food to breeding harriers to reduce their predation on grouse) on hen harrier predation rates of grouse chicks, and hen harrier breeding density and breeding success needs to be completed.

- A series of studies looking at the management of hen harrier nests, both as a potential method for limiting numbers on grouse moors and as a source for translocating birds to vacant areas, is required.

## Conservation actions

Our proposals aim to resolve one of the most divisive issues in the uplands and, we believe, will benefit hen harriers, grouse and the habitat they share. Both conservation and sporting interest groups now recognise that the current situation is unacceptable, and all key agencies and groups have pledged to work towards a resolution of this issue. In our view, a satisfactory resolution will need to:

- Remove the keepers' current incentive to get rid of harriers. We believe this will need to involve management of the harriers themselves through some sort of quota scheme.

- Ensure that proper licences and derogations under the EU Birds Directive are put in place to manage this species for sound conservation reasons.

## Sources and references

1. Gibbons, D. W., Reid, J. B. & Chapman, R. A. (1993) *The New Atlas of Breeding Birds of Britain and Ireland: 1988–1991*. British Trust for Ornithology. T. & A. D. Poyser, London.

2. Potts, G. R. (1998) Global dispersion of nesting hen harriers (*Circus cyaneus*): Implications for grouse moors in the UK. *Ibis*, **140**: 76–88.

3. Redpath, S. M. & Thirgood, S. J. (1997) *Birds of Prey and Red Grouse. Report of the Joint Raptor Study*. The Stationery Office, London.

4. Watson, D. (1977) *The Hen Harrier*. T. & A. D. Poyser, Berkhamsted, Hertfordshire.

5. Etheridge, B., Summers, R. W. & Green, R. E. (1997) The effects of illegal killing and destruction of nests by humans on the population dynamics of the hen harrier *Circus cyaneus* in Scotland. *Journal of Applied Ecology*, **34**: 1081–1105.

6. Stone, B. H., Sears, J., Cranswick, P. A., Gregory, R. D., Gibbons, D. W., Rehfisch, M. M., Aebischer, N. J. & Reid, J. B. (1997) Population estimates of birds in Britain and the United Kingdom. *British Birds*, **90**:1–22.

7. Watson, M. (1998) *Hen Harrier Translocation as a Conservation Tool in the United Kingdom – a Feasibility Study*. The Game Conservancy Trust, Fordingbridge, Hampshire.

**Goshawk habitat and distribution:** kilometre squares containing more than 5 hectares of woodland.
**Blue =** areas where goshawks are present.
**Green =** areas where goshawks are currently absent.

From ITE Land Cover map and BTO bird atlas.

# 11.2 Goshawk
*(Accipiter gentilis)*

## History and current status

The goshawk is a large and impressive bird of prey that has always been popular in the sport of falconry. Unlike the peregrine, which principally takes large birds, such as pigeons and gamebirds, on the wing, the goshawk is more versatile. It will not only take gamebirds in flight, but can also kill rabbits and snatch birds off the ground[2]. Studies in Finland show that willow grouse, black grouse, corvids and ducks are all important avian prey species, while young hares and red squirrels are important mammalian ones[3]. Like its smaller relative, the sparrowhawk, it likes mature woodland, particularly pinewoods, and prefers to hunt the glade and woodland edge for its prey. It does this by either ambushing its prey from cover or watching from lookout posts before swooping down to make its kill[2].

Although a native species, the goshawk became extinct in Britain at the end of the last century. Almost certainly poultry and game preservation interests were a major factor in its demise, but forest destruction in the preceding 200 years was also important and it may have been very sparsely distributed for some time[4]. Thus the bird has been absent from Britain for most of the last 200 years. In the early 1960s some new breeding pairs were discovered and since then the population has been rising exponentially[5]. There is little doubt that these breeding birds were deliberately released by falconers and other bird-of-prey enthusiasts.

The current population is estimated to be between 400–450 pairs[6], which have increased at a rate of 16% per year, from a mere handful in the 1960s to some 20–30 pairs in the mid-1970s and over 100 in the 1980s. The population will probably continue to expand over the next two to three decades. A similar rapid increase occurred in the Netherlands, where the population increased from 30 to 400 pairs in less than two decades[7].

## Conservation plan

Whatever one's views on birds of prey or gamebirds, we think that the re-introduction of the goshawk has been a clear example of how such an exercise should *not* be carried out. It was conducted with scant consultation and little thought was given to the likely impact on other interests and other species. This contrasts strongly with the other raptor re-introduction programmes

involving the red kite and sea eagle, which involved wide consultation and well-run public relations initiatives to encourage support from landowners and game interests.

In spite of these unfortunate beginnings we think that, because it was in Britain before, the goshawk as a species has a legitimate place in our modern countryside. It fits particularly well into the ecology of modern forestry enterprises[8]. However, it is very likely that a substantial goshawk population will have a significant impact on game interests.

Most important, and most difficult to cope with, will be the impact on wild game stocks. The appearance of goshawks in an area where arable farmland is interspersed with woodland could well put an end to a keeper's attempt to resurrect a wild pheasant population. As yet there is no research in Britain to demonstrate this, but persistent predation by goshawks along woodland edges and rides in spring, when cover is minimal, could well substantially affect the numbers of a gamebird breeding stock.

Another species of high conservation value, with which we are particularly concerned, is the black grouse. This is a declining species which is likely to be vulnerable to goshawks, just as it is in Finland[3]. There will also be an impact on released game, and keepers who rear pheasants and partridges can expect to find regular evidence of goshawk predation in and around release areas[9, 10]. Keepers may be able to reduce this by devising systems to give the game more cover[10] but losses are still likely to increase.

There has been a substantial amount of research on this species on the Continent, particularly in Scandinavia, and the evidence that they will adversely affect gamebirds is convincing[3, 9].

In view of the rapid population growth of this species, we think that the number of pairs will approach 1,000 by the year 2000. The goshawk's potential impact on game and other wildlife can therefore only increase. It is important to forestall problems by initiating research now into ways in which its predation on economically important species and species of conservation concern can be alleviated.

## Research needs

Given the way that this species has been re-established, with no proper assessment of its impact, we feel strongly that it is Government's duty to fund urgent research to assess the situation. We need a series of studies to examine how the other fauna might be affected. Particular requirements include:

- Technical research to devise rearing and releasing systems for pheasants which are likely to minimise losses to raptors.

- Determination of the likely impact of goshawks on lowland prey species, including pheasant, partridge, black grouse and woodcock.

- Investigation and modelling of past and future goshawk numbers so that the spread and growth of the population can be predicted.

## Conservation actions

The outcome of the above studies should indicate what, if any, action is appropriate.

## Sources and references

1. Gibbons, D. W., Reid, J. B. & Chapman, R. A. (1993) *The New Atlas of Breeding Birds of Britain and Ireland: 1988–1991*. British Trust for Ornithology. T. & A. D. Poyser, London.

2. Fox, N. (1981) The hunting behaviour of trained northern goshawks *Accipiter gentilis*. In: Kenward, R. E. & Lindsay, I. M. (Eds) *Understanding the Goshawk*. The International Association for Falconry and Conservation of Birds of Prey, Oxford. 121–33.

3. Tornberg, R. (1997) Prey selection of the goshawk *Accipiter gentilis* during the breeding season: The role of prey profitability and vulnerability. *Ornis Fennica*, **74**: 15–28.

4. Holloway, S. (1996) *The Historical Atlas of Breeding Birds in Britain and Ireland: 1875–1900*. British Trust for Ornithology. T. & A. D. Poyser, London.

5. Marquiss, M. (1981) The Goshawk in Britain – its provenance and current status. In: Kenward, R. E. & Lindsay, I. M. (Eds) *Understanding the Goshawk*. The International Association for Falconry and Conservation of Birds of Prey, Oxford. 43–55.

6. Stone, B. H., Sears, J., Cranswick, P. A., Gregory, R. D., Gibbons, D. W., Rehfisch, M. M., Aebischer, N. J. & Reid, J. B. (1997) Population estimates of birds in Britain and the United Kingdom. *British Birds*, **90**: 1–22.

7. Thissen, J., Müskens, G. & Opdam, P. (1981) Trends in the Dutch goshawk *Accipiter gentilis* population and their causes. In: Kenward, R. E. & Lindsay, I. M. (Eds) *Understanding the Goshawk*. The International Association for Falconry and Conservation of Birds of Prey, Oxford. 28–42.

8. Petty, S. J. (1989) Goshawks: Their status, requirements and management. *Forestry Commission Bulletin*. HMSO, London.

9. Kenward, R. E., Marcström, V. & Karlbom, M. (1981) Goshawk winter ecology in Swedish pheasant habitats. *Journal of Wildlife Management*, **45**: 397–408.

10. Kenward, R. E. & Marcström, V. (1981) Goshawk predation on game and poultry: Some problems and solutions. In: Kenward, R. E. & Lindsay, I. M. (Eds) *Understanding the Goshawk*. The International Association for Falconry and Conservation of Birds of Prey, Oxford. 152–9.

# 11.3 Sparrowhawk
*(Accipiter nisus)*

## History and current status

The sparrowhawk is primarily a species of woodland and the woodland edge. It preys on small to medium-sized birds, taking anything from a blue tit to a partridge. Female sparrowhawks are almost double the size of males and it is this sexual difference which allows them to exploit such a large range of prey sizes. Their diet is almost exclusively birds and over a year they clearly kill a considerable number. Studies at the Institute of Terrestrial Ecology suggest that a pair of sparrowhawks could consume the equivalent of 2,200 sparrows in the course of a year[1].

Sparrowhawks are once again a common bird and their numbers may be around 32,000 breeding pairs, plus a substantial number of non-breeders[2]. They are widespread throughout Britain and need only a small area of woodland for nesting. However, this was not always so and they suffered a rapid and severe decline in the 1950s as a direct consequence of the introduction of organo-chlorine insecticides. In many eastern arable areas, as a result of preying on songbirds which had eaten pesticide-treated seed, sparrowhawks were virtually wiped out as levels of these pesticides accumulated in their tissues. Sparrowhawks died and, at sublethal levels, eggshell thinning curtailed their breeding success. From the 1970s numbers began to recover and they may well now be as numerous as ever before[1].

This increased abundance has led to widespread concern about the impact these birds have on other species. Gamekeepers have always regarded sparrowhawks as game-predators and, prior to a 1961 amendment to the Protection of Birds Act (1954), keepers controlled them as part of their normal predator-control operations. Female sparrowhawks are regularly seen to kill adult partridges in spring, when there is limited cover, and broods of partridges are sometimes depleted to the last chick as result of sparrowhawk predation. Now, as well as gamekeepers, others are raising concerns about the sparrowhawk's effect on songbirds. However, there are very few scientific studies concerning the impact of sparrowhawks on other bird species.

The only substantial work was on the effect of sparrowhawks on breeding great tits and blue tits in Wytham Woods near Oxford. This study showed that, although tit mortality due to sparrowhawk predation is substantial and has a large impact on the pattern of mortality of these birds, the effect on overall breeding numbers of both species is slight[3]. It is argued that this is mainly because such mortality simply replaces losses that would otherwise occur through starvation. It is also argued that long-term data-sets for many common woodland birds do not show any changes in abundance corresponding firstly with the decline of sparrowhawks due to pesticides and, secondly, with their recovery[4]. However, not all songbird species are flourishing and it is quite possible that the impact of sparrowhawks on other species in farmland areas may be quite different from that in mature woodland. Some species are also clearly more vulnerable than others. In open habitats blackbirds, song thrushes and fieldfares, for example, are much more vulnerable than finches or tits[5]. On farmland and in rural areas, tree and house sparrows topped a vulnerability index in a recent Swedish study of sparrowhawk prey[6] and changes in the abundance of tree sparrows in Britain do, in fact, mirror the changing fortunes of the sparrowhawk[7].

## Conservation plan

In our view, the conservation status of the sparrowhawk is satisfactory. It enjoys complete protection under the Wildlife and Countryside Act (1981) and, although provisions do theoretically exist to issue licences to kill sparrowhawks, to our knowledge they have never been granted; in any case, few people apply. Some covert illegal killing certainly still persists on some estates and we condemn it entirely.

Although probably more is known about the biology of this raptor than any other, the main issue remains: to what extent do sparrowhawks affect other bird species? Their prey base is very wide and it is possible that numbers of some vulnerable birds may be affected, whereas other, more prolific species can withstand the mortality.

## Research needs

Key questions are:

- What is the impact of sparrowhawks on farmland songbirds? This work needs to examine a range of species and, ideally, should include an experimental element whereby breeding sparrowhawks are removed under licence.

- To what extent do sparrowhawks affect grey partridges? Spring predation on breeding pairs and losses of chicks during summer may be important. The overall biology of the grey partridge and the sparrowhawk is well understood, and a combination of investigation and modelling should answer this question.

## Conservation actions

We feel that no special conservation actions are needed for this species.

## Sources and references

1. Newton, I. (1986) *The Sparrowhawk*. T. & A. D. Poyser, Calton, Staffordshire.

2. Stone, B. H., Sears, J., Cranswick, P. A., Gregory, R. D., Gibbons, D. W., Rehfisch, M. M., Aebischer, N. J. & Reid, J. B. (1997) Population estimates of birds in Britain and the United Kingdom. *British Birds*, 90, 1–22.

3. McCleery, R. H. & Perrins, C. M. (1991) Effects of predation on the numbers of great tits *Parus major*. In: Perrins, C. M., Lebreton, J.-D. & Hirons, G. J. M. (Eds) *Bird Population Studies: Relevance to Conservation and Management*. Oxford University Press, Oxford. 129–47.

4. Newton, I. & Perrins, C. (1997) Sparrowhawks and songbirds. *Birds* (Summer): 65–68.

5. Cresswell, W. (1995) Selection of avian prey by wintering sparrowhawks *Accipiter nisus* in southern Scotland. *Ardea*, 83, 381–9.

6. Gotmark, F. & Post, P. (1996) Prey selection by sparrowhawks, *Accipiter nisus*: Relative predation risk for breeding passerine birds in relation to their size, ecology and behaviour. *Philosophical Transactions of the Royal Society of London (Biology)*, 351: 1559–77.

7. Summers-Smith, J. D. (1995) *The Tree Sparrow*. The Bath Press, Bath.

**Buzzard habitat and distribution:** kilometre squares containing more than 1 hectare of woodland but no more than 50 hectares of tilled ground or significant areas of urban or suburban land.
**Blue =** regions where buzzards are currently established breeders.
**Green =** areas where buzzards are largely absent.

From ITE Land Cover, OS Geographic Reference maps and BTO bird atlas.

# 11.4 Buzzard
*(Buteo buteo)*

## History and current status

Buzzards are soaring raptors that take a wide variety of vertebrate and invertebrate prey – mainly on the ground[2, 3, 4]. They nest in tall trees or occasionally on craggy outcrops, seeking their prey over open ground. In Britain they are generally regarded as being dependent on rabbits, and their numbers and productivity dropped substantially following the 1954 myxomatosis epidemic[5]. Thus, as birds of fragmented habitats, buzzards have probably profited by the pattern of woodlands and fields created by farming.

There is historical evidence that these birds spread throughout most of Britain in the 18th century and their disappearance from much of this range is blamed on game interests[5], although this is impossible to prove[6]. Furthermore, although buzzard numbers have substantially recovered in the west, they have failed to regain their former range in much of England. Gamekeepers are blamed for preventing their spread[1]. However, young buzzards are very slow to colonise new areas and the fact that parts of south-eastern England still have few buzzards may be more a reflection of past status rather than current game-keeping practice[7].

Buzzards take gamebirds but the extent to which they do so, and the seriousness of this predation, has yet to be established. In one study in the uplands, red grouse comprised 11% of all prey remains[4]. In lowland areas of western England, where buzzards are common, the two principal areas of concern for keepers are:

- On reared pheasant shoots, where buzzards perch near release pens and feed on newly released pheasant poults;

- In winter and early spring, when buzzards kill wild partridges because there is little or no escape cover available.

In areas where partridge numbers are very low these could be serious losses. The importance of this predation to wild partridges has not been quantified but we suspect it might be substantial at the margins of the grey partridge range and probably contributes to the range contraction of this species.

## Conservation plan

There is an understandable desire to see buzzards return to much of lowland England in the same

way that they now inhabit arable areas in northern France and Germany. On the Continent, the food chain in farming districts is, however, fundamentally different from that in Britain. There, most arable crops, including grass, contain large numbers of the field vole (*Microtus arvalis*), which provides the staple item of diet for most ground-hunting raptors. In Britain neither managed grass nor cereal crops contain voles. Our own voles occur only in non-farmed habitats. For this reason we think that large areas of arable farmland, dominated in summer by tall cereal crops, have an insufficient prey base to support significant numbers of buzzards. The fact that buzzards were formerly found in eastern counties may be because, before the Second World War, farms were generally mixed enterprises with livestock and cereals.

In our analysis of suitable habitat, we have included only kilometre squares which contain at least one hectare of woodland (suitable for nesting) and which are not associated with urban or suburban land. We have excluded squares that are more than 50% cultivated. The total amounts to 116,000 square kilometres, of which 79,000 square kilometres are within the bird's currently established breeding range. This represents some 68% occupancy. The current buzzard population is estimated to be about 15,000 pairs[8]. By extrapolation, one might therefore expect the habitat to limit this species to some 22,000 pairs if the unused habitat were filled to the same level as in the west. It is clear from the map that south-eastern England and the wooded part of Pennines are the main unoccupied areas most suited to buzzards.

## Research needs

Resolving the conflicts with game interests will be important for this species and most research should be geared towards this. These key questions are paramount:

- What are the factors that make reared game vulnerable to buzzards and what methods can be used to deter attack or lower its chances of success?

- What is the impact of buzzard predation on wild game?

- Can habitats be designed which provide better escape cover for partridges and pheasants in winter?

- How does buzzard density vary with habitat within its existing range and what densities could the currently unoccupied areas support?

- In areas of Europe where there are larger birds of prey (such as golden eagles and eagle owls) are buzzard numbers limited by intra-guild predation?

## Conservation actions

- On pheasant shoots with buzzards, keepers should ensure that release pens do not offer perches where buzzards can sit and pounce on newly released poults. Release sites in areas with buzzards should include dense escape cover.

## Sources and references

1. Gibbons, D. W., Reid, J. B. & Chapman, R. A. (1993) *The New Atlas of Breeding Birds of Britain and Ireland: 1988–1991*. British Trust for Ornithology. T. & A. D. Poyser, London.

2. Tubbs, C. R. (1967) Population study of buzzards in the New Forest during 1962–66. *British Birds*, **60**: 381–95.

3. Newton, I., Davis, P. E. & Davis, J. E. (1982) Ravens and buzzards in relation to sheep farming and forestry in Wales. *Journal of Applied Ecology*, **19**: 681–706.

4. Graham, I. M., Redpath, S. M. & Thirgood, S. J. (1995) The diet and breeding density of common buzzards *Buteo buteo* in relation to indices of prey abundance. *Bird Study*, **42**: 165–73.

5. Moore, N. W. (1957) The past and present status of the buzzard in the British Isles. *British Birds*, **50**: 173–96.

6. Gibbons, D., Gates, S., Green, R. E., Fuller, R. J. & Fuller, R. M. (1994) Buzzards *Buteo buteo* and ravens *Corvus corax* in the uplands of Britain: limits to distribution and abundance. *Ibis*, **137**: S75–S84.

7. Wallis, S. S. & Kenward, R. E. (1995) Movements of radio-tagged common buzzards *Buteo buteo* in their first year. *Ibis*, **137**: 177–82.

8. Stone, B. H., Sears, J., Cranswick, P. A., Gregory, R. D., Gibbons, D. W., Rehfisch, M. M., Aebischer, N. J. & Reid, J. B. (1997) Population estimates of birds in Britain and the United Kingdom. *British Birds*, **90**, 1–22.

**Golden eagle habitat and distribution:** kilometre squares where the topography has a mean slope of greater than 20 degrees. Such topography is most likely to have crags and cliffs which would make suitable nest sites. In the mainland part of the north-western Scottish Highlands this topography fits the actual distribution of birds reasonably well.
**Blue =** areas where eagles are present.
**Green =** other areas of similar topography where eagles are absent.

From OS Topographic Reference map and BTO bird atlas.

# 11.5 Golden eagle
*(Aquila chrysaetos)*

## History and current status

The golden eagle is a large and spectacular bird of prey confined mainly to the Scottish Highlands. It is a soaring species which hunts and kills its prey over open ground, taking medium-sized mammals and birds[1]. Since the prey includes lambs and gamebirds, historically the eagle has been the enemy of shepherd and gamekeeper alike. Consequently, eagle numbers and range were quickly reduced, disappearing from England in the late 18th century and from much of Scotland in the 19th century. At its lowest point, in the late 19th century, there were only about 80 eyries in regular use[2]. Generally, numbers have substantially recovered with the decline in Highland

shepherding and its replacement by deer forest.

Today there are some 422 adult pairs of eagles, as well as other unmated and juvenile birds[3]. Although numbers are currently stable there is variation between regions, ie. there are losses and gains in different local areas throughout the Highlands[3]. Illegal killing and disturbance by gamekeepers remains a problem on some grouse moor areas[4] but other factors, such as afforestation and food supply, are also contributory causes[3].

Eagle nesting density and breeding success is influenced by food supply, the abundance of carrion correlating best with nesting density, and live prey, in the form of mountain hares and grouse, having the most effect on breeding success[5]. Where there is annual variation in prey abundance, particularly as a result of the natural cycles of mountain hare and red grouse, eagle breeding success varies too. However, after a persistent food shortage, nesting density also declines[4]. Access to food is also important and commercial afforestation restricts the hunting ground available to eagles.

Apart from food and freedom from disturbance, eagles need an adequate nest site. Sometimes these can be in old pines but, since eyries can weigh several hundred kilograms[1], these must be in substantial trees. More typically, nests in Scotland are on inaccessible cliffs and crags.

## Conservation plan

In the Highlands golden eagles appear to be distributed throughout the suitable habitat. However, they are less numerous in the eastern Highlands than in the western. There are very few pairs outside the Highlands and human interference in these regions may be preventing the species from spreading.

The map suggests there may be areas, especially in Wales and the Lake District, where the landscape is suitable for eagles. Indeed there are records from the 18th and 19th centuries which indicate that eagles were once more widely dispersed in upland areas[2]. Today, however, the food supply combination of red deer carrion, mountain hares and red grouse is unique to the Highlands, so it might be unrealistic to expect good numbers of eagles to become established outside Scotland. We think the possibility of extending the range of the golden eagle warrants investigation.

## Research needs

In our view, the basic ecology of this bird is understood and the main emphasis of future work should be to devise conservation strategies to:

- Encourage the species to spread south from its current range.

- Improve its productivity in eastern Scotland, especially on grouse moors.

Additionally:

- A greater understanding of intra-guild predation among raptor species is required, eg. whether or not eagles have a limiting effect on the densities of smaller birds of prey, such as the buzzard or the hen harrier.

## Conservation actions

- Conservation agencies should bear in mind that this species is vulnerable to accidental as well as deliberate disturbance when considering increased access to upland areas.

## Sources and references

1. Watson, J. (1997) *The Golden Eagle*. T. & A. D. Poyser, London.

2. Holloway, S. (1996) *The Historical Atlas of Breeding Birds in Britain and Ireland: 1875–1900*. British Trust for Ornithology. T. & A. D. Poyser, London.

3. Green, R. E. (1996) The status of the golden eagle in Britain. *Bird Study*, **43:** 20–7.

4. Watson, A., Payne, S. & Rae, R. (1989) Golden eagles *Aquila chrysaetos*: land use and food in northeast Scotland. *Ibis*, 131: 336–48.

5. Watson, J., Rae, S. R. & Stillman, R. (1992) Nesting density and breeding success of golden eagles in relation to food supply in Scotland. *Journal of Animal Ecology*, **61:** 543–50.

# 11.6 Peregrine falcon
## *(Falco peregrinus)*

## History and current status

The peregrine is a large swift-flying falcon which specialises in killing medium to large birds on the wing. Because of the spectacular way in which its stoops to take flying gamebirds and waterfowl, it has always been the most prized of all falconry species. Since medieval times peregrines have been taken from the wild and trained for sport. Although it is not clear to what extent this affected numbers, it has been suggested that the bird's preference for nesting on inaccessible cliffs meant that many eyries escaped undisturbed[1]. In the days when falconry was a nobleman's sport, peregrines were protected to provide birds for it. Although peregrines were not subject to the effects of either persecution or pesticides, it is not clear whether they were substantially more common then than they are today. Peregrines are territorial and their distribution is largely limited by the availability of suitable nesting cliffs. Indeed, breeding numbers are currently estimated from the occupancy rates of traditional eyrie nesting sites.

With the advent of game preservation in the 19th century, numbers were probably significantly reduced by gamekeepers using poison, traps and the gun[3]. However, their impact on this bird was much less than on other species, such as harriers, which nest on the ground.

At the beginning of the Second World War, the then War Department took steps to reduce peregrine numbers in an effort to protect carrier pigeons, which were being used to send messages across the Channel from northern France to

*Estimates of changes in numbers of breeding pairs of peregrine falcons in Britain. Based on occupancy of known breeding sites[1,2].*

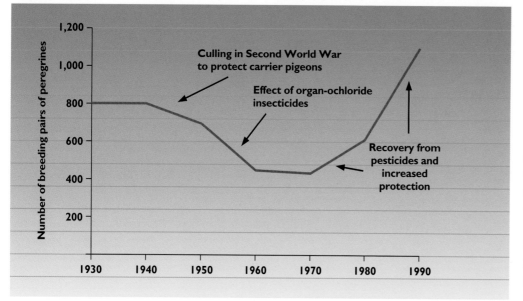

England. Naturally officials feared that coastal peregrines would intercept these returning pigeons. Even though some 600 peregrines were culled the overall population reduction was thought to have been only about 13%[1].

The most severe reduction in peregrine numbers came in the 1950s, with the introduction of organo-chlorine seed dressings. Substances such as dieldrin and dichlorodiphenyltrichlorethane (DDT) reached such concentrations in these top predators that they were poisoned directly and their breeding success was curtailed as a result of egg-shell thinning[4].

Peregrines are significant gamebird-predators, easily capable of taking adult grouse[5], partridges, pheasants and ducks. Peregrines depend on killing these and other large birds, such as pigeons and corvids, for the bulk of their diet. However, it is principally on grouse moors that peregrines are perceived to have a major detrimental impact on game stocks and where gamekeepers are blamed for the continued persecution of this species. The recently completed Joint Raptor Study showed that grouse losses to peregrines can be heavy, particularly in winter and spring, when these and other raptors can account for some 50% of all predation losses[6], although the effect on grouse density is still not known. However, the territorial nature of peregrine breeding means that peregrine numbers do not concentrate in areas with good grouse stocks. As a consequence they do not have the same limiting effect on production as the semi-colonial hen harrier.

## Conservation plan

In our view, the conservation status of the peregrine falcon, with 1,185 breeding pairs[2], is satisfactory and we do not believe that positive actions are required to build numbers further. However, in spite of the damage these birds clearly inflict on upland game stocks, and almost certainly on racing pigeon interests, we do not think that any kind of licensed cull of peregrines could be justified for two main reasons:

- The mobile nature of peregrines in winter and their territorial behaviour in summer suggest that birds killed would be quickly replaced by others, nullifying any benefits unless further peregrines were removed.

- To have any overall benefit to grouse production, culling would have to be on such a large scale that it would significantly reduce peregrine numbers and threaten their currently healthy population status. Currently, the illegal killing of adult peregrines does not seem to be a significant conservation problem as their adult survival rate is very high[7].

- We think there is little alternative at present except for grouse moors simply to sustain losses caused by peregrines. This will inevitably result in lower overall bags than in the past, which will, in turn, have an impact on the moors' economic viability and value. We therefore need to explore ways whereby the Government can financially support conservation actions in the uplands (such as heather burning), which can be undertaken by gamekeepers and thus aid the current management infrastructure on upland properties, as suggested by many Non-Government organisations[8].

## Research needs

Key questions include:

- Are different habitat management methods, such as the provision of escape cover, helpful in reducing raptor losses?

- Can the encouragement of alternative prey species (such as feral pigeons) reduce predation losses of grouse or will it increase them?

## Conservation actions

Government conservation agencies should discuss with conservation and other bodies what conservation measures could be financially supported in upland areas where losses to peregrines are currently reducing grouse revenues.

## Sources and references

1. Ratcliffe, D. (1980) *The Peregrine Falcon*. T. & A. D. Poyser, London.

2. Stone, B. H., Sears, J., Cranswick, P. A., Gregory, R. D., Gibbons, D. W., Rehfisch, M. M., Aebischer, N. J. & Reid, J. B. (1997) Population estimates of birds in Britain and the United Kingdom. *British Birds*, **90**: 1–22.

3. Holloway, S. (1996) *The Historical Atlas of Breeding Birds in Britain and Ireland: 1875–1900*. British Trust for Ornithology. T. & A. D. Poyser, London.

4. Newton, I. (1979) *Population Ecology of Raptors*. T. & A. D. Poyser, Berkhamsted, Hertfordshire.

5. Mearns, R. (1983) The diet of the peregrine *Falco peregrinus* in south Scotland during the breeding season. *Bird Study*, **30**: 81–90.

6. Redpath, S. & Thirgood, S. (1997) *Birds of Prey and Red Grouse. Report of the Joint Raptor Study*. HMSO, London.

7. Mearns, R. & Newton, I. (1984) Turnover and dispersal in a peregrine *Falco peregrinus* population. *Ibis*, **126**: 347–55.

8. Anon. (1998) *A Future for Grouse Moors: A Call to Action*. The Hawk and Owl Trust, National Trust, Royal Society for the Protection of Birds, Scottish Raptor Study Groups, Wales Raptor Study Group, North of England Raptor and Upland Bird Study Groups, Wildlife Trusts (UK), Scottish Ornithologists' Club and Worldwide Fund for Nature. Sandy, Bedfordshire.

# 12 Other predatory birds

Many predatory birds, especially most of the Corvidae, are relatively common and have become more abundant in recent decades. For some birds, predation on livestock, fish and other species is slight but, where it is significant, The Game Conservancy Trust believes landowners should continue to be allowed to cull these birds locally to reduce damage.

# 12.1 Cormorant
*(Phalacrocorax carbo)*

## History and current status

These large, fish-eating birds have always been primarily, although not exclusively, a coastal species in Britain. They need protected nest sites to breed and tend to form colonies on islands or cliffs. Inland they nest in trees. Their breeding distribution is biased to western coasts and they are largely absent along the shores of south-eastern England and East Anglia. Unlike their close relative, the shag, cormorants are willing to move inland – especially in winter, when they frequently turn up on rivers and lakes. Cormorants are predominantly bottom-feeders so they stick close to the coast-line and do not fish far out to sea.

Historical records indicate that cormorants have been infrequent visitors to inland waters in winter and occasionally small breeding colonies have sprung up – presumably where fish have been plentiful and where they have been left alone by fishermen. Inland colonies appear to have been more frequent in Ireland[1], while some very large colonies have become established on parts of the Continent.

The bulk of Britain's breeding population of some 7,200 pairs is still coastal, but at a few inland sites breeding numbers have expanded rapidly. In comparison, the much more numerous shag has a breeding population of some 38,000 pairs. The cormorant wintering population of some 20,000 is also principally coastal but it is more dispersed. Inland, birds have always been present in very small numbers and their population has probably been firmly held in check by shooting[1], as well as by the poor food availability on most inland waters.

In the last two decades inland birds have become noticeably more numerous. This stems from the protection afforded them under the Wildlife and Countryside Act (1981)[2], as well as from a substantial increase in the food supply on inland waters due to fish stocking for angling – especially trout.

## Conservation plan

The increase in inland cormorants has caused widespread concern and anger among anglers, including both still-water trout and coarse fishermen. Although scientific studies on the impact of these birds on fisheries are few[2], and many are inadequate[3], it seems that damage can be con-

siderable. They consume large numbers of fish and wound many others.

Particularly vulnerable are migrating salmon smolts, as well as stocked trout and shoaling species of coarse fish, such as roach, rudd and dace. The state of knowledge has been reviewed in a recent report to the Ministry of Agriculture, Fisheries, and Food[3], which clearly concluded that more research was needed to understand fully the predation effects. In addition, the authors under-lined the distinction that needs to be made between two types of predation mortality, namely:

- Compensatory mortality, where other mortality is reduced which compensates for the predation;

- Non-compensatory mortality, where preda-tion losses lead to a direct reduction in pop-ulation.

The latter is clearly more serious and has been shown to occur where cormorants prey on migrat-ing salmon smolts[4]. In this case there was a direct consequential loss of returning adult salmon of 51–66%. In other cases, where there is apparent compensation, such as that shown on some Swiss trout and grayling fisheries[5], there appears to be no reduction in fish stocks. However, even where losses are fully compensatory, there can be a loss of yield to the fishery because a reduced catch by anglers may form part of the compensation.

Opinions on this bird have polarised and a sensible conservation strategy for this species will inevitably be unpopular with either anglers or bird-watchers. It is our view that conservation strategies should be based on the best conservation science and that proper research studies, if not already conducted, need to be set in place. However, in the case of inland cormorants, we need an interim strategy (based on the precautionary principle) until adequate research has been done.

In most instances, the precautionary principle is invoked to protect existing species and habitats from the unknown effects of proposed development. However, in this case, the cormorant itself is the new agent acting on inland fish populations not previously subject to such intense predation in recent times. For this reason, the principle should operate in favour of the fish and fisheries, and river-keepers and others should be allowed to control cormorants without restriction on inland waters. Adequate numbers of these birds need to be retained only in areas where research projects are being conducted.

In our view it would probably be desirable to restrict cormorants to coastal areas for the foreseeable future. This would not undermine the overall conservation status of the cormorant, but would serve to protect valuable trout and coarse fisheries from terminal decline.

## Research needs

The key research question is:

- To what extent do cormorants affect populations of fish and what are the economic implications for fisheries. Some of this research is currently in progress and being funded by Government. Three types of fishery appear to be vulnerable and need investigation:

(a) Wild salmon rivers with a substantial smolt run which are in the neighbourhood of large cormorant colonies. We need to know whether or not the results found for the River Bush in Northern Ireland[4] are typical of the damage that might be expected.

(b) Coarse fisheries which depend on populations of small shoaling fish in both still waters and rivers. Anecdotal evidence suggests that cormorants essentially fish-out these waters and then move on. The fishery owner then has either to abandon the fishery or restock.

(c) On stocked trout lakes, cormorants not only consume stocked fish, which then have to be replaced, but also wound many others and reputedly prevent trout from feeding at the surface. This effectively precludes fly-fishing, which is usually the economic basis for the fishery in the first place.

## Conservation actions

- Until new research clearly demonstrates that cormorants have only a minor impact on fisheries, the Government should allow legal control of this species where fishery interests perceive damage and only retain full protection for the bird in areas within a limited distance of the coastline.

## Sources and references

1. Holloway, S. (1996) *The Historical Atlas of Breeding Birds in Britain and Ireland: 1875–1900*. British Trust for Ornithology. T. & A. D. Poyser, London.

2. Kirby, J. S., Holmes, J. S. & Sellers, R. M. (1996) Cormorants *Phalacrocorax carbo* as fish predators: An appraisal of their conservation and management in Great Britain. *Biological Conservation*, 75: 191–9.

3. Russel, I. C., Dare, P. J., Eaton, D. R. & Armstrong, J. D. (1996) *Assessment of the Problem of Fish-eating Birds in Inland Fisheries in England and Wales*. Directorate of Fisheries Research, Lowestoft.

4. Kennedy, G. J. A. & Greer, J. E. (1988) Predation by cormorants, *Phalacrocorax carbo* (L.), on the salmonid populations of an Irish river. *Aquaculture and Fisheries Management*, 19: 159–70.

5. Suter, W. (1995) The effect of predation by wintering cormorants *Phalacrocorax carbo* on grayling *Thymallus thymallus* and trout (Salmonidae) populations: Two case studies from Swiss rivers. *Journal of Applied Ecology*, 32: 29–46.

# 12.2 The crow family
## *(Corvidae)*

## Current status

With the exception of the chough and the raven, the corvids are widespread and common species. They have long been subject to human control by farmers and gamekeepers in order to prevent damage to crops, livestock and game. This control has relaxed in recent decades and we have seen a substantial increase in the numbers of some species as a consequence.

### 12.2.1 Magpie *(Pica pica)*

As with most of the common predator species, the magpie has a history intricately bound up with human land use and with human attitudes towards pests. It is generally believed that magpie numbers at the beginning of this century were suppressed following a history of intense culling. The magpie had been a 'bounty' bird since 1566[1], was conspicuous and its nest was easily located. It was easily destroyed using poisoned eggs, which in one action appeared to both prove its guilt as a predator and carry out its sentence.

Use of poisons was made illegal (except under licence) by the Protection of Animals Act 1911 and then by the Protection of Animals (Scotland) Act 1912. Magpie populations in Britain began to increase noticeably in the 1930s and blossomed during the 1940s, when magpies began to colonise suburban habitats in earnest[2]. A hiatus in rural areas during the 1950s was

attributed to the use of organo-chlorines in agriculture but Common Bird Census (CBC) data indicate a continued increase in populations since 1960[3]. These trends are reflected in National Game-Bag Census statistics[4].

As with other common predators, such as the fox and carrion crow, it is impossible to say to what extent this modern increase can be explained by reduced culling and exploitation of new habitats. However, magpie numbers have increased throughout Europe during the same period[2]. The British magpie population is now estimated at over 590,000 territorial pairs[5], representing a substantial increase over 19th-century levels.

The impact of the magpie itself as a predator is also unresolved. One study found population declines of songbirds were not related to the increase in magpie numbers[6]. On the other hand, in our Salisbury Plain experiment, the magpie was one of the suite of common predators whose control led to substantially improved grey partridge productivity[7]. It is undoubtedly an egg- and chick-predator, and songbird-lovers unable to stomach visible losses often take up magpie control. However, no research has yet estimated

its impact on either gamebird or songbird populations, except on a very local scale[8, 9], nor the cost of failing to control its numbers compared with other predator species.

Magpies, like other corvid birds, exhibit two distinct types of behaviour[2]:

- Pairs defend their own exclusive territory when breeding;

- Non-breeding birds gather in loose flocks to forage.

These two behaviour patterns almost certainly

## Larsen trap

By far the most successful tool for crow and magpie management is the Larsen trap, used either with food bait or preferably with a live call-bird (decoy). Use of a call-bird vastly increases the target-specificity of these traps. In trials, only 1% of over 10,000 captures were non-target birds and, since this is a live-capture trap, non-target captures can be readily released. Placed within the territory of a breeding pair,

the call-bird emulates an intruder and territory-holders are captured as they try to drive it away. Owing to a natural hierarchy among corvid species, carrion crows and occasionally rooks and jackdaws may be caught when using a magpie call-bird, although carrion crows are usually only caught when a carrion crow call-bird is used.

As magpies are conspicuous birds, monitoring the occupancy of territories is not a problem. However, there is often a large local reservoir of

non-breeding birds eager to take up vacated territories, so that culled birds are rapidly replaced and replacement birds must be actively removed throughout the gamebird breeding season.

Important properties of the Larsen trap include its size (for ease of handling) and low cost, and the fact that fresh captures can be used as call-birds in other traps. Together these mean that trapping effort can escalate quickly, allowing a short, focused (and therefore efficient), local spring/summer campaign.

result in different feeding strategies and may result from the availability of different food sources.

## 12.2.2 Jackdaw (*Corvus monedula*)

In 1900 the jackdaw was apparently common throughout most of Britain, but both anecdotal evidence and CBC data since 1963 suggest that it has increased in numbers throughout the century. Game-Bag data, however, suggest a four-fold decline in numbers killed on shooting estates during the late 1950s and 1960s, which exactly parallels that of the rook[4]. Given the close foraging relationship of jackdaws and rooks in many areas, and the ecological contrast between these and other corvid species, it seems reasonable to speculate that the Game-Bag trend records a common sensitivity to an agricultural practice during that period – eduction in ley farming. Latest estimates put the population at 390,000 territories in Britain[5].

The diet of the jackdaw most closely resembles that of the magpie[10] and, indeed, size and bill shape are very similar in the two species. Like the magpie, jackdaws form territorial pairs to breed, although they nest in holes rather than building twig nests and are at all times more inclined to join flocks of other jackdaws or rooks to forage.

The jackdaw is a known predator of gamebird and songbird eggs. The contribution of these to its diet is undetermined, as is its impact on these prey populations, which is thought to be much less significant than that of the carrion crow.

## 12.2.3 Rook (*Corvus frugilegus*)

The rook population of Britain probably increased considerably during the 18th and early 19th centuries[11], beginning at the time of enclosures and wide-scale tree planting and continuing into the present century. During the late 1950s and 1960s it suffered a severe decline – reflected in shooting bags – which was almost certainly due to the widespread use of organo-chlorine pesticides. The loss of nest sites through Dutch elm disease occurred too late to have played a part in this decline[12, 13]. Rook numbers remained low until the mid-1970s, when a steady recovery began[3]. Latest estimates put the population at 853,000–857,000 pairs in Britain in 1980[5, 14].

Although primarily invertebrate-feeders, at least some rooks are egg-predators, as can be testified by anyone who has run traps baited with eggs near a rook colony. Partridge nest record books from gamekeepered estates in the early 20th century demonstrate that rooks can be a frequent and serious predators of partridge eggs. There is therefore some justification for limiting rook numbers for the purposes of wild game conservation, although we know nothing about the prevalence of egg-eating within the rook population. Unlike magpies, carrion crows and jackdaws, rooks are flock feeders throughout the year, showing territorial behaviour only in defence of the nest structure itself. This may mean that, in general, they are behaviourally less suited to detecting nests of ground-nesting birds.

The rook can be an agricultural pest, but is perceived on balance to do more good than harm to agriculture because of the number of pest invertebrates it eats. Thus, for the farmer, scaring rooks from vulnerable crops is probably more appropriate than population control. The rook was formerly considered a challenging quarry species in both falconry and shooting[15] and the young were an acceptable food species. Fledglings are still shot (with a 0.22 rifle, air rifle or shotgun), both to eat and to limit numbers. Recorded bags of rooks therefore tend to reflect population changes in response to the agricultural environment.

One important line of research is to discover whether egg-predation is a standard in-bred behaviour of all rooks or a matter of individual specialisation. The answer will influence the choice of appropriate management techniques.

## 12.2.4 Carrion crow and hooded crow (*Corvus corone corone* and *C. c. cornix*)

Hooded and carrion crows are northern and southern forms of a single species, with a zone of hybridisation between them[16]. This zone has shifted northwards since the mid-19th century, possibly in response to warmer winters[17]. Hybrids, despite being fertile, are generally supposed to be less prolific than pure strains, although field data contradict this[18]. The two subspecies are very similar in habits (although the hooded crow is better adapted to cold wet conditions) and, from the management point of view, can be considered together.

Like the magpie, the crow has been culled as a pest of agriculture for centuries[1]. During the 19th century, a significant work-force of professional gamekeepers, combined with effective methods (especially poisoned eggs), intensified the scale of culling. By 1900 crows were uncommon over large parts of Britain[11] and the regional abundance of crows mirrored that of gamekeepers. Since the beginning of the 1940s, there has been a general increase in abundance in all regions[3], which probably represents a recovery from earlier suppression. According to CBC data, numbers more than doubled between 1962 and 1988. There is some evidence that the resurgence of crows has been slower in the south and east of Britain than elsewhere. According to the data available, similar pronounced increases have occurred in Ireland and the Netherlands, but not in Denmark and Sweden[19, 20]. The British population of crows is estimated at 970,000 territorial pairs[5].

The crow was less affected than other corvid birds by changes in farming since the 1950s probably because of its lower dependence on insect food[3,21]. Like magpies, crows have colonised many suburban habitats. Although breeding success is habitat specific, populations can move freely between, for instance, upland and lowland habitats. Breeding success is highest in sheep country and high sheep densities provide substantial food sources.

Like magpies, crows behave either as territorial breeding pairs or join flocks of non-territorial non-breeding birds. Crows are aggressive and dominant towards magpies and are indeed the major natural predator of magpie nests apart from man[22, 23, 24]. They have even been known to kill adult magpies[2].

As with the magpie, the specific impact of the crow as a predator is unquantified. Again, in our Salisbury Plain experiment, the crow was one of the common predators whose control led to substantially improved grey partridge productivity[7]. As far as diet is concerned, the crow is considerably more carnivorous than the magpie[25] and its impact on gamebirds is likely to be far greater than that of the magpie. Unfortunately, the likelihood of compensatory predation by one predator species if another is absent or removed makes comparative research of this kind extremely difficult.

## Control of crows

Larsen traps, particularly modified forms with side-entrances, are an efficient tool for the control of territorial crows. Where conditions allow, small-bore rifles can also be used. Effort should be con-

centrated during spring and summer when both predator and prey are breeding.

On upland areas particularly, flock birds may be present in much larger numbers but are more difficult to catch because they are not motivated by territorial behaviour. Undertaking to control a large flock is an altogether more ambitious task than selective removal of territorial birds. Large cage-traps with provision (perches, shelter, food and water) for housing a small group of call-birds attract further birds to join them through the flocking instinct. The use of carrion crows as decoys makes either Larsen traps or larger cage-traps almost entirely specific.

Carrion from dead stock or wild mammals should not be used as bait or food in any cage-trap, as this would contravene the Animal By-Products Order 1992.

While culling territorial crows in most arable farming areas has a local impact and benefit, it seems likely that in other areas – particularly upland areas where territories are few and flocks large – any attempt to reduce crow numbers can only be a regional issue.

## Conservation plan

All bird species enjoy the basic status of legal protection under the EEC Birds Directive, although member countries may derogate from this provision in the case of certain common pest species. The facility to cull corvids and other pest birds using approved methods is provided under British legislation by this derogation.

Because wording of the Wildlife and Countryside Act (1981) was ambiguous in places, use of the Larsen trap with a call-bird is specifically allowed by an Open General Licence from Department of the Environment, Transport and Regions. This requires annual renewal at the discretion of the Secretary of State.

The above provisions are satisfactory provided they are not changed by whim. Continued justification for control certainly requires monitoring of population size and culls, but as time goes by it will become increasingly important to demonstrate that culling is beneficial.

## Research needs

The following areas need to be addressed:

- The predatory role of the different corvid species on songbirds and gamebirds needs to be more precisely quantified, both within predator communities and during control of other common predator species. It is in nobody's interest to engage in unprofitable control effort.

- It would be useful to understand the influence of urban areas on the magpie population of surrounding rural areas.

- The most promising non-lethal methods of controlling corvid predation should be explored. Given that some are territorial birds, a viable non-lethal technique may be both more efficient and publicly acceptable.

## Conservation actions

- Given the healthy status of these species and the need to prevent damage, we think the existing arrangements allowing authorised persons to exert local control by trapping and shooting should continue. As yet there is insufficient evidence to warrant concerted regional control on a wide scale for any of them.

- To satisfy EU Directives that the conservation status of pest birds is not threatened by culling, it is necessary to continue to monitor – in all regions – corvid population status through the Breeding Bird Survey (carried out by the British Trust for Ornithology); and the annual cull using National Game-Bag Census data (from The Game Conservancy Trust).

# Sources and references

1. Dannenfeldt, K.H. (1982) The control of vertebrate pests in Renaissance agriculture. *Agricultural History*, 56, 542–59.

2. Birkhead, T. R. (1991) *The Magpies: The Ecology and Behaviour of Black-billed and Yellow-billed Magpies*. T. & A. D. Poyser, London.

3. Marchant, J. H., Hudson, R., Carter, S. P. & Whittington, P. (1990) *Population Trends in British Breeding Birds*. British Trust for Ornithology, Tring, Hertfordshire.

4. Tapper, S. C. (1992) *Game Heritage: An Ecological Review from Shooting and Gamekeeping Records*. Game Conservancy Limited, Fordingbridge, Hampshire.

5. Stone, B. H., Sears, J., Cranswick, P. A., Gregory, R. D., Gibbons, D. W., Rehfisch, M. M., Aebischer, N. J. & Reid, J. B. (1997) Population estimates of birds in Britain and the United Kingdom. *British Birds*, 90, 1–22.

6. Gooch, S., Baillie, S. R. & Birkhead, T. R. (1991) Magpie *Pica pica* and songbird populations. Retrospective investigation of trends in population density and breeding success. *Journal of Applied Ecology*; 28: 1068–86.

7. Tapper, S. C., Potts, G. R. & Brockless, M. (1996) The effect of an experimental reduction in predation pressure on the breeding success and population density of grey partridges (*Perdix perdix*). *Journal of Applied Ecology*, 33: 965–78.

8. Groom, D. W. (1993) Magpie *Pica pica* predation on blackbird *Turdus merula* nests in urban areas. *Bird Study*; 40: 55–62.

9. Miller, A. P. (1988) Nest predation and nest site choice in passerine birds in habitat patches of different size – a study of magpies and blackbirds. *Oikos*, 53: 215–21.

10. Holyoak, D. (1968) A comparative study of the food of some British Corvidae. *Bird Study*, 15: 147–53.

11. Holloway, S. (1996) *The Historical Atlas of Breeding Birds in Britain and Ireland: 1875–1900*. British Trust for Ornithology. T. & A. D. Poyser, London.

12. Tapper, S. C. (1981) The effects of farming and Dutch elm disease on corvids. *The Game Conservancy Review of 1980*, 18: 98–101.

13. Osborne, P. (1982) Some effects of Dutch Elm disease on nesting farmland birds. *Bird Study*, 29: 2–16.

14. Sage, B. L. & Whittington, P. A. (1985) The 1980 sample of rookeries. *Bird Study*: 32, 77–81.

15. Blaine, D. P. (1858) *An Encyclopedia of Rural Sports*. Longmans, Brown & Co., London.

16. Picozzi, N. (1976) Hybridization of carrion and hooded crows *Corvus c. corone* and *Corvus c. cornix* in northeastern Scotland. *Ibis*, 118: 254–7.

17. Cook, A. (1975) Changes in the carrion/hooded crow hybrid zone and the possible importance of climate. *Bird Study*, 22:165–8.

18. Kryukov, A. P. & Blinov, V. N. (1989) Interaction of hooded and carrion crows (*Corvus cornix* L. and *Corvus corone* L.) in the zone of sympatry and hybridization: is there a selection against hybrids? *Zhurnal Obshchei Biologii*, 1:12 8–35.

19. Hustings, F. (1988) *European Monitoring Studies of Breeding Birds*. A report of Samenwerkunde Organisaties Vogelonderzoek Nederland (SOVON), Beek, Netherlands.

20. Anon. (1989) *Ynglefuglerapport 1988*. Dansk Ornitologisk Forenings Fugleregistreringsgruppe, Copenhagen.

21. Prestt, I. (1965) An enquiry into the recent breeding status of some of the smaller birds of prey and crows in Britain. *Bird Study*, 12: 196–221.

22. Baeyens, G. (1981) Magpie breeding success and carrion crow interference. *Ardea*, 69: 125–39.

23. Ellenberg, H. (1983) Habicht und beute. *Allgemeine Forstzeitschrift (München)*, 44: 1195–201.

24. Balanÿa, G. (1984) Le déterminisme du succès de la reproduction chez une population de pies bavardes (*Pica pica*). *Gibier Faune Sauvage*, 1 (4): 5–25.

25. Holyoak, D. (1974) Territorial and feeding behaviour of the magpie. *Bird Study*, 21: 117–28.

# Appendix 1 Mapping methods

In order to draw up a set of conservation plans for different birds, mammals and fish, we needed a simple basis for comparing the status and distribution of each species across the whole of Britain. Furthermore, for *A Question of Balance* we also wanted a method of assessing the potential expansion of some of these species in terms of abundance and distribution. Ultimately this is limited by the size of Britain itself, but only in our imagination can we plant the whole country with Scots pine and have capercaillie living in every county. We wanted a sensible and practical approach which would give us realistic conservation targets for each species and which could be accommodated within the current basic pattern of agriculture.

The basis for comparison which we have adopted is the Countryside Information System (CIS). This is a computer program developed jointly by the Natural Environment Research Council (NERC) and Department of the Environment, Transport and Regions and issued in 1995. It draws heavily on research carried out by the Institute of Terrestrial Ecology. The program displays database information on Britain's landscape down to the level of a one-kilometre square (100 hectares, or about 250 acres). Thus, for the purposes of comparison, everything was mapped to either include or exclude selected squares.

The databases contain various information about each square, eg. the proportion of woodland or the average height above sea level. Thus, by relating this information to the habitat requirements of each species, we could map out where an animal might be expected to occur. At its simplest, we would not expect to find capercaillie in squares with no Scots pine woods. For other species we might make a more precise definition, eg. we could select all squares containing at least 20% arable ground and 5% woodland that did not, at the same time, contain any suburban or urban area, motorways or 'A' roads. However, habitat definitions finer than this, eg. details of quality, such as the availability of dead grass for partridge nesting, is really beyond the system's scope.

Within the CIS two alternative strategies are available:

- **Census data.** These provide information for every square in Britain and then map the specified habitat requirements directly. At present

*Comparison of the distribution of roads using Ordnance Survey Census data* (left) *and*
*Countryside Survey 1990 sample data extrapolated to Land Class* (right).

*Comparison of the distribution of deciduous woodlands using the Institute of Terrestrial Ecology's Land Cover map (left) and Countryside Survey 1990 sample data of broad-leaved woodlands extrapolated to Land Class (right).*

there are sets provided by Ordnance Survey which give the essential features found on a map of 1:100,000 scale, as well as topography. There is also a Land Cover data-set (provided by the Institute of Terrestrial Ecology) which has been derived from satellite imagery (Landsat). This distinguishes broad habitat categories, eg. tilled land, grassland, coniferous and deciduous woodlands. There are problems in interpreting some of these data which imposes limitations on how finely some habitats can be differentiated. The satellite imagery has been derived from several fly-bys which occurred in winter and summer. Data from these images were processed automatically but, because the fly-bys occurred at different times, different cover types are not always picked out consistently. Furthermore the range of different habitats that can be recognised is rather limited.

- **Sampled data.** These are based on detailed habitat surveys that were undertaken for a large number of squares during the Countryside Surveys of 1978, 1984 and 1990. Details of hedgerows, stone walls and crops being grown were all recorded in these surveys. In order to produce a distribution map of one of these sampled characters one has to use the land classification system developed by the Institute of Terrestrial Ecology. This separates Britain into 32 different land classes which were derived from a statistical analysis of the main physical and geographical features of all squares in Britain. Therefore, to map a habitat feature, average values are calculated for each land class from samples taken during the Countryside Survey. Because the land classes themselves are mapped to the nearest square kilometre and are often fragmented,

maps produced using land classes appear to show a detailed distribution of a particular feature. In reality they don't. They show an extrapolation from the sample, which assumes that the pattern of abundance will conform to the land class classification.

To demonstrate the difference between these approaches, we show maps of the same habitat features produced by these two forms of mapping.

- In the first example (page 275), typical Ordnance Survey census information (roads) is compared with the extrapolated sample based on land classes. In this example one can see a very broad similarity in that the middle and south of England have lots of roads compared with Wales, the Pennines or the Highlands. However, beyond that, it is clear that local patterns are overlooked or over-simplified by the land class mapping. For example, the map suggests that Staffordshire has few roads, in fact as few as the North York Moors, while Leeds and Bradford appear to be more road-free than anywhere in East Anglia.

- In the second example (page 276), Land Cover census data obtained from satellite imagery (deciduous woodland) is compared with the sample data of broad-leaved woodlands extrapolated to land classes. Again, although there is a similarity between the two maps, it is clear that the land-class approach tends to produce an over-polarised view and eliminates a lot of detail that can be picked out from the Landsat data. Open-country areas, such as the South Downs and Salisbury Plain, do not appear on the land class map and are lumped in with the heavily wooded areas of the

Weald and the New Forest.

In our analyses for *A Question of Balance* we have adopted the census approach using both the Ordnance Survey and the Land Cover data-sets. We believe it to be the most flexible approach and the one most likely to reflect the true geographical pattern of the habitats in which we are interested.

We have therefore constructed the habitat map for individual species which we think best shows each animal's requirements. In some cases this is sketchy and some animals are more cosmopolitan than others. In some cases we have been able to define good and poor habitats. In other cases an animal's geographical range only partially covers the entire extent of the available habitat. In these cases we may discuss why this should be and whether or not encouraging the animal to spread would be appropriate.

An important feature of the CIS system is that, during the course of mapping the kilometre squares, the program keeps a tally of exactly how many squares have been selected. Given certain average densities of a game population, it then becomes quite straightforward to estimate a total population figure and to forecast the effects of various conservation measures on this figure.

However, our knowledge is much better for some species than for others and so our projections sometimes have to be highly qualified and may be speculative. In other cases the scientific knowledge may be so sparse that we have been unable to set any serious conservation targets.

Finally, we should stress that, in all our plans, we have not assumed or advocated an increase in the extent of game management for shooting or indeed for any other purpose. We have assumed the existing level of interest in game as remaining stable or changing only slowly.

Key

a = adults
f = nesting females
m = displaying males
p = pairs or territories with pairs
r = adult fish in rivers
w = wintering number

# Appendix 2 Summary of the conservation and legal status of the main game and predator species

| English name | Latin name | Population estimate | Trend | Game interest | Main legal statute | Notes |
|---|---|---|---|---|---|---|
| **Brown hare** | *Lepus europaeus* | 800,000 a | Stable | Shooting & hunting quarry. Minor pest. | Hares Preservation Act Ground Game Act | Not for sale 1 March – 31 July. |
| **Mountain hare** | *Lepus timidus* | 350,000 a | Stable | Minor upland quarry & minor pest. | Hares Preservation Act Ground Game Act | Not for sale 1 March – 31 July. |
| **Rabbit** | *Oryctolagus cuniculus* | 37 million a | Increasing | Major agricultural pest species. | Ground Game Act | – |
| **Muntjac deer** | *Muntiacus reevesi* | 40,000 a | Increasing | Minor quarry. Forest & woodland damage. | Wildlife & Countryside Act Schedule 9 Part 1 | No close season. Year-round breeder. |
| **Fallow deer** | *Dama dama* | 100,000 a | Stable | Stalking quarry. Forest damage. | Deer Act Statutory close seasons | – |
| **Red deer** | *Cervus elaphus* | 360,000 a | Increasing | Important stalking quarry. Forest damage. | Deer Act Statutory close seasons | – |
| **Sika deer** | *Cervus nippon* | 11,500 a | Increasing | Stalking quarry. Forest damage. | Deer Act Statutory close seasons | – |

| English name | Latin name | Population estimate | Trend | Game interest | Main legal statute | Notes |
|---|---|---|---|---|---|---|
| **Roe deer** | *Capreolus capreolus* | 500,000 a | Increasing | Stalking quarry. Forest damage. | Deer Act Statutory close seasons | – |
| **Red grouse** | *Lagopus lagopus scoticus* | 250,000 p | Declining | Valuable upland gamebird. | Game Act Statutory close season | – |
| **Black grouse** | *Tetrao tetrix* | 6,500 m | Declining | Valuable gamebird. | Game Act Statutory close season | – |
| **Capercaillie** | *Tetrao urogallus* | 2,200 a | Declining | Trophy gamebird. | Wildlife & Countryside Act Schedule 2 Part I | Voluntary shooting ban in force. |
| **Red-legged partridge** | *Alectoris rufa* | 170,000 p | Stable | Important farm gamebird. | Game Act Statutory close season | – |
| **Grey partridge** | *Perdix perdix* | 145,000 p | Stable | Important farm gamebird. | Game Act Statutory close season | – |
| **Pheasant** | *Phasianus colchicus* | 1.5 million f | Stable | Important lowland gamebird. | Game Act Statutory close season | – |
| **Stock dove** | *Columba oenas* | 240,000 p | Increasing | Protected farmland bird. | Wildlife & Countryside Act | Former quarry. Protected. |
| **Woodpigeon** | *Columba palumbus* | 2.3 million p | Increasing | Popular shooting quarry & farm pest. | Wildlife & Countryside Act Schedule 2 Part II | General licence for control for agricultural puposes. |
| **Greylag goose** | *Anser anser* | 14,300 a >100,000 w | Increasing | Resident and migratory wildfowl quarry. | Wildlife & Countryside Act Schedule 2 Part I | Protected in Scotland. |
| **Pink-footed goose** | *Anser brachyrhynchus* | 192,000 w | Increasing | Migratory wildfowl quarry. Crop damage. | Wildlife & Countryside Act Schedule 2 Part I | – |
| **White-fronted goose** | *Anser albifrons* | 19,800 w | Increasing | Migratory wildfowl quarry. | Wildlife & Countryside Act Schedule 2 Part I | Protected in Scotland on Islay. |

| English name | Latin name | Population estimate | Trend | Game interest | Main legal statute | Notes |
|---|---|---|---|---|---|---|
| **Canada goose** | *Branta canadensis* | 46,700 a<br>61,000 w | Increasing | Resident wildfowl quarry. Minor pest. | Wildlife & Countryside Act Schedule 2  Part I | – |
| **Barnacle goose** | *Branta leucopsis* | 53,000 w | Stable | Protected migratory or increasing | Wildlife & Countryside Act wildfowl. Crop damage. | Notable local increase on Islay |
| **Brent goose** | *Branta bernicla* | >125,000 w | Dark form | Protected migratory increasing; light form stable | Wildlife & Countryside Act wildfowl. | – |
| **Wigeon** | *Anas penelope* | 400 p<br>277,800 w | Stable | Important wildfowling quarry. | Wildlife & Countryside Act Schedule 2 Part I | All waterfowl may be subject to cold-weather shooting bans. |
| **Gadwall** | *Anas strepera* | 770 p<br>8,200 w | Increasing | Uncommon wildfowling quarry. | Wildlife & Countryside Act Schedule 2 Part I | – |
| **Teal** | *Anas crecca* | 2,050 p<br>135,800 w | Stable in | Important winter wildfowling quarry. | Wildlife & Countryside Act Schedule 2 Part I | – |
| **Mallard** | *Anas platyrhynchos* | 125,000 p<br>500,000 w | Stable | Important wildfowling quarry. | Wildlife & Countryside Act Schedule 2 Part I | – |
| **Pintail** | *Anas acuta* | 50 p<br>27,800 w | Stable in | Important winter wildfowling quarry. | Wildlife & Countryside Act Schedule 2 Part I | – |
| **Shoveler** | *Anas clypeata* | 1,250 p<br>10,300 w | Stable | Uncommon wildfowling quarry. | Wildlife & Countryside Act Schedule 2 Part I | – |
| **Pochard** | *Aythya ferina* | 328 p<br>43,700 w | Stable | Uncommon wildfowling quarry. | Wildlife & Countryside Act Schedule 2 Part I | – |
| **Tufted duck** | *Aythya fuligula* | 6,000 p<br>60,600 w | Increasing | Increasing wildfowling quarry – inland only. | Wildlife & Countryside Act Schedule 2 Part I | – |

| English name | Latin name | Population estimate | Trend | Game interest | Main legal statute | Notes |
|---|---|---|---|---|---|---|
| **Snipe** | *Gallinago gallinago* | 55,000 p 100,000 w | Stable after decline | Resident & migratory wader. Quarry species. | Wildlife & Countryside Act Schedule 2 Part I | – |
| **Woodcock** | *Scolopax rusticola* | 15,000 p >200,000 | Summer decline; winter increase | Resident & migratory wader. Quarry species. | Wildlife & Countryside Act Schedule 2 Part I | A polygynous species so true breeding pairs do not occur. |
| **Atlantic salmon** | *Salmo salar* | > 2 million r | Long-term decline | Migratory gamefish. | Salmon & Freshwater Fisheries Act | See also Salmon Act. |
| **Brown and Sea trout** | *Salmo trutta* | Unknown | General decline | Migratory & resident gamefish. | Salmon & Freshwater Fisheries Act | – |
| **Arctic char** | *Salvelinus alpinus* | Unknown | Shrinking range; otherwise stable | Gamefish of northern cold deep lakes. | Salmon & Freshwater Fisheries Act | – |
| **Grayling** | *Thymallus thymallus* | Unknown | Probable decline | Game & coarse fish of river & stream. | Salmon & Freshwater Fisheries Act | – |
| **Pike** | *Esox lucius* | Unknown | Stable or increasing | Predator & trophy coarse fish. | Salmon & Freshwater Fisheries Act | – |
| **Fox** | *Vulpes vulpes* | 240,000 a | Increasing in most areas | Predator of game and livestock. | – | Certain methods of control outlawed by various Acts. |
| **Stoat** | *Mustela erminea* | 462,000 a | Stable | Predator of rabbits & medium sized birds. | – | Use of spring-traps restricted by Pests Act. |
| **Weasel** | *Mustela nivalis* | 450,000 a | Declining | Predator of voles, mice & small birds. | – | Use of spring-traps restricted by Pests Act. |
| **American mink** | *Mustela vison* | 110,000 a | Spreading range | General semi-aquatic predator. | Wildlife & Countryside Act Schedule 9 | Use of spring-traps restricted by Pests Act. |

| English name | Latin name | Population estimate | Trend | Game interest | Main legal statute | Notes |
|---|---|---|---|---|---|---|
| **Polecat** | *Mustela putorius* | 15,000 a | Increasing | Part-protected predator of mammals & birds. | Wildlife & Countryside Act Schedule 6 | – |
| **Pine marten** | *Martes martes* | 3,650 a | Scotland stable; E & W unknown | Protected predator of birds & mammals. | Wildlife & Countryside Act Schedule 5 | – |
| **Badger** | *Meles meles* | >250,000 a | Increasing | Protected omnivore. | Protection of Badgers Acts | Population estimate now probably some 75% higher. |
| **Otter** | *Lutra lutra* | 7,350 a | Slow increase | Protected predator of fish. | Wildlife & Countryside Act Schedule 5 | – |
| **Wildcat** | *Felis sylvestris* | 3,500 a | Stable | Protected predator of small birds & mammals | Wildlife & Countryside Act Schedule 5 | – |
| **Cormorant** | *Phalacrocorax carbo* | 7,000 p | Spreading inland | Protected predator of game & coarse fish. | Wildlife & Countryside Act | Limited licences issued by MAFF to prevent damage. |
| **Hen harrier** | *Circus cyaneus* | 630 f | Stable | Specially protected predator of grouse. | Wildlife & Countryside Act Schedule 1 | – |
| **Goshawk** | *Accipiter gentilis* | 425 p | Increasing | Specially protected predator of gamebirds. | Wildlife & Countryside Act Schedule 1 | – |
| **Sparrowhawk** | *Accipiter nisus* | 32,000 p | Increasing | Protected predator of game and small birds. | Wildlife & Countryside Act | – |
| **Buzzard** | *Buteo buteo* | 15,000 p | Increasing | Protected predator occasionally of game. | Wildlife & Countryside Act | – |
| **Golden eagle** | *Aquila chrysaetos* | 422 p | Stable | Specially protected upland predator. | Wildlife & Countryside Act Schedule 1 | – |

| English name | Latin name | Population estimate | Trend | Game interest | Main legal statute | Notes |
|---|---|---|---|---|---|---|
| Peregrine falcon | *Falco peregrinus* | 1,000 p | Increasing | Specially protected predator of large birds. | Wildlife & Countryside Act Schedule 1 | – |
| Magpie | *Pica pica* | 590,000 p | Increasing | Predator of eggs & nestlings. | Wildlife & Countryside Act Schedule 2 Part II | Year-round control under licence. Open licence for Larsen traps. |
| Jackdaw | *Corvus monedula* | 390,000 p | Recovered after decline | Occasional predator of eggs. | Wildlife & Countryside Act Schedule 2 Part II | Year-round control under licence. |
| Rook | *Corvus frugilegus* | 855,000 p | Recovered after decline | Occasional predator of eggs. | Wildlife & Countryside Act Schedule 2 Part II | Year-round control under licence. |
| Carrion crow | *Corvus corone* | 970,000 p | Increasing | Predator of game & livestock. | Wildlife & Countryside Act Schedule 2 Part II | Year-round control under licence. Open licence for Larsen traps. |

## Acts of Parliament referred to above:

**Deer Act (1991)** A consolidation of earlier acts. In Scotland see Deer (Scotland) Act (1959) amended 1967 and 1982.

**Game Act (1831)** Amended in 1970. Equivalent in Scotland is Game (Scotland) Acts 1772 and 1832.

**Ground Game Act (1880)** Allows farmers to kill hares and rabbits year round.

**Hares Preservation Act (1892)** Prevents the sale of hares during their breeding season.

**Pests Act (1954)** Restricts the use of spring-traps to those approved by the Minister.

**Protection of Badgers Act (1992)** A consolidation and strengthening of previous acts.

**Salmon Act (1986)** Covers sale of salmon.

**Salmon and Freshwater Fisheries Act (1975)** Main legislation for England & Wales.

**Wildlife and Countryside Act (1981)** Covers all of Britain.

## Population estimates are based largely on the following:

Anon. (1996) *Wild Geese and Agriculture in Scotland. A Discussion Paper.* Scottish Office Agriculture, Environment and Fisheries Department, Edinburgh.

Harris, S., Morris, P., Wray, S. & Yalden. D. (1995) *A Review of British Mammals.* Joint Nature Conservation Committee. Peterborough.

Rose, P. M. (Ed.) (1994) Western Palaearctic and South-West Asia waterfowl census 1994. *IWRB Publication* No. 35, Slimbridge.

Stone, B. H., Sears, J., Cranswick, P. A., Gregory, R. D., Gibbons, D. W., Rehfisch, M. M., Aebischer, N. J. & Reid, J. B. (1997) Population estimates of birds in Britain and the United Kingdom. *British Birds*, 90: 1–22.

# Appendix 3 Other minor game and predatory species for which we have developed no specific conservation plan

**Hedgehog** (*Erinaceus europaeus*) Occasional predator of gamebird nests. Has been known to kill young pheasant poults in release pens. Semi-protected under Wildlife & Countryside Act (1981) Schedule 6.

**Chinese water deer** (*Hydropotes inermis*) Small feral deer which became established in some eastern Midland and East Anglian localities in the middle of this century. Probably not expanding its range. Should be eliminated where possible.

**Bean goose** (*Anser fabalis*) Large numbers of bean goose of three different subspecies winter in Europe. In 1993 well over 300,000 were counted. However, only about 400–500 occur in Britain and there are small flocks in East Anglia and Scotland, especially in the Yare and Carron Valleys. They seem to prefer unimproved pasture for feeding and small water-bodies for resting. The bean goose is a fully protected species and there is no justification for a change in this status. Conservation efforts should aim to ensure adequate feeding sites in wintering areas through the Agri-environment Measures.

**Goldeneye** (*Bucephala clangula*) A diving duck occasionally bagged by the wildfowler. Normally stays well out of range in open expanses of water in winter. A hole-nester in summer. Population expanding.

**Merganser** (*Mergus serrator*) Fish-eating duck found in northern freshwater and coastal habitats. Mainly coastal in winter. Feeds on large numbers of salmon and trout parr and therefore of concern to salmon anglers. Research needed to properly assess this type of predation on migratory fish stocks.

**Goosander** (*Mergus merganser*) Similar ecology to merganser, but spreading further south. Tends to winter inland and may therefore have more impact on salmonid fry. As with the merganser, research on the impact on fish stocks is needed to justify the licensed control that exists under the Wildlife & Countryside Act (1981). If this shows their effect to be significant, licences should be made easier to obtain.

**Ruddy duck** (*Oxyura jamaicensis*) Aggressive North American alien species which threatens the genetic integrity of the European white-headed duck. Of no sporting interest. The British breeding population should be eliminated as soon as possible.

**Kestrel** (*Falco tinnunculus*) Small-mammal-dependent falcon that likes to hunt over open long-grass habitats. Over-grazing by livestock and expansion of rabbit numbers may have reduced field vole numbers, with a consequent decline in kestrels in northern and western districts. Has been seen to take gamebird chicks in situations of poor cover.

**Ptarmigan** (*Lagopus mutus*) Sometimes shot on mountainous parts of Scottish estates. There has been some range contraction. Probably benefits from the predator control associated with grouse moors but, like other upland species, may be suffering through habitat degradation caused by over-grazing.

**Coot** (*Fulica atra*) Like the moorhen, the coot is thought to rob duck nests and does, indeed, sometimes kill ducklings.

**Moorhen** (*Gallinula chloropus*) Sometimes shot by gamekeepers because it is thought to rob duck nests. However, it is protected during the breeding season.

**Golden plover** (*Pluvialis apricaria*) A minor quarry species still valued by a few people. There is no evidence that the small amount of shooting does any harm. In fact, the species certainly benefits from game management on upland estates.

**Curlew** (*Numenius arquata*) Formerly shot occasionally by wildfowlers, but was removed from the quarry list in 1981. This is a species that benefits from game management in the uplands and we see no good reason why it should not be returned to the quarry list.

**Tawny owl** (*Strix aluco*) Predator that lives primarily on woodland small mammals. Will take young pheasant poults. In some release pen situations, large numbers may be killed each night because of surplus killing. Owls characteristically bite the heads off pheasant poults.

**Little owl** (*Athene noctua*) Common introduced farmland species that has declined in some intensively farmed regions. Sometimes takes gamebird chicks and is particularly adept at getting in through the roofs of farm buildings where large numbers of gamebird chicks are sometimes raised.

**Raven** (*Corvus corax*) Protected corvid which can be a significant predator of lambs in some hill-farming areas.

**Jay** (*Garrulus glandarius*) Occasionally shot by gamekeepers year round and on pheasant shoots in winter. Perceived to be a predator of gamebird nests and particularly a predator of nesting songbirds. There are too few data at present to make a clear case one way or another for changing its legal status.

# List of abbreviations

## Government departments

**DETR**
Department of the Environment, Transport and Regions
**MAFF**
Ministry of Agriculture, Fisheries and Food
**SOAEFD**
Scottish Office Agriculture, Environment and Fisheries Department

## Government-funded agencies

**ADAS**
Agricultural Development Advisory Service
**BRC**
Biological Records Centre
**CCW**
Countryside Council for Wales
**CSL**
Central Science Laboratory
**EA**
Environment Agency (former National Rivers Authority)
**EPA**
Environmental Protection Agency
**EN**
English Nature
**FRCA**
Farming and Rural Conservation Agency (former policy division of ADAS)
**ITE**
Institute of Terrestrial Ecology
**JNCC**
Joint Nature Conservation Committee
**NERC**
Natural Environment Research Council
**OS**
Ordnance Survey
**SEPA**
Scottish Environmental Protection Agency

**SNH**
Scottish Natural Heritage
**VIC**
Veterinary Investigation Centre

## Non-Governmental organisations (NGOs)

**BASC**
British Association for Shooting and Conservation
**BDS**
British Deer Society
**BTO**
British Trust for Ornithology
**CA**
Countryside Alliance (incorporating the British Field Sports Society or BFSS)
**FWAG**
Farming and Wildlife Advisory Group
**HOT**
The Hawk and Owl Trust
**IUCN**
International Union for the Conservation of Nature and Natural Resources
**IWRB**
International Waterfowl and Wetlands Research Bureau
**NT**
National Trust
**RSPB**
Royal Society for the Protection of Birds
**RSPCA**
Royal Society for the Prevention of Cruelty to Animals
**SOC**
Scottish Ornithologists' Club
**SRSG**
Scottish Raptor Study Groups
**WI**
Wetlands International
**WRSG**
Wales Raptor Study Group

**WWF**
Worldwide Fund for Nature
**WWT**
Wildfowl and Wetlands Trust (formerly Wildfowl Trust or WT)

## Miscellaneous

**BASIS**
British Agro-chemicals Standards Inspection Scheme
**BBS**
British Bird Survey
**BWP**
Birds of the Western Palearctic
**CBC**
Common Bird Census
**CIS**
Countryside Information System
**DDT**
Dichlorodiphenyltrichloroethane
**ESA**
Environmentally Sensitive Area
**GMO**
Genetically modified organism
**HLCA**
Hill Livestock Compensatory Allowance
**IACS**
Integrated Administration and Control Scheme
**LEAF**
Linking Environment and Farming
**LFA**
Less Favoured Area
**PCB**
Polychlorinated biphenyl
**SAC**
Special Area of Conservation
**SDA**
Severely Disadvantaged Area
**SPA**
Special Protection Area
**SSSI**
Site of Special Scientific Interest
**WeBS**
Wetland Bird Survey

# Glossary of terms

**Alevin** A young trout or salmon which has just hatched and which still carries a yolk sac.

**Arable Stewardship Scheme** Set of management options available to farmers under the EU Agri-environment Measures. Farmers receive payments for managing cereal fields in ways which benefit wildlife. Currently in the pilot phase.

**Auto-ecology** Ecology of a single species.

**Channelisation** The straightening and dredging in small rivers and streams to improve drainage – turning them into channels.

**Coble** Small flat-bottomed boat used by salmon netsmen.

**Conditioned taste aversion** A technique designed to deter animals from eating a particular food by lacing a bait with an undetectable substance that makes them briefly sick.

**Control** Used in the sense of a scientific experiment, a control is a sample which has not undergone the experimental treatment and can therefore be used as a comparison. Correctly all experiments by definition need controls.

**Countryside Stewardship Scheme** Run by the Ministry of Agriculture, Fisheries and Food to pay farmers grants to enhance the countryside.

**Coupe** A section of woodland managed as a unit.

**Covey** A family group of partridges or grouse.

**Cyprinid** A fish belonging to the carp family *(Cyprinidae)*, which includes carp, bream, roach and rudd.

**Dimethoate** An organophosphate insecticide. Toxic and has a wide spectrum of action.

**Ephemerid** A fly belonging to the family Ephemeridae, typically the mayflies and their relatives.

**Ericaceous** Plant species belonging to the family Ericaceae.

**Eutrophic** Warm, nutrient-rich water.

**Extensification** The opposite of intensification, a term mainly applied to agriculture.

**Farm Woodland Premium Scheme** Grant scheme for planting and maintaining woodlands.

**Fennoscandia** Finland, Sweden and Norway.

**Fothering** Grazing sheep on open moorland.

**Fray** Bark stripping and other damage to trees caused by deer, often as they clean velvet from their antlers.

**Fry** A young fish. For trout and salmon it is correctly defined as the stage before it starts to feed actively, although it is commonly used in reference to small fish less than a year old.

**Functional response** The action of a predator which increases its consumption of a prey species as prey abundance increases. There are different kinds of functional response depending largely on whether the predator gradually increases its prey consumption or makes a switch from one prey type to another. In any case, beyond a certain limit of prey numbers, most predators do not go on taking further prey. They become sated and the response is said to tend towards an asymptote (a line that continually approaches a curve but never meets it).

**Gralloch** Deer entrails. Usually removed from the carcass after shooting.

**Grilse** A small salmon that has spent only one winter in the sea and returns to the river, usually in late summer.

**Gripping** Moorland draining using a network of ditches.

**Hacking** A method of restocking raptor populations by rearing young birds in areas where they are to be released.

**Immunocontraception** A method of contraception which works by making the immune system of a female react against the sperm (usually) of its own species, thus rendering the animal barren.

**Intra-guild predation** Where one predator kills another, usually smaller, predator. There is growing appreciation that these interactions between predators may be an important factor influencing the abundance of some predators and their prey.

**Kelt** An adult salmon that has bred in the preceding summer, remained in the river and is slowly dropping back to the sea. Kelts are usually very thin and in poor condition; a high proportion die.

**Lek** A group of displaying male birds or mammals, notably black grouse, during the breeding season.

**Lepidoptera** An order of insects that includes butterflies and moths.

**Moorland Scheme** A scheme to encourage hill-farmers to reduce sheep numbers in the uplands.

**Mustelid** A member of the family Mustelidae. This group of mammalian predators (carnivores) characteristically possess a pair of anal scent glands which give them an often pungent aroma. Weasels, stoats, mink, otters and badgers are all mustelids.

**Mycetophagous** Fungus-eating. Species of animals that eat fungi. Many insects that live in cereal crops are mycetophagous.

**National Game Bag Census** An annual return of game shot on farms and estates across Britain. Run by The Game Conservancy Trust.

**Natural Areas** Regions of England defined by English Nature as having similar fauna, flora and landscape. A map of Natural Areas was published in 1996 defining these, as well as how they dovetail with a man-made character map defined by the Countryside Commission (the Countryside Agency).

**Numerical response** An increase (or decrease) of predator numbers associated with rising (or declining) numbers of their prey.

**Oligotrophic** Normally cold, nutrient-poor water.

**Parr** A young trout over one year old or a young salmon living in fresh water before it begins its migration to the sea. Parr have a line of dark blotches on their sides which they lose with age.

**Philopatry** An animal's tendency to remain close to where it was reared.

**Population viability analysis** A computer simulation to predict the probability of extinction of a population based on known population parameters, such as mortality, reproduction, etc.

**Pyrethroid** A naturally occurring plant chemical which has strong insecticidal properties. Now manufactured artificially, these chemicals make very safe insecticides, but because of their high lethality to insects they can have a wide ecological impact if used extensively, ie. on cereal fields or in sheep dips.

**Raptor** A bird of prey.

**Riffle** Shallow part of a river where the water runs over a gravel bottom; often between pools, which tend to be on bends. The fast current and shallow depth cause surface turbulence, giving the water a 'riffled' appearance.

**Roding** The display flight of breeding male woodcock.

**Salmonid** A fish belong to the family Salmonidae. These are mainly gamefish, such as salmon, trout and char, but also include grayling. All species have a second small dorsal fin – the adipose (fatty) fin – just in front of the tail.

**Satyrid** A butterfly, such as the grayling, belonging to the Satyridae family.

**Scottish Countryside Premium Scheme** Set of financial incentives to help farmers take up conservation measures in Scotland.

**Set-aside** Arable land taken out of agricultural production for either one or several seasons. A fixed area is set for farmers receiving arable area payments as part of an EU subsidy.

**Smolt** A young salmon (usually around 10 centimetres in length) which has turned silver and begun its journey from a river's headwaters downstream to the sea.

**Spate** River in flood.

**Spraint** Otter faeces.

**Springer** An adult salmon which has spent two or more winters at sea and returns to the river in spring in order to breed the following winter.

**Tir Gofal** Welsh countryside stewardship and farming scheme.

**Woodland Grant Scheme** Scheme run by the Forestry Commission.